COALS FROM NEWCASTLE

An Introduction to the Northumberland and Durham Coalfield

by Les Turnbull B.A. (Hons), M.Ed

Published by
CHAPMAN RESEARCH PUBLISHING

ISBN 978-0-9561248-0-7

Chapman Research Publishing
18 Paradise Square
Oxford OX1 1TW

Willington Colliery

Typeset by A G Thompson

Printed by Newcastle Print Solutions Limited

CONTENTS

Introduction - In Search of the Great Northern Coalfield Page 1

Chapter One - From Fossils to Fuel Page 7

Chapter Two - The Coal Mine: a Study of the Manor of Heaton Page 28

Chapter Three - Mining Accidents Page 71

Chapter Four - Colliery Villages Page 83

Chapter Five - Glimpses of the Lost Railways of Newcastle Page 103

Old Hartley Colliery

ACKNOWLEDGEMENTS

Many people have given their time and expertise to assist with the reseach behind the writing of this book. The staff of the Northumberland County Record Office, Durham County Record Office, Tyne and Wear Archive Office, the National Archives of Scotland, Newcastle Public Library, Gateshead Public Library, North Shields Public Library, South Shields Public Library, and the Literary and Philosophical Society of Newcastle upon Tyne have been very helpful. A special debt of gratitude is owed to the staff of the North of England Institute of Mining and Mechanical Engineers for the bulk of the research has been carried out there. Furthermore, the majority of the maps and illustrations in the book are reproduced with the permission of the Institute. The watercolours of Thomas Hair are reproduced with the permission of the Hatton Gallery and Beamish Museum has been very helpful in supplying photographs to supplement the author's collection.

When I was an undergraduate at Durham University, my interest in industrial archaeology was fostered by a young lecturer in the history department of King's College. It is particularly gratifying that having risen to the heights of Emeritus Professor of Social History in the University of Newcastle upon Tyne, Norman McCord readily agreed to read the draft of this book. His comments are greatly appreciated: I am indebted to an inspiring teacher.

I am also indebted to Alan Thompson who has not only contributed immensely to the design of this book but has also managed the production process.

Hetton Colliery

Introduction – In Search of the Great Northern Coalfield

'The coal from Northumberland and Durham made a vital contribution to the evolution of modern Britain and a wider world beyond; it was won at a high cost in death, injury and suffering. The remains of this great industrial interest, now in marked decline, are among the most precious elements in the region's archaeological heritage for the collieries and the staiths, the waggonways and the pit villages, provided a vital element in the world's energy supplies during a major period of historical transformation'.

Norman McCord, Emeritus Professor of Social History in the University of Newcastle upon Tyne, North East History from the Air, 1991.

In 2005, Ellington Colliery, the last deep coal mine in the North East of England, closed. This event was of more than local significance since it marked the end of deep shaft mining in the Northumberland and Durham coalfield, a region which had played a pivotal role in the economic history of England since the sixteenth century. For much of the time since the reign of Elizabeth I, this coalfield was the most important in Britain and consequently it was known as the Great Northern Coalfield. Until the beginning of the twentieth century, the North East produced more coal than any other coalfield in the United Kingdom. Furthermore, the region was widely regarded as the leading centre of technical expertise. Visitors from elsewhere in Britain and abroad came to learn from the mining engineers of the North East of England. The collieries of this region were at the centre of the industrialisation of the country providing the fuel for the steam engines which made the industrial revolution possible. Britain's economic power, which established the nation as the world's first industrial superpower, was based upon coal; and the world's first carbon based economy was created in the United Kingdom as a result primarily of the skills of the miners of Northumberland and Durham.

St Hilda's Colliery, Wallsend

The importance of the Great Northern Coalfield was not confined to British history, for this coalfield also played an important role in European history as the provider of energy supplies for the continent. The immense growth of the export trade in coal from the region during the nineteenth and early twentieth centuries was an essential element in the industrialisation and urbanisation of Europe. Coal from the North East of England provided the power for the factories and the railways of Europe; it also provided gas to light the streets of many European cities. Furthermore, this was a time when the continent of Europe, through the imperial possessions of its principal members, was of enormous global importance. Coal from the Northumberland and Durham was shipped to coaling stations throughout the world to fuel the steam-powered ships which made possible the enormous expansion in world trade during Victoria's reign. The offices of the major coal companies in Newcastle at, for example, Milburn House and Cathedral Buildings administered a network of connections supplying Europe and the wider world beyond with energy.

Now that collieries, steam engines and even coal fires are museum exhibits, it is difficult to realise the dominant part coal mining once played in the lives of the people of Northumberland and Durham. Fifty years ago, the coal mines were not only a major source of employment in the region but coal itself was at the centre of everyday life: open coal fires heated the home; coal was used to produce gas and electricity for lighting and cooking; and even the air people breathed was blackened by the smoke from factory chimneys, steam locomotives and domestic coal fires. As a contrast today, most school children have never seen coal. Coal is still used, primarily to generate electricity, but it is only mined in the North East by opencast workings which quarry coal left behind by the inefficient mining techniques of former generations. The change since the 1950's is also illustrated by the fact that Tyne Dock, once the largest coal exporting facility in the world, is in 2008 scheduled to import three million tons of coals to Newcastle.

The traffic in coal from the North East ports, primarily to London, the South East of England, Europe and Scandinavia, was known as the seacoal trade. The Great Northern Coalfield was the name given to the area where the collieries which produced coal for the seacoal trade were located. Amble marked the northern limit and Hartlepool the southern boundary of this coalfield; and, at its widest, between Consett and the Durham coast, it was twenty fives miles across. These collieries were the largest and most technically advanced in the world during their heyday, the impetus for their development springing from the wealth to be made from the seacoal trade. Major industrial empires were created by, for example, Lord Londonderry in Durham and the Ashington Coal Company in Northumberland. Many of these large collieries also sold their coal locally but the domestic market was usually a less important part of their business.

The importance of the Great Northern Coalfield in the economic history of Europe is an established fact but it should not be forgotten that coal was mined in other areas of North East England. At Scremerston in north Northumberland, at Shilbottle and Whittle near Alnwick, at Plashetts and Bellingham in the North Tyne valley, at Acomb, Bardon Mill and Blenkinsop in the mid Tyne valley, important landsale collieries existed which mainly supplied only a local market. These mines provided coal not

Lighting up at Heaton Locomotive Depot

only for domestic use but also for local industries such as brick and tile works, lime kilns and farms which increasingly used steam powered agricultural machinery. These pits employed a few dozen men in contrast to the thousand and more working in the major collieries. Although they did not have the international stature of the seacoal collieries, these mines are an important part of our regional history.

This book is written to help the general reader appreciate the richness of our mining heritage by providing an outline of the history and industrial archaeology of the Great Northern Coalfield. Chapter One provides an introduction to the geology of the coalfield and an outline history of its development from Roman times to the present. Coal mining and the coal trade provided the impetus for the development of the iron and steel, chemical, shipbuilding and engineering industries in the North East; and this interdependent spiral of growth is the main theme of the history of the coalfield. When the coal industry began to contract after the First World

War, the process moved into reverse and a spiral of decline set in making the years of depression in the 1920s and 1930s more severe because of the interdependence of the major industries in the region.

Chapter Two examines the development of the coal mine through a detailed study of mining in the manor of Heaton, now a suburb of Newcastle. Beginning with the quarrying of coal at the outcrop of the High Main seam, mining progressed until major seacoal collieries were developed during the seventeenth, eighteenth and nineteenth centuries making Heaton one of the great coal mining royalties of the region. It could be argued that such a detailed study is inappropriate in a book that purports to be a general introduction. However, the study is presented as an example of how coal mining changed as new technologies were developed and a similar story could be written for other royalties in the North East. Indeed, it is hoped that the study will provide a framework to assist and encourage others to write a detailed study of their local colliery.

The emotive subject of mining accidents is the subject of Chapter Three. Again, rather than writing a general survey of the many disasters which afflicted the coalfield, a detailed study of three different types of accident is presented. The death of 204 miners at Hartley Colliery in 1862, when a cast iron beam fractured and blocked the only entrance into the mine; the explosion of methane gas at Felling Colliery in 1812, which resulted in the death of 92 miners; and the flooding of Heaton Main Colliery in 1815, which caused 75 men and boys to be suffocated are only three of the many accidents in the coalfield. Each of these accidents was of more than local significance for they led to efforts to improve safety in the mines. Furthermore, they illustrate the price that was paid for the world's energy supplies by the miners of the Great Northern Coalfield. It should not be forgotten that the publicity given to major disasters, such as these three, often masked the fact that death on a smaller scale, serious injury and permanent disablement were an everyday aspect of life in the pits. Significantly, amongst all the advertisements for mining equipment in Reid's 'Handy Colliery Guide' of 1921 are advertisements for ambulances and artificial limbs.

Colliery villages and the social life of the mining communities is the subject of Chapter Four. Through a detailed study of three different villages – Bigges Main, Gosforth and Chopwell – the reader is introduced to the principal sources of evidence for a study of a colliery village – namely, early Ordnance Survey maps, census returns, oral evidence, local newspaper reports and old photographs. Once more it is hoped that this example will encourage others to write the history of their local mining community. It is easy to emphasise the solidarity, friendliness and humanity of the mining communities which was a very real and admirable aspect of the history of these villages; but the history of the Methodist church in the region and the writings of local authors, like the miner Sid Chaplin, reveal that there was another side of village life which was less endearing where gambling, drunkenness and violence were prominent aspects of daily life.

The final chapter 'Glimpses of the Lost Railways of Newcastle' is more than a study of the waggonways which once transported coal from the royalties which today make up the City of Newcastle upon Tyne. Now that this area is almost entirely urbanised and the former collieries, together with their transport systems, have been lost to housing and industrial estates, this chapter is an attempt to answer the question – where were the coal mines of Newcastle and the railways which served them. This is a question which can be asked of other parts of the coalfield. To illustrate this chapter several of the rare maps within the archive of the Mining Institute have been used. These present a picture of the city in the eighteenth and early nineteenth centuries before urbanisation had created the landscape we know today. They have a fascination in themselves because they show a different world of watermills and windmills, open fields and country houses, turnpike roads and waggonways – all of which have either disappeared or have been radically changed as the urban sprawl of later centuries encroached upon the countryside.

Woodhorn Colliery Museum

Horse Gin at Beamish Museum

Although the Great Northern Coalfield played a pivotal role in the development of the British economy and also in the industrialisation and urbanisation of Europe at a time when that continent was of such immense global importance, the notion of preserving the heritage of the coal mining industry of Northumberland and Durham did not attract widespread interest in the new Elizabethan age. The legacy of the Roman occupation of the region and the interest in medieval studies determined that more public funding was spent on Roman forts and medieval castles than on the industrial archaeology of the coalfield even though the region's mines and railways had played a more significant role in world history. As the coal mining industry of the North East contracted, the movement to record and preserve some of this heritage for posterity gathered pace. Professor Norman McCord through his aerial surveys of the region; Frank Atkinson through the establishment of Beamish Museum; the Tyne and Wear Industrial Monuments Trust through its work to conserve industrial remains; Colin Mountford through his championship of the Bowes Railway; Les Charlton through his efforts to record the industrial railways of the area; Eric Maxwell, Alan Thompson and their colleagues who fought to preserve the Tanfield waggonway; and a host of other individuals who assisted with these projects, or simply took photographs before the demolition teams moved in; all strived to record the heritage of the Great Northern Coalfield before coal mining ended.

Today, the success of their work can be seen at Beamish Museum where the colliery village, dominated by the pithead winding gear, is a very good reconstruction of a typical colliery village of the early twentieth century and the regional studies centre at Beamish contains an impressive photographic archive; at Woodhorn Colliery Museum where the buildings of one of the Ashington Coal Company's former collieries house the museum but alas the massive pit heap and the all pervading grime, smoke and bustle which were

Netherton Colliery - now farmland (Norman McCord)

Seaham Harbour and Dawdon Colliery (Norman McCord)

the lifeblood of the pit are absent; and at the Bowes Railway and Tanfield Railway where enthusiasts have restored two of the former waggonways which were once essential to the development and operation of the mining industry.

Beyond the museums, remains of the Great Northern Coalfield are not easy to find. Certainly numerous pithead winding wheels and colliery tubs mark the entrance to former mining villages often as result of successful campaigning by former miners like Ralph Wilson at Burradon. Other traces are less obvious, largely because there has been a deliberate policy to remove the grime of industrialisation and to transform the image of the region. Memories are stirred by the sight of the low hills of the landscaped pitheaps, some now nature reserves like the spoil heaps of Weetslade Colliery and the Rising Sun Colliery. The impressive offices of the major companies, such as Milburn House and Cathedral Buildings, are now used by other enterprises but the quality of their architecture is testimony to the importance of the coal trade. The graveyard memorials to the victims of the major accidents are a sober reminder of the dangers faced by the coal miners especially in the fiery pits of the North East. The routes of abandoned waggonways now used as footpaths, like the waggonway from Killingworth Colliery where George Stephenson experimented with the steam locomotive; the forlorn riverside staiths at Dunston and Derwenthaugh, and the former coal ports, like Seaton Sluice, Cullercoats and Seaham Harbour, all are mementos of the transport infrastructure established for the coal industry.

There is an abundance of place name evidence such as Colliery Road, Pit Lane, Coley Hill, Middle Engine Lane and Buddle Street, the last named after perhaps the most famous colliery engineer of the coalfield, John Buddle. Also, many of the public houses in the region are named after the coal owners such as the Brandling Hotel found in both Jesmond and Gosforth. The great estates and country mansions like Seaton Delaval Hall of the Delaval family; Gibside Hall belonging to the Bowes family; the Ridley's residence at Blagdon Hall and Lord Londonderry's home at Wynyard serve as a statement of the wealth which could be acquired by those who gambled successfully in the coal trade. The old colliery rows which once housed the miners and their families; the Methodist chapels and Co-operative stores, which are often converted to other uses; the colliery welfare halls and the aged miners cottages; the rich dialect and folk music of the region – all are reminders of the distinctive communities which coal mining created.

Jowl, jowl and listen lads
You'll hear the coalface working
There's many a marrer missing lads
Because he wouldn't listen lads.

The coalfield had a language of its own known as pitmatic, with several variations of dialect, and this speech was sometimes unintelligible even to others living in the region. Words such as jowl – to tap the roof as a safety measure to check its solidity – and marrer, a workmate, were part of this language. Much of the terminology was technical and is encountered in the following chapters. To assist the reader, there is a short glossary at the back of the book but a more detailed study can be found in a recent anthology by Bill Griffiths entitled 'Pitmatic: the Talk of the North East Coalfield'.

There is also a large body of evidence relating to the history of the coalfield in the museums, libraries and record offices of the region and the staff of these institutions have been very helpful in assisting with the research for this book. The collections of official documents, family papers, photographs, oral recollections, maps and a host of other items provide the basis for discovering the history and industrial archaeology of the coalfield. The most extensive collection is housed in the North of England Institute of Mining and Mechanical Engineers and this book draws heavily upon this archive.

It needs to be emphasised that this book is not a comprehensive history of the Northumberland and Durham coalfield but only an introduction to the subject. It is hoped that by providing an overview of the history of the industry, and examples of studies in depth of important elements in that history, others will be encouraged to research into this important part of the region's heritage. For as J. R. Leifchild, a mines inspector with considerable experience of the area, wrote in 1862 expressing undisguised pride: 'No one would dream of making an excursion for pleasure to this great district of subterranean blackness; yet few places in our country, and certainly not in any other, are so full of real interest'. In the search for the Great Northern Coalfield, it is this 'real interest' which the book now hopes to explore.

This publication is dedicated to the members and staff, both past and present, of the North of England Institute of Mining and Mechanical Engineers: without their patient acquisition and care of the records of the Great Northern Coalfield this book could not have been written.

Chapter One – From Fossils to Fuel

'Imagine then a village consisting of a few shops, a public-house, and a clutter of dirty houses, all at the base of what looked at first like an active volcano'.

J. B. Priestley, English Journey.

The East Durham Village of Shotton, dominated and polluted by its infamous colliery tip, was visited by the Yorkshire writer J. B. Priestley in 1933 on his journey through the areas of England gripped by the deep economic depression of the thirties. The burning, smoking mountain was created from the waste generated by the colliery; but the process which created the coal and the waste began many millions of years earlier when the landscape of northern England was formed by the deposition of sedimentary rocks – sandstones, limestones, shales and coal seams. About 300 million years ago, huge deltas spread southwards from an ancient landmass to the north and the millstone grits were formed by the deposition of materials carried down by rivers and deposited in the shallow seas at the mouths of these deltas. Later still, a succession of huge swamps clothed with dense vegetation existed in the area. The vegetable matter died and decayed. It was compressed by later deposits to form the coal measures many containing the visible fossilised remains of these plants. Next, the area was covered by a deep sea and the magnesian limestone was formed by the deposition of dead marine creatures

Massive forces springing from the centre of the earth have disrupted these horizontal layers of sedimentary rocks which are no longer horizontal. Furthermore, the layers have been fractured by the movement of the earth's crust, forming faults in the stratification. Sometimes these faults were filled with igneous rocks, bursting up in a molten state from the earth's core, which cooled to form whinstone dykes. On other occasions they were filled with gases which condensed to form mineral veins. These natural forces have been continuously at work and are still moulding the landscape.

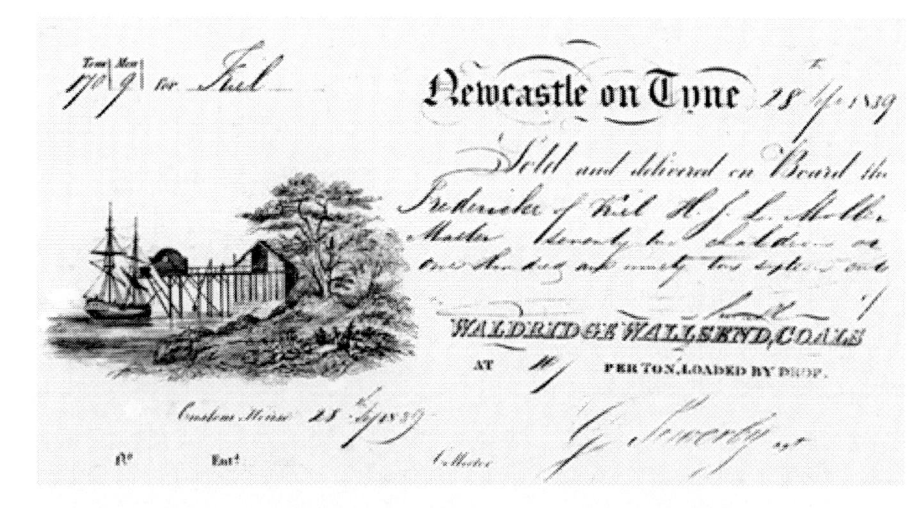
Newcastle on Tyne

WALDRIDGE WALLSEND COALS

AT PER TON, LOADED BY DROP.

The action of ice, wind and water during the course of millions of years has resulted in the wearing away of the surface rocks. Thus, in the far west, the coal measures have disappeared completely and the millstone grit forms the present surface; further east, beneath the western suburbs of Newcastle for example, the coal measures are exposed; while near the Durham coast they are hidden by the magnesian limestone of the Durham plateau. A major geological fault north and west of Newcastle, the Ninety Fathom Dyke, throws the seams to the north downward from 250 to 1,000 feet. In the south of the coalfield another major fault, the Butterknowle Dyke, throws the seams to the south downward from 300 to 900 feet. This geological framework has determined the development of the coalfield and the colonisation of the area. All these events occurred before man began making his mark on the landscape some 10,000 years ago.

A section of a map of the strata beneath Newcastle, dated 1831, is reproduced below. It shows the impact of these geological forces upon the coal seams. Three principal coal seams are marked – the High Main, the Low Main and the Beaumont – dipping from the aptly named Coley Hill in the west, where they outcrop, to the Ouseburn, now running through the eastern suburbs of Newcastle. The disruption caused by the Ninety Fathom Fault (the Main Dyke) in Denton Burn is dramatically illustrated. At the Charlotte Pit in Benwell Colliery, the High Main seam was 48 feet from the surface, the Low Main 382 feet and the Beaumont 572 feet.

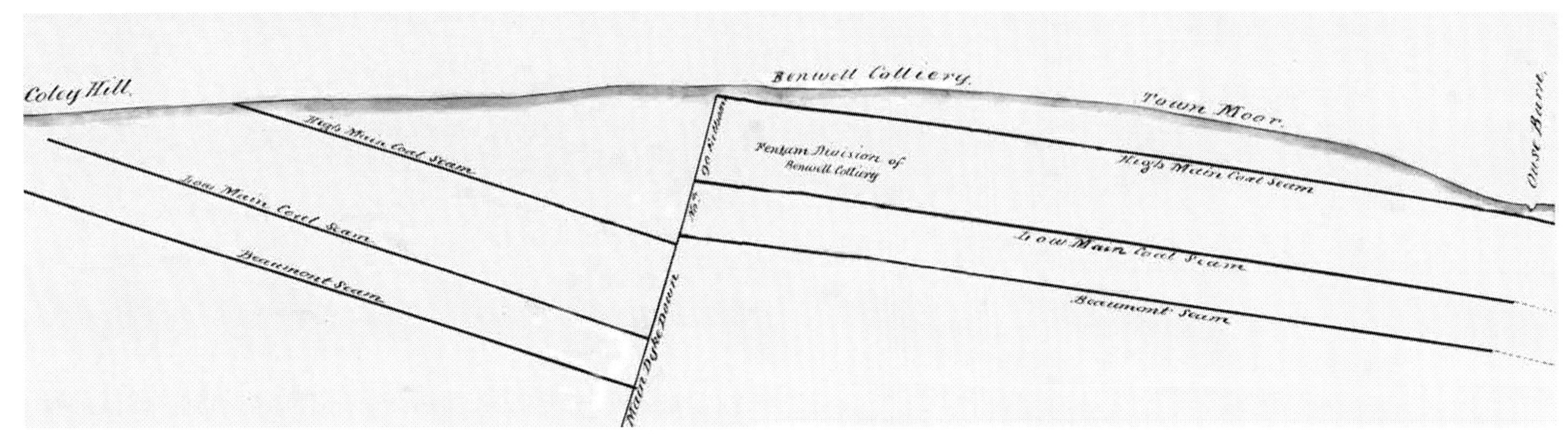

Immediately to the west of this major fault the High Main is about 600 feet from the surface.

In a journey across the City of Newcastle, the traveller moves from the exposed coalfield to the hidden coalfield: in Walker, at the eastern end of the city, the same High Main seam that outcropped east of Coley Hill is 100 fathoms deep. Further east past Wallsend Colliery, the coal seams turned upwards and outcropped between Billy Mill and the coast. This formed a basin in the area between the Ouseburn and North Shields known as the Tyne Basin where some of the greatest mines were won after the improvement of pumping technology.

The section from an early nineteenth century map shows the Walker Estate and Colliery divided by a series of geological faults which disrupted the working of the colliery. One fault with a downcast of 3.5 fathoms thrusts the coal seams to the north a further 21 feet down which was followed by another which cast the seams 5 fathoms (30 feet) upwards to the north. Another fault, the Whin Dyke or Jane Pit Dyke, was a vertical intrusion of basalt rock, one of the hardest rocks of the area, which effectively sealed off one part of the colliery from the other. The Thistle Pit Dyke separated the north western corner of the estate from Walker Colliery and this area was mined from Byker – the Endeavour Pit being part of Lawson's Main Colliery.

Within the coalfield at large, the coal measures are over 2,000 feet in thickness at their deepest but the upper half of the strata, the barren coal measures, has no seams worthy of mining. In the lower half, the productive coal measures, there are ten principal seams varying in thickness generally from two to six feet. The High Main seam is the highest and the Brockwell the lowest. Unfortunately, the name given to a seam is not consistent throughout the coalfield which is confusing. For example, miners on Tyneside referred to the Yard and Bensham seams: these were known as the Main and the Maudlin seams on Wearside. Part of the reason for this inconsistency is that the concept of stratification was only developed in the early nineteenth century many years after the miners had named and started working the coal seams. It should not be forgotten that geology is a modern science.

The nature of the coal from different seams at a particular colliery and from different parts of the coalfield varies considerably. Tyneside produced the best household coal, the High Main seam being prized above all other coal in the London market for domestic use; the west Durham collieries mined

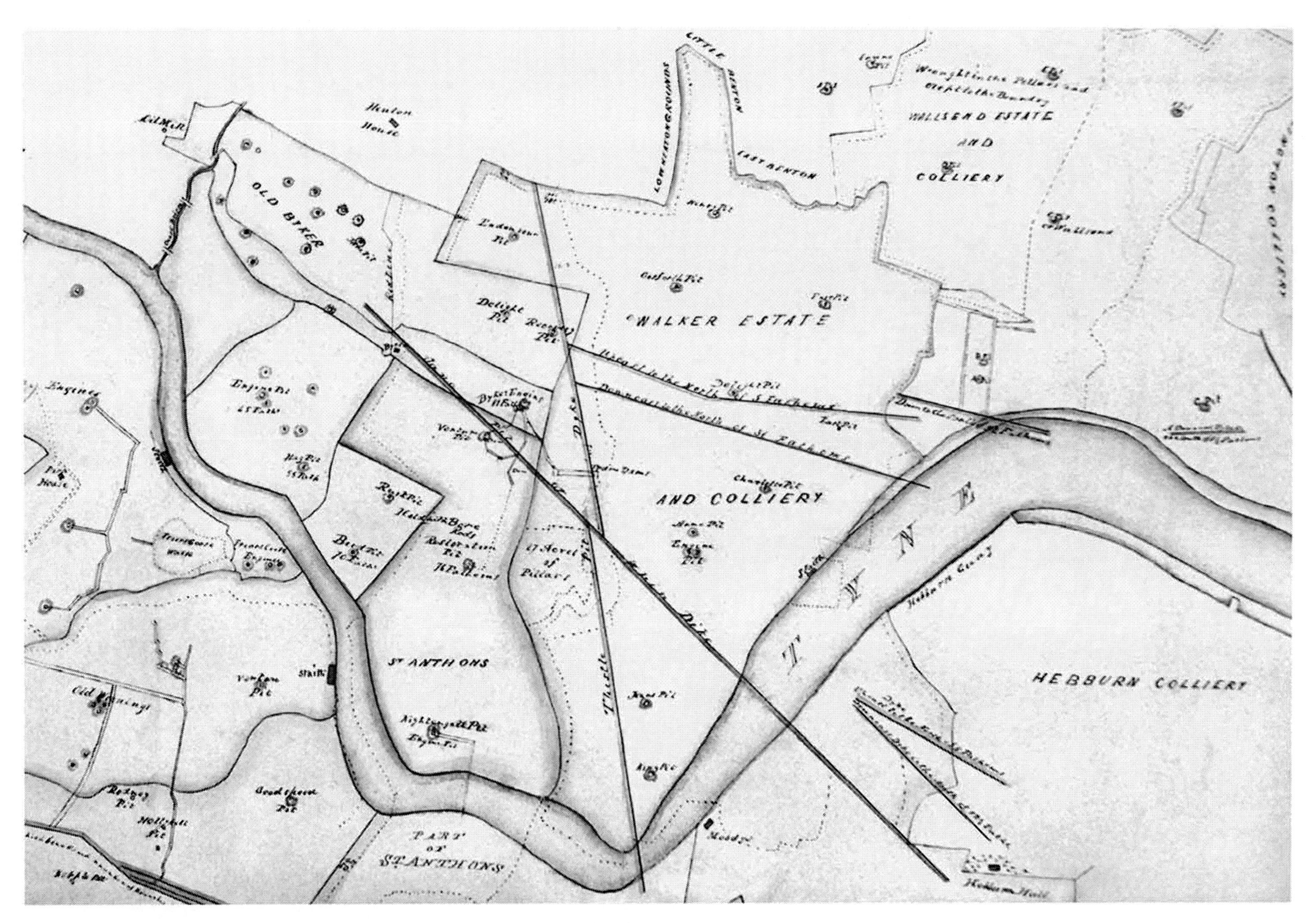

Walker Colliery

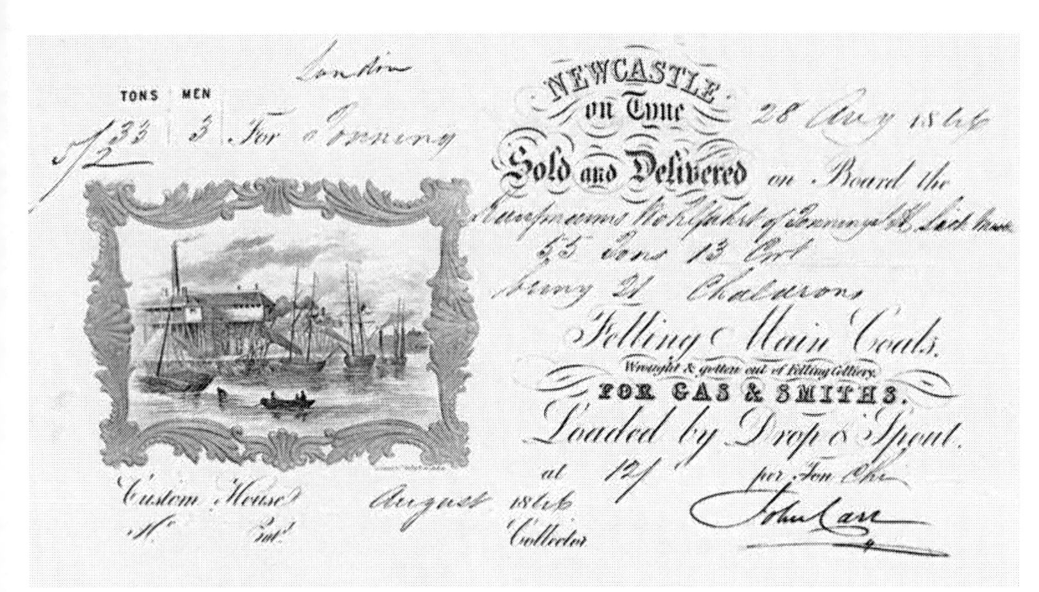
London
TONS MEN
33 3 For [illegible]
NEWCASTLE on Tyne 28 Aug 1846
Sold and Delivered on Board the [illegible]
55 Tons 13 Cwt
being 21 Chaldrons
Felling Main Coals.
Wrought & gotten out of Felling Colliery.
FOR GAS & SMITHS.
Loaded by Drop & Spout.
at 12/ per Ton Chr
Custom House August 1846
No. Ent. Collector
John Carr

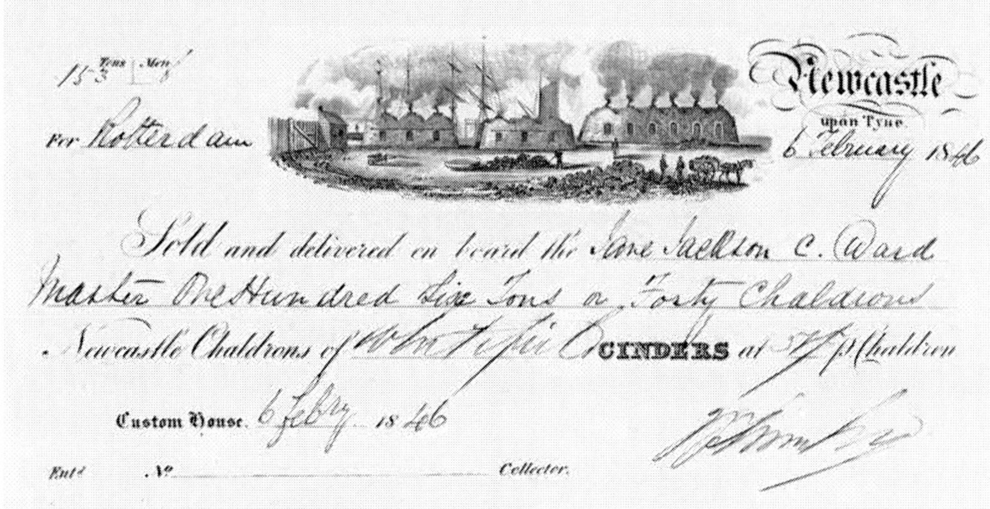
153 Tons Men
For Rotterdam
Newcastle upon Tyne. 6 February 1846
Sold and delivered on board the Jane Jackson C. Ward master One Hundred Six Tons or Forty Chaldrons Newcastle Chaldrons of Whitefield CINDERS at [illegible] Chaldron
Custom House. 6 Feby 1846
Ent. No. Collector.

excellent coking coal which was important for the development of the Teesside iron industry in the second half of the nineteenth century; the east Durham collieries mined good quality gas coals; and the pits of south east Northumberland produced high quality steam coal. Thus, the word 'coal' embraced a variety of products. This point is illustrated in the bills of lading. The first is a cargo of household coal from Waldridge Colliery (p7); the second is for coal 'wrought and gotten out of Felling Colliery for gas and smiths'; the third is for a cargo of 'celebrated Carr's Hartley steam coals' from Seghill Colliery; the fourth for coke or cinders from Whitefield Colliery and the fifth for Garesfield cinders.

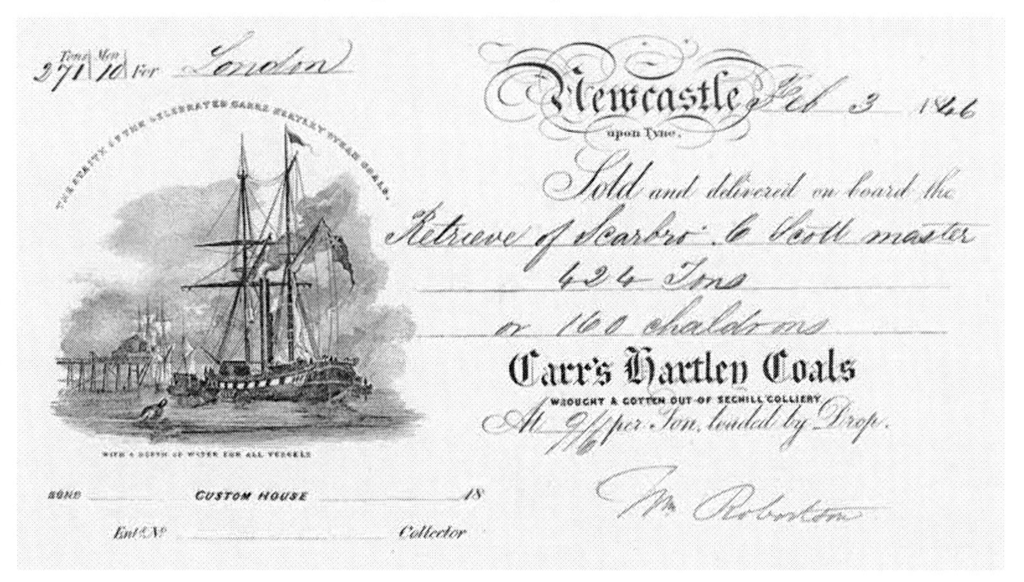
Tons Men 271 10 For London
Newcastle upon Tyne. Feb 3 1846
Sold and delivered on board the Retrieve of Scarbro C Scott master 424 Tons or 160 chaldrons
Carr's Hartley Coals
Wrought & gotten out of Seghill Colliery
At [illegible] per Ton, loaded by Drop.
Bond Custom House 18
Ent. No. Collector
Wm Robertson

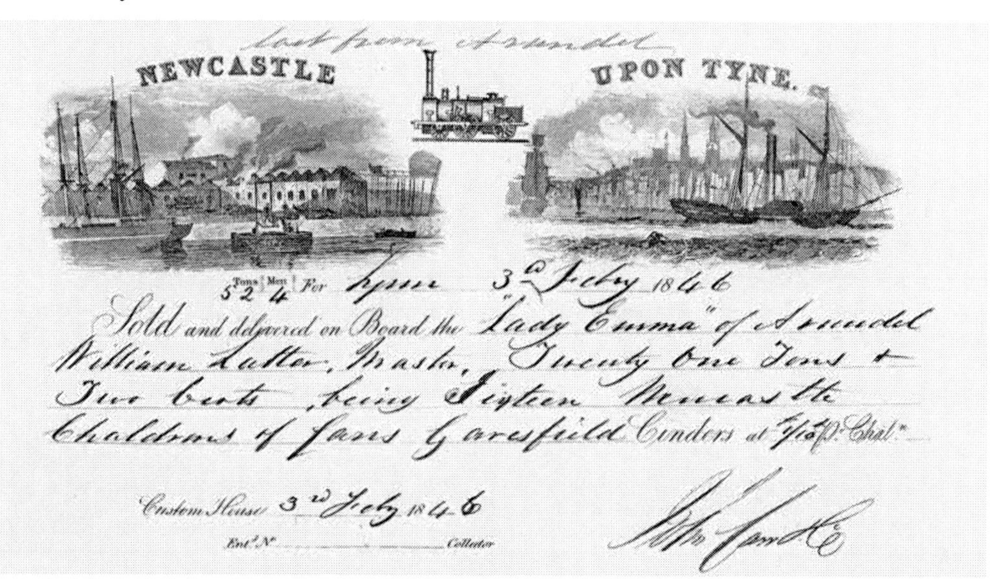
Last from Arundel
NEWCASTLE UPON TYNE.
Tons Men 52 4 For Lynn 3d Feby 1846
Sold and delivered on Board the "Lady Emma" of Arundel William Latter, Master, Twenty One Tons & Two Cwts, being Sixteen Newcastle Chaldrons of [illegible] Garesfield Cinders at [illegible] Chal.
Custom House 3d Feby 1846
Ent. No. Collector

An Outline History

Coal has been found in several forts along Hadrian's Wall indicating that coal was mined in Roman times. The coal was used to provide heating for the regimental bath houses and for the workshops. At Benwell fort to the west of Newcastle an altar to the Roman god of mining Jupiter Dolichenus was discovered near the outcrop of the High Main seam. However, it is important to distinguish between coal being mined for local use as at Benwell and coal being mined for a distant market. Because of the weight of coal, the cost of transport overland is high. Before the development of the railway, overland transport costs exceeded production costs when the coal was moved more than two or three miles. Therefore production was generally for a local market. What made the North East different from other areas of Britain was the fact that the coal seams outcropped near to the banks of rivers deep enough to enable the coalfield to use water transport to supply London and south east. When Bobby Shafto mined the same High Main coal seam at Benwell that the Roman army had mined, his was an entirely different enterprise. It was the difference between a landsale pit providing for local needs and a seacoal pit serving a distant and more lucrative market.

The coal trade developed during the Middle Ages when most of the mining was in the hands of the church, a principal landowner. The monks of Tynemouth priory were shipping coal from Tynemouth by 1269 and by the fourteenth century coal was being mined from their lands at Elswick and Benwell. The bishop of Durham had pits south of the River Tyne in the manors of Gateshead and Whickham where the coal seams also outcropped. The burgesses of Newcastle were allowed to dig for coal from pits in the Forth and Castle Leazes. During medieval times there was a perpetual struggle between these two powerful ecclesiastical neighbours and the burgesses of Newcastle who tried to control the export trade in coal from the river by forcing the prior and bishop to sell their coal exclusively through Newcastle merchants. The burgesses insisted upon the right of acting as a host to foreign merchants who could only trade through the burgesses. For this reason, by Tudor times, the coal merchants of Newcastle were known as hostmen.

Coal was mined in several other places during medieval times for local use such as Blyth and Wylam in Northumberland, around Chester-le-Street on the Wear and Bishop Auckland in Durham. However, it was the merchants of Tyneside who were able to develop an export trade because the best quality household coal seam – the High Main – was exposed at the surface near to the banks of the River Tyne. At a time when it was very difficult to transport heavy goods by road, the river provided the means of transport. During the fourteenth and fifteenth centuries about 15,000 tons per annum was shipped from Tyneside to London where it was in demand by large fuel users such as the lime-burners, bakers, smiths and brewers. Increasingly, as wood became expensive in the capital, people turned to coal for domestic use. However, there was considerable resistance to burning coal because of the pollution it caused. London was not the only market for Newcastle's coal: vessels from France, the Low Countries and the Baltic brought cargoes to Tyneside and returned with coal as ballast. Although the coal trade was important, the main exports from Tyneside in the Middle Ages were wool, hides and grindstones. It is significant that Roger Thornton, one of the great medieval merchants of Newcastle, whose monumental brass adorns his burial spot in St. Nicholas Cathedral, traded in wool rather than coal.

Elizabethan Times

At the dissolution of the monasteries in 1536 and 1539, these lands of the church became crown property. Subsequently, through grants and leases large areas of the coalfield passed into the possession of entrepreneurs who were stimulated to increase production by the demand for coal as a domestic and industrial fuel. During the reign of Elizabeth I, there was a dramatic increase in the coastal trade from the River Tyne which grew from about 35,000 tons in 1550 to about 165,000 tons in 1600. Incredibly, by 1625, production had expanded to 400,000 tons. This dramatic rise in demand was caused primarily by the rapid increase in the population of London. Tyneside became known as the 'Black Indies' and the name of Newcastle became synonymous with coal.

The trade in seacoal, which was the name given to the coal shipped from the Tyne, was controlled by the Company of Hostmen in Newcastle. In 1600, Elizabeth I granted the hostmen a charter, by which in return for a tax of one shilling per chaldron of coal shipped coastwise from Newcastle, the hostmen were granted the exclusive right to trade in coal from Tyneside. It also sanctioned electoral arrangements which gave them virtual monopoly of municipal offices. Members of the company owned most of the principal collieries on Tyneside and they tried to regulate the output of the pits to maintain a high price for their coal on the London market. Understandably, there were frequent complaints to parliament from the London merchants and the East Anglian shippers about the perceived injustice of their activities.

The principal mining areas for seacoal in Elizabethan times were the manors of Gateshead and Whickham on the south bank and Benwell, Elswick, Denton and Newburn on the north bank of the River Tyne. This was a very limited area of the coalfield where the High Main and other lower seams outcropped near to the banks of the River Tyne. The low medieval bridge at Newcastle and the shallow nature of parts of the river prevented sea-going vessels reaching the area of mining west of the bridge. The coal was ferried down the river in keels by the keelman to larger vessels, the colliers, at Shields near the mouth of the River Tyne. The keelman were a distinctive group living principally at Sandgate in the east of Newcastle but also at other riverside communities like Dunston and Swalwell. Many keelmen came from the border country for this seasonal work and returned to their families during slack periods of mid summer and mid winter. The market demanded large coal and it required some skill by the keelmen in handling the cargo to prevent breakages. Small coals could be sold to lime-burners, glassmakers and salt producers but at much inferior price. The Keelmen's Hospital, which was established in 1701 to provide welfare facilities for these workmen, still stands in Sandgate. The hospital and the popular folk song 'The Keel Row' are reminders of this distinctive group of Tyneside workers.

As I went thro Sandgate, thro Sandgate, thro Sandgate,
As I went thro Sandgate, I heard the lassies sing;
Weel may the keel row, the keel row, the keel row,
Weel may the keel row that my laddie's in.

The engraving shows a keelboat passing through the low bridge at Newcastle which had replaced the medieval bridge destroyed by flooding in 1781.

The ships engaged in the coastal trade to London and the South East in Elizabethan times were mainly owned by traders from the ports of Ipswich, King's Lynn and Yarmouth in East Anglia. These colliers were vessels of about 200 to 300 tons and made perhaps six trips during the summer season. Often the ships arrived in the River Tyne carrying flint, clay or sand as ballast which, when it could not be dumped at sea to avoid tolls, was off-loaded onto the shore to create the ballast hills of Tyneside folklore.

Eventually, these ballast cargoes give rise to the glassmaking and pottery industries of Tyneside since they provided these industries with cheap raw materials. During the mid nineteenth century the region produced about 40% of the nation's glass: the glass cone at Lemington is a reminder of this important industry. Also, Newcastle and Sunderland were major centres of pottery manufacture in Victoria's reign. The Maling pottery in Byker became one of the largest potteries in Britain employing 1,200 workers. Clay was imported as ballast but it was also found in association with the coal seams.

Some Elizabethan merchant's houses survive in the Close off Newcastle's quayside. These houses were built with pantile roofs and Flemish bricks brought back as ballast by colliers from Europe. The tall chimney was developed in Elizabethan times to deal with the problem of pollution from open coal fires. The export trade to the continent – France, Germany and the Low Countries – was chiefly in the hands of Dutch and French ships. However, in the seventeenth century, the Newcastle merchants began to build ships especially for the coal trade which was a major stimulus to the development of the shipbuilding industry on Tyneside.

Early Modern Times

In 1637, Charles I attempted to consolidate the hostmen's monopoly in return for an additional tax which was vitally important in his efforts to secure financial independence of parliament. However, the puritan merchants in London and shippers from East Anglia resisted by boycotting Tyne coal. In 1638, Charles was forced to concede and in the following year the Scots invaded and occupied Newcastle in a successful attempt to seize the coalfield and embarrass the king. In 1641, parliament abolished the right of the king to collect tax from seacoal. When civil war finally broke out in 1642, Newcastle supported the king against the Scots and the puritans. The parliamentarians, who controlled the navy, blockaded the River Tyne in 1644: in that year fewer than 200 ships entered the Tyne compared with 3,000 in a normal year and only 3,000 tons of coal were shipped as against 450,000 tons. Newcastle's difficulties provided the opportunities for others to step into the breach notably Sunderland whose trade with London expanded during this time. The coal shipped from Sunderland was mined from a small area of outcrops near Chester-le-Street with easy access to the River Wear. However, this was a brief recession for London needed coals from Newcastle.

In 1625, about 400 ships were engaged in the coastal trade alone: but by the end of the century there were about 1,000 making several trips a year. These ships carried the large coal demanded by the London market. Much of the small coal was left in the pits or burnt at the pithead but there was a local market for the some of the small coals despised by the London merchants. The manufacture of salt from seawater was extensive in the area because of the availability of cheap coal. South Shields was the principal centre for this industry and by 1750 there were 200 pans for boiling seawater. These pans consumed over a quarter of a million tons of coal per annum. The area became the largest producer of salt in the country and exported about 10,000 tons to the Baltic and northern Europe.

Transporting coal by land was both difficult and expensive. After a distance of about two to three miles the cost of transport exceeded the cost of extraction. Coal was carried by packhorses, two-wheeled carts known as cowps or the larger four wheeled waggon known as a wain. The major collieries used the wain which carried 17.5 cwt. The collieries had dedicated wainroads but even these were useless in wet weather because the heavy vehicles churned up the land. As the accessible coal near the river became exhausted the attention of the coal owners turned to the more distant outcrops of coal. The need to transport large quantities of coal several miles to the staiths at the riverside led to the development of the waggonway, the precursor of the modern railway, in the early seventeenth century.

The first waggonways in the region were built by Huntington Beaumont in about 1608 to transport coal from his pits at Bedlington, Cowpen and

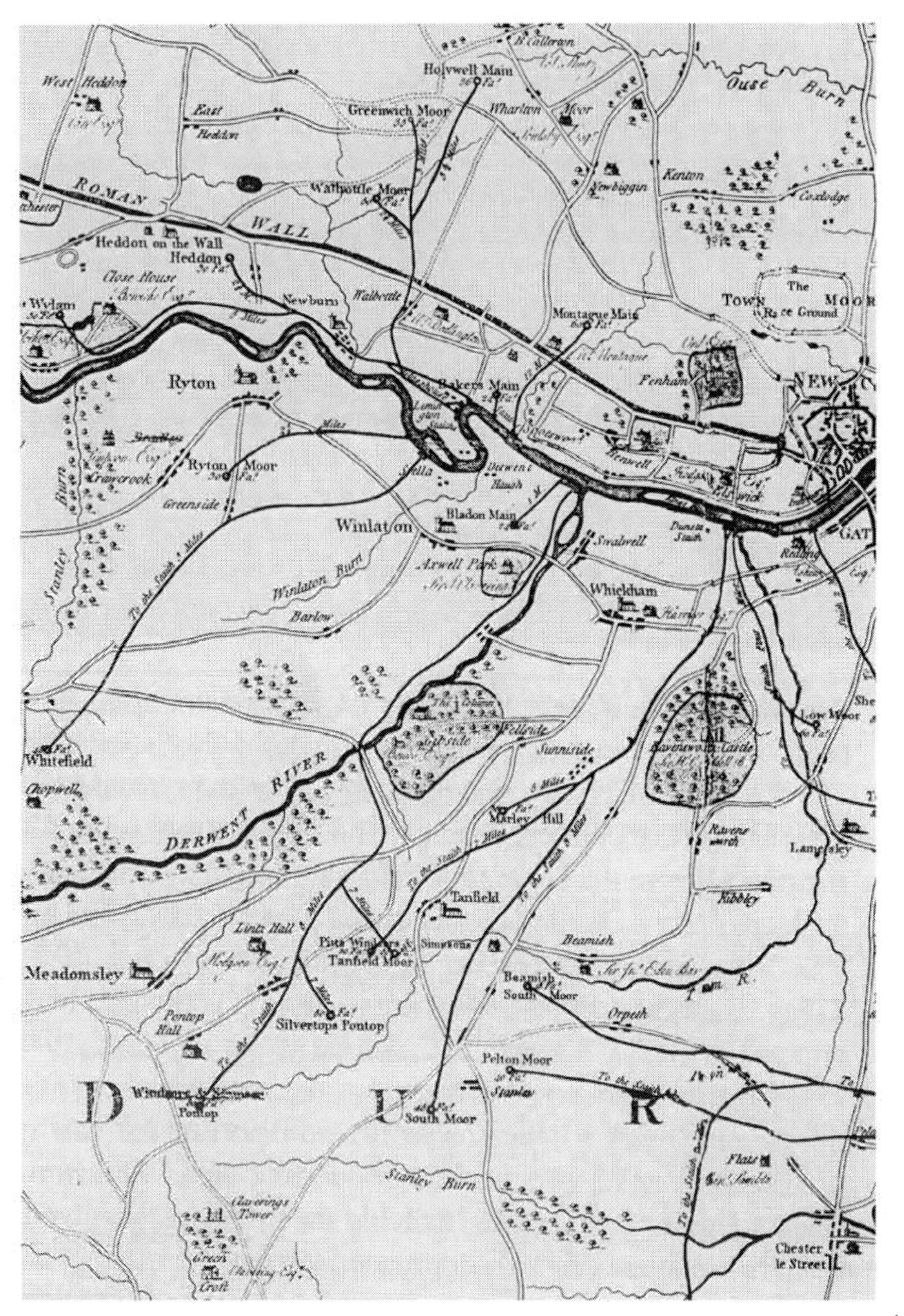

Bebside to the port of Blyth. Unfortunately, the system closed down when he became bankrupt in 1618 having failed in his attempt to break the monopoly of the Newcastle merchants. In 1624, he died in the debtor's prison in Nottingham. From 1621 the Whickham collieries were served by a waggonway from the mines to the staiths at Dunston. Across the River Tyne, in the royal manor of Benwell, the pits were now as far north as Hadrian's Wall, and they were served by a waggonway to the Tyne from about 1637. On these early waggonways a single horse was used to haul a chaldron waggon along wooden rails to the staiths. Where possible the force of gravity was also used: the weight of the loaded waggons descending an incline pulled empty wagons up the hill on their return journey. Benwell was one of the first collieries in the region to use an inclined plane.

By the mid eighteenth century, a network of wooden waggonways linked the collieries with the staiths on the rivers Tyne and Wear. Perhaps the most famous was the Tanfield Waggonway which was opened in 1725 and carried coal trains until 1962. The line is shown on the section from Gibson's map of the coalfield dated 1788 running from Tanfield Moor to the River Tyne passing en route the estates of two of the great coal owning families – the Bowes' at Gibside and the Liddells at Ravensworth. The scale of the civil engineering on the waggonway astounded contemporaries who compared it to the great works of Rome. The antiquarian William Stukeley wrote in 1725 that 'we saw Colonel Lyddels coal-works at Tanfield where he carries the road over valleys filled with earth, 100 foot high, 300 foot broad at bottom; other valleys as large have a stone bridge laid across; and in this manner a road is made, and frames of timber laid for five miles to the river side'. In the eighteenth century, the Tanfield way carried about a third of the total production of the Great Northern Coalfield. The world's oldest railway bridge and embankment can still be seen at Causey.

Daniel Defoe, writing in 1726, described how the waggonway carried coal to 'a great storehouse called a Stethe .... with one part close to or hanging

over the Water that lighters or keels came close or under it and the coals at once shot out of the Waggon into the said lighters which carry them to the Ships'. At this time the coal was stored undercover to prevent it from weathering which lowered its value on the London market. These huge wooden structures can be seen in the engravings of the Team staith above and the Hollywell staith at Lemington below, both situated up river from the medieval bridge at Newcastle. Large coal was prized on the London market and in 1807 the coal drop was invented by William Chapman to reduce breakages. It was first used at Coxlodge Colliery's staith at Wallsend. Traditionally, coal had been loaded from spouts as shown on the engravings of Oakwellgate staith above, where a keel boat is being loaded, and Carr Hill staith below, where a collier is being loaded. At the drops, the chaldron waggon was lowered directly onto the deck of the collier and a counterbalance was used to return the empty waggon. Often the water was too shallow to enable the collier to be fully loaded: then it was moved into the river and topped up from the keel boat. At the Washington staith a chaldron waggon is being lowered onto the collier while the keelmen stand by.

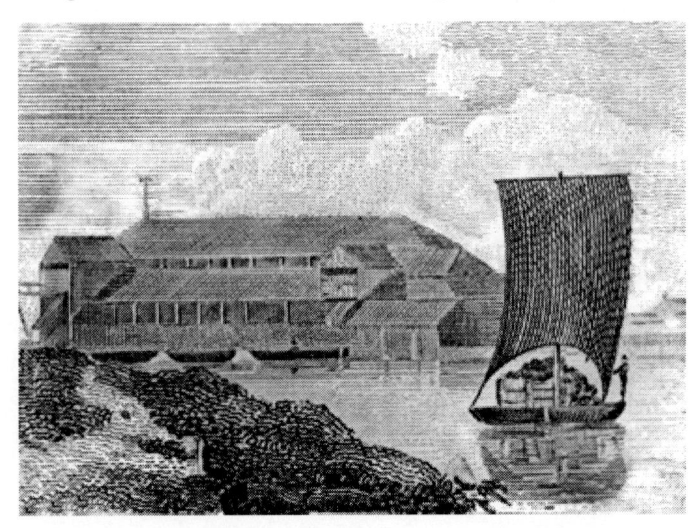

Further expansion – The Iron Industry.

During the seventeenth and eighteenth centuries, the coal trade continued to increase stimulated not only by the increasing demand for coal as a domestic fuel, but also by the development of new industrial processes. In the iron industry, the shortage of timber had resulted in the ironmasters experimenting with coke as an alternative fuel to charcoal for their furnaces. Abraham Darby I (1677-1717) made coke from coal by cooking the coal in heaps like the charcoal burners. His son, Abraham Darby II (1711-1763) improved upon this method by using special coking ovens and also by improving his furnaces with stronger bellows to provide a better blast during smelting. By using coke as a fuel he was able to produce good quality pig iron which was suitable both for castings and for refining into bar iron at the forge. As the demands for iron products increased so did the demand for coking coal.

In the eighteenth century iron making in the North East was chiefly centred upon the Derwent valley where some of the principal collieries of the day were situated. Here Ambrose Crowley had established workshops at Winlaton and Swalwell. He won substantial contracts with the royal navy to supply nails, chains and anchors. In 1770, his works were described as 'the greatest manufactory of its kind in Europe'. Important as these development were, they do not compare with the great development of the iron industry on Teesside in the later nineteenth century, when the iron ore deposits of Cleveland and Weardale were exploited. As a consequence, Middlesborough was transformed from farmland into a great industrial town during the early years of Victoria's reign.

Steel was also produced in the Derwent valley at Blackhall Mill and Derwentcote by the cementation process. In the eighteenth century the North East produced about 400 tons, half of Britain's annual output of steel, mainly using imported Swedish wrought iron often brought to the Tyne as ballast in the colliers. By the nineteenth century the North East had lost its leadership in this field to Sheffield. One old cementation furnace still exists at Derwentcote near Hamsterley Mill.

From the middle of the nineteenth century, coke making became an important industry at many collieries in west Durham. Indeed, some of the ironmasters owned collieries producing coking coal as part of their industrial empire. The illustrations show the beehive coke ovens at Rowlands Gill prior to their closure in 1958. First the oven was loaded from the top with small coals which were levelled by means of a long rake resting on an iron bar suspended by chains at the doorway of the oven. The coal was heated in the oven and afterwards it was cooled with water. It could then be removed from the oven by means of a 'reel' or long handled shovel hung on a pivoted crane. The 'reel' was used to throw the coke out onto a loading bench to allow it to cool before being loaded onto waggons for transport to Consett iron works nearby.

Coal as a Source of Power

During the eighteenth century, coal came to be used as a source of power as a result of the development of the steam engine. In 1705, Thomas Newcomen produced his steam atmospheric engine to pump water from the Cornish tin mines. Steam was used to drive a piston which forced a rocker beam upwards; the steam was condensed with water and the weight of the beam forced the piston down. This see-saw motion was used to drive pumping rods which sucked up the water. These Newcomen engines were very inefficient and therefore consumed a lot of fuel. Consequently, they were not widely used in Cornwall where coal was expensive. However, this was not a problem to the coal owners of the North East where the pumping engines were seen as the solution to draining the flooded Tyne Basin east of Newcastle. A Newcomen engine was in action at Tanfield Lea in 1715 and at Byker in 1717. By 1720 these engines were in general use and by 1769 more than one hundred were in operation in the Northumberland and Durham coalfield.

The efficiency of the Newcomen engines was improved by James Watt who added a separate condenser and valve box. He applied steam to both ends of the piston and the steam engine as opposed to the atmospheric engine was born. More important, in 1781, by using a connecting rod at the end of a beam to turn a flywheel, he converted the rocking motion of the beam into the rotary motion of the wheel. The steam engine could now be used to drive a wide range of machinery. In the pits it was now used for winding as well as pumping and the steam engine was quickly adopted by the ironmasters to drive bellows, rollers and hammers. Later, it was used by the cotton manufacturers to drive spinning and weaving machinery. Because of this development of steam power produced by burning coal to boil water, the major centres of industry became concentrated near the coalfields.

Steam Power for Transport

Steam power was soon applied to transport. In 1802, William Symington, a Scottish millwright, launched the steamship 'Charlotte Dundas' which hauled two barges for twenty miles along the Forth-Clyde canal. By 1818, a regular steam ferry service was in operation between Dover and Calais; and a steam powered tug was used to move colliers at the mouth of the River Tyne. However, it was not until later in the nineteenth century that steam power replaced sail on the main ocean routes and in the coal trade.

In contrast, the development of steam power for transport on land was a much quicker affair. Early railways, known as waggonways, had existed since the seventeenth century on which horses were used to haul waggons along wooden railways. Because of the shortage of horses and the high price of fodder during the time of the Napoleonic wars, several attempts were made to replace horses with a steam engine. In 1804, Richard Trevithick used a steam locomotive to haul waggons on the Penydaren tramway in South Wales. During the following year a Trevithick locomotive was built in Gateshead but it was too heavy for the track of the Wylam waggonway and was used as a stationary engine at the Gateshead workshops. Other engineers were quick to follow Trevithick's lead. In

1813, William Hedley built 'Puffing Billy' for the Wylam waggonway (a relica of this engine can be seen at Beamish Museum). The locomotive could haul nine full waggons at 5 mph and was a source of inspiration to the great locomotive engineer George Stephenson – generally accepted as the father of the modern railway. The opening of the Stockton and Darlington Railway in 1825, two hundred years after the first waggonways had been built, is usually regarded as the beginning of the public railway system. During the nineteenth century, the railway powered by steam locomotives became the principal method of transporting goods and people throughout Britain, Europe and many other parts of the world. Tyneside became a centre for locomotive building and Stephenson's factory, the first locomotive works in the world, still survives in South Street behind Newcastle Central Station. The railways stimulated a demand for coal but they also provided the means by which other coalfields could compete with Newcastle for the London market.

The engraving of Hetton Colliery, dated about 1840, shows steam power being used for pumping water and drawing coals – it also shows one of Stephenson's early steam locomotives in action hauling a rake of chaldron wagons.

Coal Gas.

Methane gas – or fire damp as the miners called it – occurs naturally in some coal seams. It was the cause of some of the most horrific accidents in the northern coalfield such as the disasters at Wallsend Colliery in 1835, which killed 101 miners, and at Seaham in 1880, which killed 164 miners. In 1765, Carlisle Spedding, the agent for Lord Lonsdale in Cumbria, used methane to light the colliery office at Whitehaven. Two years later, in 1767, Richard Watson, the professor of chemistry at Cambridge University, published an account of the preparation of inflammable gas by carbonising coal. However, it was William Murdock, the foreman of the famous Soho Works of Boulton and Watt, north of Birmingham, who pioneered the commercial manufacture of coal gas in England. In 1802, the Soho

Foundry was illuminated by gas lighting to celebrate the Peace of Amiens – a brief interlude of respite during the Napoleonic Wars. By 1805, coal gas was being used to light cotton mills in Manchester and Halifax and shops in London and Glasgow. In 1812, the London Light and Coke Company was established and in 1816 the first provincial gas company was founded at Preston in Lancashire. The following year, 1817, the Newcastle and Gateshead Gas Company was established and street lighting by gas was introduced into Newcastle in 1818 and into Gateshead in 1821. Gradually, gas lighting was introduced into homes to replace oil lamps. In 1855, R.W.Bunsen invented the aerated gas burner named after him and this stimulated a great interest in cooking and heating by coal gas. By 1869, about six million tons of coal were being used to produce household gas and the circular gas holder, some of which still survive, was a familiar site in even the smallest town. The aerial photograph of the Redheugh gas works in Gateshead was taken in the 1950's. The works opened in 1876 and occupied a site between the Tanfield railway line and the Dunston staiths. Gas coal became an important export from the collieries in eastern County Durham: coal from Horden Colliery was used to produce gas to light the streets of Hamburg.

The Chemical Industry

When coal is heated in an oven to produce coke, it gives off a thick brown smoke which contains gas, tar and ammonia liquor. The early beehive coal ovens, although they produced excellent coke for the blast furnaces, did not recover the by-products of tar and ammonia liquor. Later in the nineteenth century, with the development of the science of chemistry, the value of these by-products of coke production began to be understood. In 1883, John Jameson of Newcastle devised an improved method of recovering the by-products through the floor of the beehive oven. However, by this time the first battery of by-product recovery coke ovens in Britain had been built at Crook in Weardale. In the course of the last 150 years, chemists have discovered a large range of substances which can be made from these by-products including fertilisers, explosives, nylon, plastics and disinfectants.

Furthermore, the abundant supply of cheap fuel in the form of the small coals led to the development of other chemical factories on Tyneside. Iron pyrites, fool's gold, known to the miners as brasses, is frequently found amongst the coal. The miner's brasses were exposed to the weather for several years at the copperas works and then roasted in an oven. The process was used to produce colours (Venetian red and Prussian blue), ink and sulphuric acid. The acid was mixed with magnesium limestone to produce Epsom salts and with alum shales to produce alum. Epsom salts and alum were both used as mordants in the textile industry. Sulphuric acid was used in the alkali industry.

Alkali is of considerable economic importance since it is an essential ingredient in the manufacture of soap and glass. Traditionally, it was produced from the seaweed kelp but towards the end of the eighteenth century manufacturers, such as Isaac Cookson of South Shields, began to examine the possibilities of producing alkali from salt. In 1791, the Frenchman Nicholas Leblanc discovered a process for converting salt into soda using sulphuric acid. The first alkali works in Britain to use the Leblanc process was built at Walker in 1796 by the chemist William Losh who was a partner in Walker Colliery. A major industry developed particularly on the south side of the river between Gateshead and South Shields. By the 1860's Tyneside was producing more than half the national output of alkali and the Tyneside chemical industry was consuming 300,000 tons of coal each year. The engraving of the staiths for St. Lawrence's Colliery in Byker shows the large chimney of the Felling chemical works in the background. These tall chimneys were used to dissipate the hydrochloric acid gas produced when salt was mixed with sulphuric acid: they were only partly successful and acid rain was a feature of the Tyneside climate in the late nineteenth century. 'The Alkali', a public house near Tyne Dock, is one of the few reminders of this important Tyneside industry.

Felling Staiths

Increased Production.

Thus, during the eighteenth and nineteenth centuries, the demand for coal increased considerably. Coal was used as a domestic fuel by the growing urban population of industrial Britain; as the means of generating steam power for industry and transport; as the source of coke for iron and steel making; as the raw material for producing coal gas used for lighting and cooking in the expanding towns; and as a source of valuable by-products for the emerging chemical industry. Coal was at the centre of the industrial revolution first in Britain and then elsewhere in Europe and America. From this time the carbon based economy was established and one source for global warming created. The Great Northern Coalfield was at the heart of this revolution and Newcastle was the leading centre of mining technology at a time when Britain was largest producer of coal in the world. At the North of England Mining Institute, still standing at the foot of Westgate Road, the world's foremost mining engineers, who were running the great collieries in the North East, met to share their mining expertise. Their skills were used to develop mines throughout the world. Today, coal is at the centre of the industrialisation of China adding to the growing concern over carbon emissions.

The effect of the growing demand for coal was reflected in the increased output from the mines of Northumberland and Durham and in the increased number of men employed in the mining industry. Technical developments in pumping, ventilation and haulage enabled deep mines to be sunk beneath the magnesian limestone plateau in east Durham and beyond the Ninety Fathom Dyke in Northumberland. The winning of these mines was achieved only with considerable capital outlay and often after initial setbacks. The sinking of Hetton Colliery, the first to break though the porous magnesian limestone plateau, in the 1820's cost £50,000; the attempt to win the neighbouring Haswell Colliery in 1831 ended in failure after £60,000 had been spent, because the sinkers were unable to stem the flow of water.

The following table shows the increase in production during the nineteenth century to the peak year of 1911. It also shows a fall in productivity.

Year	Production	Workforce	Productivity
1800	c. 4.5 million tons	c. 12,000	375 tons per man
1844	c. 10.0 million tons	c. 34,000	294 tons per man
1873	c. 29.5 million tons	c. 77,000	383 tons per man
1900	46.3 million tons	153,000	303 tons per man
1911	56.4 million tons	227,000	248 tons per man

Although these statistics show the enormous development of the northern coalfield they hide two factors of great importance. Firstly, the dominance of the North East was beginning to wane as other coalfields developed at a more spectacular rate because the building of a network of railways throughout Britain enabled them to reach a wider market. At the end of the Napoleonic Wars, the Great Northern Coalfield produced about 40% of U.K. output; at the outbreak of the Crimean War in 1854, it produced about 25% and by the beginning of the First World War, the North East produced only 20%. Thus, increasing competition in the domestic market from other British coalfields, brought about principally by the development of the railways, meant that the domestic market for Newcastle's coal rose only gradually from about two million to over five million tons a year. Secondly, the bulk of the increase in production from North East mines in the nineteenth century was sold to the expanding overseas export markets especially in France, Germany and Italy where factories and industrial towns were being built as the industrial revolution spread throughout Europe. The North East became heavily dependent upon this export trade.

The massive development of the coal trade from the North East was possible because of the development of the ports and their transport infrastructure, the building of bigger and faster colliers and the availability of migrant labour from elsewhere in Britain attracted by the wages available to those working in the pits. Prior to its transformation by the Tyne

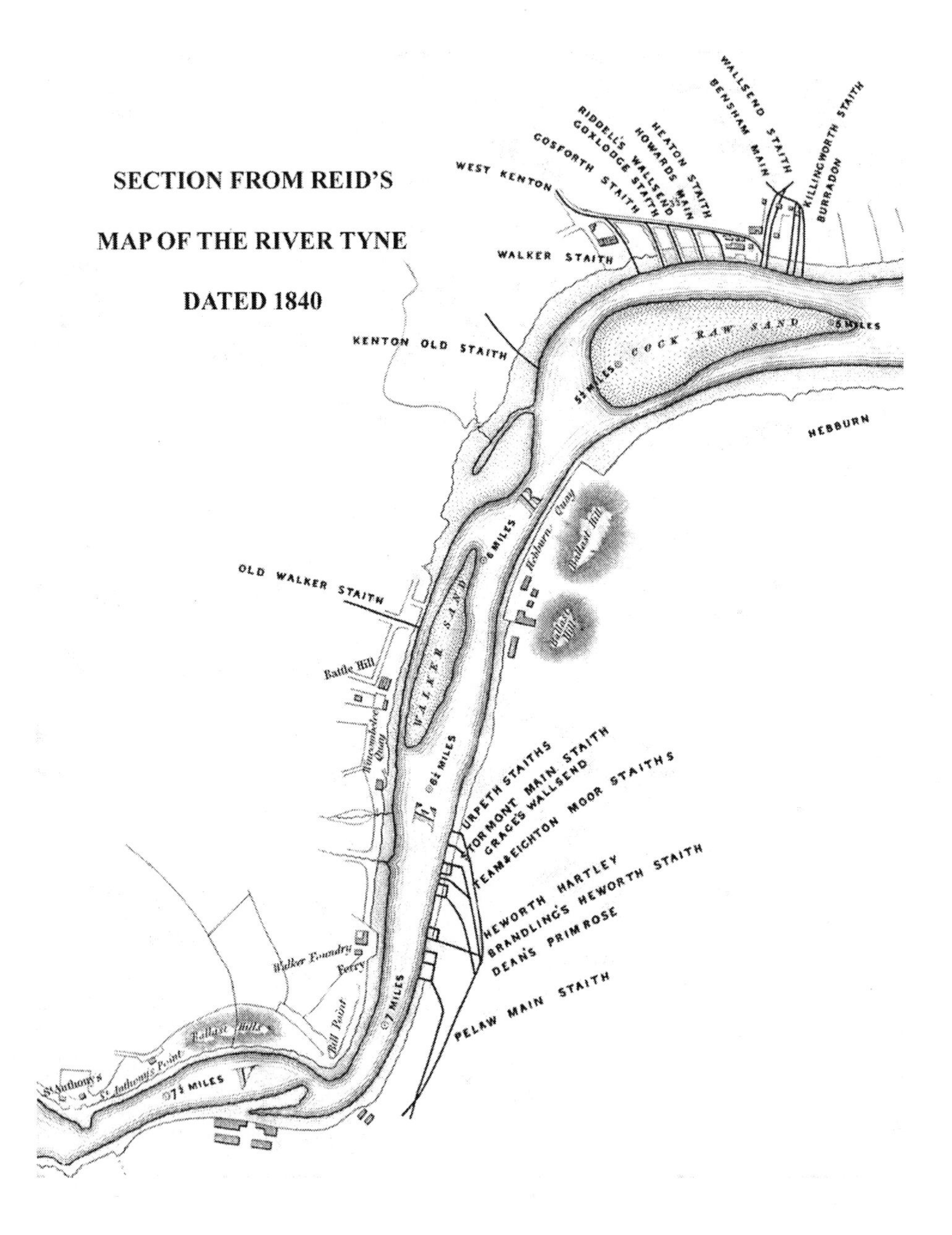

Improvement Commission in the second half of the nineteenth century, the River Tyne was not an easy river to navigate largely because Newcastle Corporation failed to invest enough of the taxes from the coal trade into improving the river. The shallow waters at the bar, the Black Midden rocks and the Herd Sands at the mouth, the moving sandbanks and the failure to dredge a deep channel, all created major problems for the captains of the collier ships. The old bridge at Newcastle was an obstacle to large vessels until the opening of Armstrong's Swing Bridge in 1876. Before this date all coal from above bridge was carried in keel boats to colliers moored downstream principally at Shields. In 1850, the establishment of the Tyne Improvement Commission marked the beginning of a period of great change. Northumberland Dock was built by the T.I.C. to serve the collieries of south east Northumberland. A further five staiths were built at Whitehall Point. On the south bank the North Eastern Railway constructed Tyne Dock and Dunston Staiths to serve the Durham collieries. Tyne Dock had four staiths with forty two spouts and was capable of loading sixteen vessels simultaneously – it shipped more coal than any other dock in the world. These improvements led to a five fold increase in coal exports from the Tyne: from just under four million tons in 1850 to over twenty million tons in 1911.

Dunston Staiths

The port facilities at Amble, Blyth, Sunderland, West Hartlepool, Stockton and Middlesborough were also greatly improved to handle the increased trade with railways linking the ports directly to the pits. The Stockton and Darlington Railway was opened in 1825 essentially to carry coal from the pits of south west Durham to the River Tees. It was extended to Middlesborough in 1834 as a consequence of the building of a rival line by the Clarence Railway Company to Haverton Hill. In 1831, the first coal was shipped from Seaham Harbour where the Marquis of Londonderry had built an entirely new port linked by rail to his collieries at Rainton. In the following year, the Hartlepool Dock and Railway Company began transforming the old port, which had become a rubbish dump, into an important coal shipment facility linked by rail to the pits around Moorsley. The railway king George Hudson, M.P. for Sunderland, built the new South Dock between 1846 and 1850. Large vessels were able to avoid the dangerous bar at the mouth of the River Wear by using the new southern outlet. The Newcastle and Berwick Railway Company opened a five mile branch line to Amble in 1849, linking Earl Grey's colliery at Broomhill with the port then known as Warkworth Harbour. Much of this early development was conducted amid fierce competition by the railway companies to capture the coal trade. Later, in 1884, the North Eastern Railway Company, which had absorbed most of these small companies, built new staiths at Blyth to rejuvenate the port and improve facilities for the new collieries in the Ashington area.

The launching of the first sucessful iron built and screw propelled ship, the 'John Bowes', at Palmer's shipyard in Jarrow in 1852 revolutionised the transport of coal. She carried 650 tons compared to the 280 tons of a good sailing collier; but more importantly, steaming at nine miles an hour, she made the return journey between the Tyne and the Thames in five days compared with the month taken by a sailing ship. Having a twin hull she was able to use water as ballast and at the port of London hydraulic cranes, built by William Armstrong's engineering firm on Tyneside, also facilitated the quick turn round of the collier. The success of this type of vessel is seen by the fact that in 1855 there were 60 screw colliers based in

the Tyne and the number continued to grow rapidly. Not only did the screw colliers make the development of the export trade possible but their success stimulated a large expansion of the shipbuilding industry on the Tyne. The photograph shows the 'John Bowes' lying off Pelaw Main Staiths with Walker Iron Works just visible in the background. The shipbuilding industry on the Wear also began to build in iron – the first iron ship, the Loftus being launched in 1852.

The expansion of the coalfield, particularly during Victoria's reign, acted as magnet drawing people into the region from Scotland, Ireland, Wales and other parts of England. The offer of relatively high wages and good housing encouraged men like the redundant textile workers of Norfolk to move to the North East. There was a large influx of catholic Irish particularly into County Durham. New villages were created by the mining companies to accommodate this migration such as at Chopwell in Durham and at Ashington in Northumberland. These villages became close-knit communities, dominated by the colliery, and fiercely loyal to miners' trade union and later to the Labour Party. The regimented terraces of colliery houses, the non conformist chapels, the social clubs and allotment gardens, clustered around the mine, became a distinctive feature of the region.

The importance of the mining communities in the development of the labour movement, which led to the improvement of the living condition of the working classes in Britain, should not be forgotten amid all these statistics of production. Trade unionism was born in the protracted struggles against the miners' bond, their annual contract of employment which tied them to a particular colliery for one year. The bitter and unsuccessful strikes of 1831-2 and 1844 ultimately led to the formation of the Northumberland Miners' Union in 1862 and the Durham Miners' Association in 1869. Welbourne, in his history of these two unions, commented that by 1882 the Northumberland and Durham unions were 'unrivalled in financial strength, organisation and firm purpose'. These unions played a central role in the management of labour relations at the colliery. The wages of the miners were based upon the amount of coal they produced and one of the unions' first victories was to secure the appointment in 1872 of checkweighmen at the pithead. These union officials worked alongside the owners representatives to verify the production of individual miners. The Northumberland miners' leader Thomas Burt was returned to parliament by the Morpeth miners after the election of 1874. As a member of the Liberal Party, he was one of the first working class M.Ps. in the country. The Northumberland and Durham miners' unions became part of the Mineworkers Federation of Great Britain which was formed in 1889. The decision of the M.F.G.B. to affiliate to the Labour Party in 1909 was a major landmark in British political history. The leaders of the miners were prominent in the development of the Labour Party which in the twentieth century played a dominant role in local politics throughout the coalfield and an increasing role in national politics. Coal was at the foundation of the national economy and the miners used this fact for political ends.

The photograph shows the leaders of the 1925-26 strike at Chopwell gathered beneath their banner in front of the miners' institute. Second on the left is Will Lawther who became president of the National Union of Mineworkers between 1945 and 1954 and played an important role in the early years of the nationalised coal industry.

Banner of Chopwell Lodge

From the mid nineteenth century the government began to interfere in the mining industry to protect the workforce. The report of the Children's Commission in 1842 shocked the House of Commons with its illustrated accounts of the work of children and women down the mines. It led to legislation banning all women and children under ten from working underground. Although there is evidence that women were employed during the early eighteenth century in mines on the River Wear, by the nineteenth century women did not work in the mines of the Great Northern Coalfield. However, young boys were employed as trappers underground and at the screens on the surface. Concern over the increasing loss of life from mining accidents led to the establishment of the mines inspectorate. The 1842 Mines Act resulted in the appointment of S. Tremenheare as the first government inspector and by 1850 four had been appointed to cover the whole of Britain. Mathias Dunn, a very experienced colliery viewer from Tyneside, was given responsibility for the whole of the North East and Cumbria. The reports of these inspectors led to further legislation. In 1862, following the Hartley Colliery disaster, when 199 men were entombed in the pit when the engine beam broke and tumbled down the only shaft blocking any escape from the mine, legislation was passed which required collieries to have a minimum of two shafts. The Mines Act of 1887 required the management – the overmen and deputies - to be trained in mining practice including mine safety. In this education the North of England Institute of Mining and Mechanical Engineering, famous throughout the mining world as a centre of expertise, played a seminal role. At a time when government interference in industry was limited these were bold developments.

The Decline of Coal Mining.

Coal production in the North East reached its peak in the years immediately before the First World War. The decline of the coal industry after the war had far reaching effects for the independent spiral of growth which linked the coal industry with the iron and steel industry, shipbuilding and the engineering industries was thrown into reverse causing an interdependent spiral of decline. This contraction not only resulted in the transformation of the mining communities and the distinctive society which the mining industry had created but affected the region as a whole. The decline of the coal industry was not a sudden collapse but a process of change which began at the end of the First World War and then gathered pace during the twentieth century. There were moments of optimism such in 1947 when the coal mines were nationalised or when the super pits were opened along the North East coast mining coal several miles offshore beneath the North Sea. However, throughout the twentieth century, the Great Northern Coalfield continued to contract and the gradual decline resulted in pit closures, the emigration of miners from the region and ultimately, the death of mining communities.The statistics below show the fall in production and the consequent reduction in the workforce. They also show the impact of mechanisation upon productivity after the nationalisation of the coal mines in 1947.

Year	Production	Workforce	Productivity
1911	56.4 million tons	227,000	248 tons per man
1929	53.5 million tons	208,000	257 tons per man
1938	44.7 million tons	160,000	279 tons per man
1948	36.8 million tons	149,000	247 tons per man
1964/65	31.2 million tons	93,000	335 tons per man
1980/81	14.0 million tons	32,000	438 tons per man

One major reason for the decline of the coal industry was the shrinkage of the export trade. The terms of the Treaty of Versailles which ended the First World War damaged the Tyneside coal trade since Germany was compelled to pay reparations in the form of coal to France and Italy, formerly two of the principal export markets for Tyneside coal. In addition, cheap coal from Germany and Poland undermined the North East's export market to Scandinavia. Because of the lack of investment in new mining technology by the coal owners, which was perhaps understandable at a time of recession, Tyneside was ill equipped to face the growth of international competition in worldwide export markets. The coal owners were competing against highly mechanised collieries from overseas often working thicker seams. Consequently, coal shipments from the River Tyne fell from 21 to 13 million tons between 1925 and 1935.

Another reason for the deceleration in the demand for coal was the development of alternative sources of power for heating and lighting. The North East played a major part in the creation of electrical power generation through the development of the steam turbine by Charles Parsons at Heaton; through the development of switch gear by Reyrolles of Hebburn and the improvement of the boilers by Clarke Chapman of Gateshead. As a consequence, electricity began to replace coal as a source of power to industry and for heating and lighting in the home. Furthermore, with the development of hydro-electricity and power stations using oil, natural gas and later nuclear power, the steam to generate the turbines, which produced the electricity, was no longer exclusively produced by burning coal. These changes particularly affected the export market upon which the North East was so dependent. The domestic market was also affected: for example, the ending of steam power on the railways in 1968 removed a major market which at its peak, in 1949, had used 15 million tons of coal - much of which was from collieries in the North East.

The growing concern about pollution was another cause of the decline in the popularity of coal, especially after London's 'black fog' of December 1952, when visibility was limited to eleven inches and hundreds were killed by smoke related diseases. Public concern led to the Clean Air Act of 1956 which restricted the type of coal which could be used on open coal fires in city homes. The use of coal in the home fell from over forty six million tons in 1940 to eight million in 1978. Gas and electricity, rather than coal, were used for domestic central heating, which was widely introduced into British homes from the 1960's onwards. Later, the concern over carbon emissions and their impact on global warming added to the unpopularity of coal.

The nationalisation of the coal mines in 1947 and the subsequent large-scale investment in the mechanisation of the mines created optimism in the industry. The pits had been nationalised during the First World War and the miners had wished them to remain under government control afterwards. The post war depression led to conflict with the owners who demanded a reduction in the men's wages and an increase in their working hours as a solution to the collapsing market for British coal. The miners resisted with strike action culminating in the General Strike of 1926. The miners lost these struggles and the fortunes of the coal industry did not improve during the difficult economic conditions of the 1930s. Lack of investment in the collieries by the private owners during the depression rendered them less able to compete with the mechanised coal mines of Europe and America. For every coal mine which was mechanised in Britain, fifty were working by outdated methods which relied mainly on physical labour. One of the earliest underground photographs, taken by the Gateshead photographer C.E.Ruddock in 1893, shows hewers at work in Dunston Colliery: such conditions still existed in the 1940's. The deprivation faced by many mining communities during the inter-war years left a lasting impression upon the

workforce: their memories of personal hardship, frustration and humiliation influenced trade union affairs and local politics for many years.The approach of war ended the depression. During the Second World War the mines were once again under government control. The problem of recruitment was acerbated by men leaving the mines to join the armed forces. Conscripts known as 'Bevin Boys' were directed into the pits to solve the shortage of manpower. When the war ended a Labour government was returned to Westminster. One of their major concerns was to modernise the mining industry and tackle problems of recruitment and industrial unrest. A secure national fuel policy was essential for post war development. It was widely felt that the only practical solution was nationalisation. Consequently, on 1st January 1947 the National Coal Board was created. With almost one thousand collieries and many ancilliary industries such as coke and brick works, the N.C.B. was the largest and most complex industrial organisation in Britain – and possibly the world.

In the course of the debate over nationalisation, the National Union of Miners, led by Will Lawther of Chopwell, submitted the Miners' Charter to the former Scottish miner, Emanuel Shinwell, M.P. for Easington and Minister of Fuel in Atlee's Labour government. The charter was a set of demands which the miners believed would improve recruitment to the industry – it is also an illustration of the working conditions in the mining industry at this time. These demands included the rapid modernisation of the pits; enhanced training opportunities for the men; the maintenance of the miners' pay at the top of the wages league; a five day week for all workers; a limit of seven hours per day for underground workers and 40 hours per week for surface workers; two weeks paid holiday and six days public holidays each year; pensions for men above 55 unable to work; and new towns with improved housing. These were indicative of the grievances of the miners at that time – and they blamed the coal owners for their working and living conditions.

Coal provided 90% of Britain's fuel and in order to meet the demand a massive programme of modernisation was introduced, changing the miner from a skilled manual worker to a skilled technician. Initially, £150 million was set aside for mechanisation during the first five years but more was to follow. Power-loaders, which both cut and loaded the coal at the coal face, supplanted men with pneumatic drills; the old system of supporting the roof with pit-props was replaced by hydraulic supports which advanced as the face advanced; electric trains hauled the men to the coal face and the coal to the shaft for winding. The super pits along the coast - collieries like Seaham, Vane Tempest, Wearmouth, Whitburn and Ellington - were at the leading edge of mining technology extracting coal from many miles beneath the North Sea. Once again Britain led the world in techniques for cutting and loading coal underground. In the financial year 1980/81, the North East Division of the National Coal Board employed 32,000 people and had a turnover of £615 million. Therefore, despite the contraction of the industry, the chairman could rightly claim in his annual report that the N.C.B. was the largest employer in the region.

During this period of rapid technological change, the labour force and the number of collieries were greatly reduced: in 1960 there were 698 collieries in Britain employing 602,100 men – by 1970 there were 299 collieries employing 305,100 men. The miners co-operated in the modernisation of their industry and their productivity rose from 25 cwt per man shift in 1951 to 45 cwt in 1970. However, the miners found that their wages were falling behind those of workers in other industries; and they were also concerned about the programme of further pit closures. These concerns led to the national strikes of 1972 and 1974 which threatened the country's power supplies by preventing coal reaching the power stations. The Labour government of Harold Wilson met the miners' demands but many in the country at large, who had suffered from power cuts and a reduced working week, felt that the nation had been held to ransom.

In particular, Margaret Thatcher was greatly influenced by these strikes and when she came to power her Conservative government withdrew subsidies and privatised the coal industry. Market forces were allowed to rule: it had become cheaper to buy coal on the world market than mine it in Britain and the country now became a major importer of coal. Furthermore, with the development of the North Sea oil and gas industry, the role of coal as the foundation of the nation's power supply was being eroded. Many in the region believed that a political decision had been made to destroy the influence of the miners' union by running down the industry following the national strikes of 1972 and 1974. The final battle came in the bitter strike of 1984-85. This was an attempt to stop the new NCB chairman, Ian MacGregor, from implementing a programme of further pit closures. The strike was seen as a battle to save mining communities and reject the crude economics of market forces espoused by the Conservative government: it failed and by 1993 all the collieries in County Durham had been shut down. The end came in February 2005 when Ellington, the last of the super pits, was closed. Coal is still extracted but from opencast workings ironically removing the coal left by the former miners to support the roof of their working spaces.

A great industry has gone and with it the distinctive communities it had created. The visitor can no longer, like Inspector Leifchild, wander amongst the collieries 'to witness the extraordinary mechanisms and erections for the extraction of coal and its delivery to the collier vessels; to note the hundred tall chimneys, and the perplexed network of colliery railways'.

Chapter Two - The Coal Mine

'In order to understand my coal affairs I thought for to take a trip to Newcastle for there I understand that the perfection of coaling was to be learned both in relation to the machines necessary above ground and the easiest ways of working below ground'.

From the Journal of Sir John Clerk of Penicuik - April 1724

Sir John Clerk of Penicuik, the owner of several coal mines in Midlothian, visited Tyneside in April 1724 because the Great Northern Coalfield was acknowledged to be at the forefront of mining practise. A century later, in 1816, when the Grand Duke Nicholas of Russia visited England, Wallsend Colliery was included in his itinerary because this colliery, under the direction of the eminent mining engineer John Buddle, was believed to be a model for the industry. Both examples serve to illustrate the high esteem in which the coal mines in the North East of England were held by previous generations. Since Tudor times the Northumberland and Durham Coalfield was seen as the foremost repository of coal mining expertise and it held this reputation throughout most of its history.

The major technical problems encountered in operating a coal mine are providing light for the workplace; ventilating the mine to remove bad air and dangerous gases; draining the influx of water to prevent flooding; safely extracting the coal from the seam; providing haulage underground to get the coal to the shaft bottom; generating winding power to raise the coal to the surface; and organising transport above ground to get the coal to market. These problems remained a constant headache for all colliery engineers but the solutions to the problems changed as different technologies were developed. Consequently, there is a world of difference between the collieries of Elizabeth I's time and the super pits of Elizabeth II's reign.

The history of the exploitation of the coal reserves within the Heaton royalty is worthy of a detailed study because it represents in microcosm the history

St Lawrence's Colliery Byker

of the development of the coalfield in general. The history of Heaton illustrates the relationship between the geological framework of an area, the development of technology and the exploitation of the coal deposits. This was the change from a dozen men working with simple tools at shallow pits near the outcrop of the seam, to many hundred of men mining from deep pits covering several square miles with sophisticated machinery for coal cutting, ventilation, drainage, haulage and transport. The history of Heaton also illustrates the commercial rivalries surrounding the winning of the coal including the bitter battles fought for waggonway access to the River Tyne.

The medieval manor of Heaton lay to the east of Newcastle beyond the Ouseburn, a tributary of the River Tyne, which formed its western boundary. Today, the main east coast railway line roughly follows the southern and eastern boundaries of the old manor while the DHSS building and the Freeman Hospital roughly mark the northern boundary. At present, the manor is largely covered with housing apart from the valuable recreational areas of Heaton Park, Armstrong Park and Jesmond Dene which interestingly occupy much of the site of the former Heaton Banks Colliery. To the east another small park off Newton Road, known locally as the Spinney, occupies the site of the Far Pit of Heaton Main Colliery; and according to the local folklore the ghost of a trapper boy wanders amongst

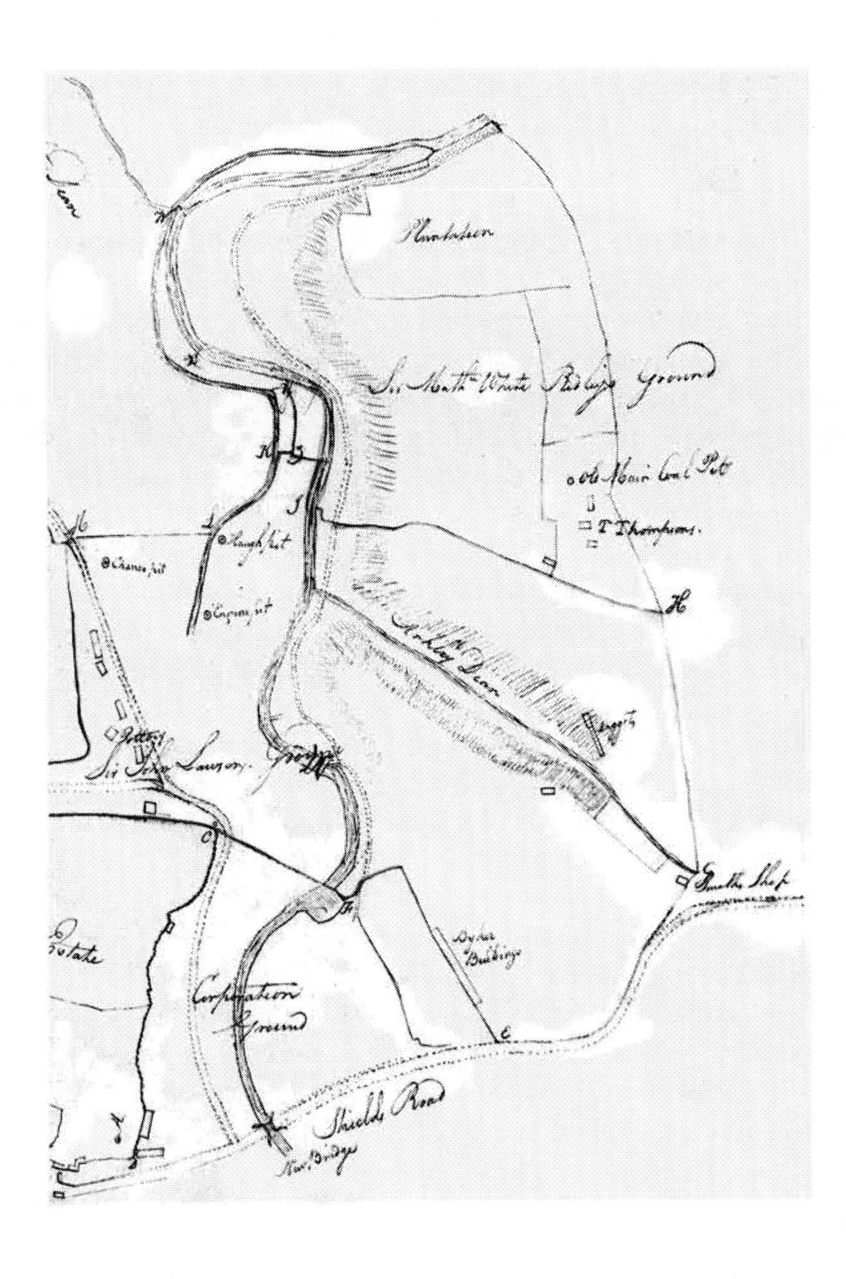

the sycamore trees planted to commemorate the seventy five miners lost in the disaster of 1815 when the mine was flooded.

The principal geological features of the royalty are the outcrop of the High Main seam in the south west corner of Heaton where the Ouseburn now runs through a concrete culvert; the general dip of the coal seams from west to east; and two major faults, the Thistle Pit and Plain Pit dykes which made the seams more difficult to access in the east. Mining began at the outcrop and, as the technology was developed, operations moved eastwards first with Heaton Banks Colliery and then with Heaton Main Colliery.

The section from a late eighteenth century map of the lower Ouseburn valley shows Arkley Dene and the escarpment about one hundred feet in height to the north where the coal outcropped. In this area the High Main seam was over six feet thick. The easiest method of accessing the coal was to quarry it from the outcrop which was a short distance from the navigable tidal waters of the Ouseburn. This was important because of the difficulty and expense of transporting heavy goods over land: the pit head price of coal was doubled when it was carted two to three miles.

It is not known for certain when mining first began. Two valuations of the estate survive dated 1421 and 1454. Although they describe in detail the farmsteads of the manor, no mention is made of coal mining. However, when the lord of the manor Thomas Musgrave died in 1482, the estate was divided equally between his two grandsons John Fenwick and Robert Mitford. John Fenwick was given the lands in the eastern half and Robert Mitford the lands in the western half with a significant exception. Heaton Hall and a corridor of land linking the east with the Ouseburn and the accessible coal was reserved for John Fenwick. Not only was the farmland divided in two equal parts but the coal outcrop seems to have been similarly divided between the grandsons. This would suggest that by the end of the fifteenth century the landowners were well aware of the importance of the coal deposits at least for domestic purposes.

What part Heaton played in the great expansion of the Tyneside coal trade in the sixteenth century is not documented; but it is likely that the collieries along the banks of the Ouseburn where the principal coal seam was near the surface made a significant contribution towards this early industrial development in the region. A map of Castle Ward (south east Northumberland) dated circa 1600 shows three pits in Heaton, two in Byker and five in Jesmond near the outcrop - all mining the valuable High Main seam. This map is reproduced in the Northumberland County History Volume IX.

The coal trade on Tyneside was hampered by both domestic and foreign wars in the middle of the seventeenth century. Although the pace of development slackened, the coal trade nevertheless continued to expand but the part Heaton played in this expansion is difficult to determine. The major source of information is the Cotesworth papers which contain a schedule of deeds in the custody of Christopher Mitford relating to the estate. Some of the deeds link the name of Sir Peter Riddell with Heaton. Like the Mitfords, the Riddell family had been merchants of Newcastle involved with the coal trade since at least the fourteenth century. Both families had been associated with the Grand Lease collieries in the manor of Whickham - at that time the principal source of Tyneside coal. Sir Thomas Riddell had served as governor of the Company of Hostmen which controlled the coal trade from the river and Sir Peter Riddell was the principal partner in Benwell Colliery one of the leading collieries of the period. His precise interest in the manor of Heaton is a matter of speculation but he cannot have been unaware of the rich coal deposits within the estate.

Robert Mitford's Colliery

During the sixteenth century Sir Ralph Lawson of Cramlington acquired the Fenwick half of the Heaton estate. In 1613 Dorothy Lawson sold these lands to Henry Babington and moved to St. Anthony's Byker, at that time a more secluded spot, where her home became a refuge for followers of the Roman Catholic faith. When James I visited Newcastle in 1617, he was hosted by Henry Babington at Heaton Hall and the king was so pleased with his entertainment that he rewarded his host with a knighthood. Sir Henry died in 1634 and was succeeded by his son William. When William died in 1648 the Babington half of the manor passed to his son Philip. An indenture dated 1st December 1677 between Robert Mitford, Philip Babington and Henry Brabant 'for working several Collierys in Heaton and Jesmond' survives among the Cotesworth papers. Another document, a lease from the Mayor and Burgesses of Newcastle to Mitford dated January 1678, mentions 'three keelrooms or keelbirths lying on the east side of the Ouseburn'. The lease also granted free wayleave for the leading of coals to the keelrooms through the Corporation's ground for eleven years for an annual rent of £10. Three keelrooms would indicate a large colliery at that time with an output of over 10,000 tons a year. The eighteenth century map of Arkley Dene shows the escarpment where the coal seam was exposed and a track leading down the lower Ouseburn valley, through Sir John Lawson's ground in Byker, to a basin in the Corporation's ground in St. Lawrence's, Byker. It is likely that this was the route from the pits to the keelbirths on the basin. The map also shows the Haugh, Chance and Engine pits of Shieldfield Colliery; and the Old Mair Pit in Low Heaton which was probably part of Mitford's Colliery.

The Ouseburn was navigatable at high tide almost to the boundary of Heaton manor - approximately to where the railway bridge now crosses the river. The keels, which carried eight Newcastle chaldrons (about 21 tons), left on the ebb tide for the colliers moored at the mouth of the Tyne. In the seventeenth century, the trading season lasted for six months from September to May with a break of two months during the winter when the colliers were unable to sail because of the weather: there were times when the River Tyne was frozen over. Although the exact location of the pits is not known, Mitford's colliery would have been in the south west corner of the manor - the only place where coal was accessible at this time because of the limitations of the pumping technology of the period. How the coal was transported from the pits to the keelbirths is not known. At the end of the seventeenth century, large four wheeled waggons known as wains were the usual method of transport. The wain carried a third of a chaldron (about 17.6 cwt) and travelled along a dedicated route known as the wain road. Extra horsepower was often necessary because of the poor condition of the roads at this time particularly in bad weather. However, it is also possible, because of the size of Mitford's colliery, that a waggonway was in use. Certainly, by 1706, there was a waggonway down the Ouseburn valley carrying the coal from Jesmond Colliery.

The Heaton estate lay on the north western edge of a major geological feature - the Tyne Basin - whereby the coal seams dipped from different directions to form a bowl. As a consequence the underground drainage was in general towards the south and the east. Water from Jesmond estate to the west, from Gosforth, Longbenton and the northern part of Heaton royalty flowed towards the southern part of Heaton and to Byker and Gateshead beyond. The chain pump, a continuous chain of buckets driven by horse power or by a water wheel, was the principal method of pumping at this time. The nineteenth century colliery engineer Matthias Dunn noted that water wheels driven by the Ouseburn were used for pumping at Heaton and Jesmond collieries. Certainly, the chain pump was in use at Heaton in 1677. The effectiveness of these pumps was limited to depths of twenty to thirty fathoms which is the basis for thinking that Mitford's Colliery was in Low Heaton, east of the outcrop, in the area between Stratford Grove and the railway. Difficulties with drainage was probably the reason why Mitford abandoned the colliery in 1689: mining had reached the limits of the pumping technology of the day.

In April 1692, Robert Mitford leased part of his interests in the manor of Heaton to Nicholas Ridley, a prominent Newcastle merchant and a former Mayor of Newcastle, for £2,948. Significantly, a clause was included which exempted 'all the collieries, coalmines and seams of coal'. Mitford also retained the right of wayleave through the estate for his colliery: the right of 'full and free liberty to carry by carts or wains, waggon or waggons … all coles as shall … hearafter be mined … and to make wainways or waggonways'. Also reserved was the right to 'dig, sink, ridd, win, work, pit or pits …. And also sufficient groundroom and heaproom to lay rubbish Gravell and Coles as shall be got out of the said colemines… and afford liberty to erect stables, shops, hovels and lodges'. Robert Mitford was to erect gates 'in any hedge upon the way employed in leading the coals' and to employ gatekeepers who were responsible for any act of trespass. However, Nicholas Ridley and his tenants had the right during the quiet time of the coal trade ' betwixt 1st May and 1st September to load lime, manure, timber or other materials to be used' on the estate. They also had the right to all the manure from 'pit horses or any other horses or beasts employed in working … the said colemines'; the contract for supplying all straw for bedding horses employed in the coal mines and the opportunity to be employed in leading coal out of the estate. There was thus a community of interest between the owner of the land and the owner of the colliery; between the farmers and the miners.

Heaton Banks Colliery

At the beginning of the eighteenth century, the development of the Newcomen steam pump gave the major coal entrepreneurs the opportunity to win collieries to the east of Newcastle by draining the Tyne Basin. These collieries were nearer the river than the Tanfield Moor pits which at that time were the principal source of coal for the London market. In June 1717, Robert and Christopher Mitford, the owners of the mineral rights in the western half of Heaton, signed an agreement with William Cotesworth of Gateshead and his partner George Liddell of Ravensworth whereby they let their colliery in Heaton for a term of twenty five years subject to certain conditions. Firstly, 'Wm. Cotesworth should use his utmost endeavours … to win and work the said Colliery within the space of three years'. The owners of the mineral rights sought to protect themselves from the practice of entrepreneurs securing leases simply to prevent them being acquired by business rivals. This was one strategy by which mine owners attempted to limit the output of coal onto the market to keep prices high. Secondly, after the colliery had been won, it should 'not cease working for a month together except occasioned by extremity of water, stythe (gas) or fire, foreign or domestic wars or a general obstruction of the coal trade' all of which were very real threats at the time. After the period allowed for the opening up of the colliery, 1717-1720, a fixed rent (known as certain rent) was to be paid together with another rent (known as tentale rent) based upon the production of the colliery. The Mitfords reserved the right to inspect the colliery accounts and to inspect the mine to ensure that it was being properly managed.

The owner of the surface rights, Nicholas Ridley, died in 1711 and the Heaton estate, excluding the mineral rights, was inherited by his eldest surviving son Richard who rebuilt Heaton Hall in 1713. Like his father, Richard was very influential in local business and politics. He had been Mayor of Newcastle in 1713–14. Richard Ridley was a major figure in mining circles: he had won the neighbouring colliery at Byker by installing a Newcomen engine in 1717, only the second to be erected in the northern coalfield. In April 1724 Sir John Clerk of Penicuik visited Alderman Ridley's colliery because it was a centre of excellence and noted that 'the three coalries are managed with three fire Engines at a vast charge'. Ridley also had a share in Jesmond Colliery with Matthew White. Not unnaturally, he was infuriated at Cotesworth's interest in the Heaton estate which he regarded with some justification as his domain. Moreover, there was a history of conflict between the two men, who had previously crossed swords over colliery matters in the Derwent valley, and a bitter struggle developed over Heaton - a struggle between an established Newcastle family and the newcomer from Gateshead.

In 1715, Newcastle Corporation purchased the manor of Walker primarily to use the river frontage as a ballast dump. Alderman Ridley used his influence with Newcastle Council to prevent Cotesworth from securing a wayleave through the neighbouring estate of Walker, thereby blocking Cotesworth's preferred route to the River Tyne for the waggonway of the new colliery. The London merchants had protested that the self interest of Newcastle Corporation - led by Ridley - was preventing Heaton Colliery from supplying the market with about 50,000 tons annually. The merchants argued that 'for the sake of the Collieries they (Newcastle Corporation) already have in Town Moor, Nuns Moor, the Leases and in Willington, and of the very large and beneficial collieries they have in Walker lands…. in order to sell their own coals at a higher price they will hinder the other persons from bringing any coals to the Tyne'. An alternative route was surveyed by the Heaton viewers through the lands of Thomas Bigge, Thomas Hindmarsh, Mr Hewbank and Mr Durham to a place in Wallsend about half a mile upriver from Willington Quay. However, Hewbank was bought out of the agreement by Ridley. There was action in the High Court and the intervention of the Secretary of State before a wayleave was eventually granted in 1725. The agreement was for 14 to 16 keel rooms, each 15 yards in length, to be built at the west end of Walker Quay and served by a waggonway 14 yards wide. Significantly, the agreement stipulated that 'no coles shall be put on board any ships from the spouts at the trunks to the detriment of the keelmen'. The keelmen, who were employed by the Newcastle hostmen, were suffering hardship through changes in the trade and a mutiny had taken place in 1710.

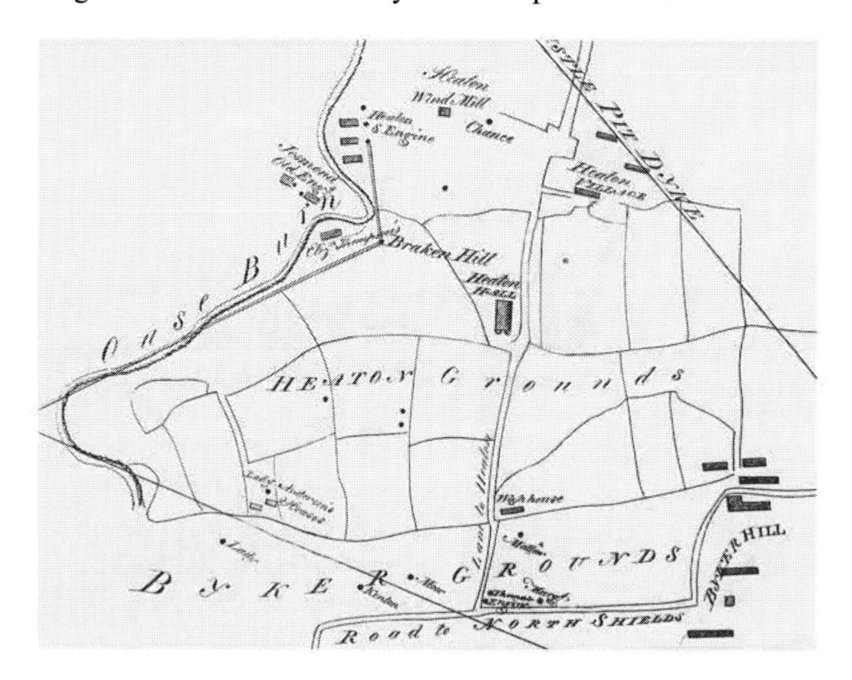

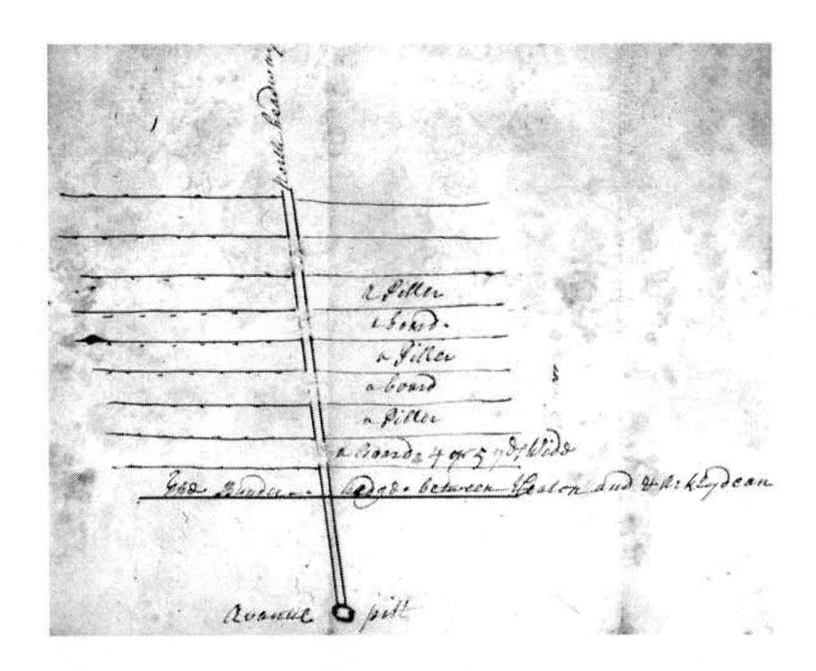

Cotesworth's approach to winning the coal in Heaton manor seems to have been two fold. Firstly, to open a colliery in Low Heaton near the area which had been worked by Mitford; and secondly, to develop Heaton Banks Colliery to the north which could also give access to coal in Gosforth and Longbenton. A section from a map dated circa 1740 is reproduced above. It shows the named pits of Byker Colliery to the north of Shields Road including one of the three engine pits; and six unnamed pits in Low Heaton where Cotesworth first mined coal. The major development was to the north of Heaton Hall near the windmill and the Chance Pit. The three engine pits sunk to win Heaton Banks Colliery to the north are shown linked to the Tyne Level Drift, a major drainage level.

In Low Heaton conflict occurred at the boundary between Heaton and Byker collieries where Cotesworth claimed that Ridley's men had interfered with the ventilation system in Heaton by putting a dead dog and onions down the mine. More seriously, Ridley was also accused of trespassing underground from the Avenue and Matthew Pits in Byker to rob coal from Heaton royalty. Incredibly, a sketch map survives of the trespass from the Avenue Pit (also known as the Moor Pit) showing a headway driven about 50 yards into Heaton estate. Ridley had attempted to prevent discovery of the trespass by building dams to flood the area where the coal had been extracted. There are several affidavits which accused Ridley's men of intimidating the Heaton pitmen who were trying to descend the Avenue Pit to investigate the trespass. 'Joseph Gill, a viewer for Mr.Ridley, threatened that if they did not go away he would shoot a pistol through their heads and swore many profane oaths at them'. Matt Dixon, Ridley's under viewer, 'threatened to take away the rope by which the men were to ascend … and swore they should never come up alive for he should nail deals over the shaft'. Despite these difficulties, the Heaton viewers, Jonathan Bullock and Jonathan Barnes, had established a colliery in Low Heaton by 1727 which had a waggonway to transport the coal to the Tyne at Wincomblee.

William Cotesworth and his partner George Liddell were trying to purchase Newcomen pumping engines for Park Colliery in Gateshead as well as Heaton Colliery. The sole proprietor was the Staffordshire firm of Stonier Parrot with whom Cotesworth had been in negotiation since 1715; but by 1724 he was still without an engine. Certainly, production of the engines was slow because of the difficulties in manufacturing the cylinders and boilers at this time. However, the more relevant reason for the delay was that Ridley had bribed Parrot to frustrate Cotesworth with the offer of shares in his collieries. Ridley had hoped that 'his inveterate enemy', Cotesworth, would give up the venture in Heaton and Cotesworth seems to have been waivering. In January 1724, George Liddell wrote to Cotesworth warning him of the tactics: 'if you do quit Heaton, when she's all retaken by the enemy (Ridley, he will)… admit Mr.P. to 1/6 throughout the whole of both collieries' i.e. Heaton and Byker.

William Cotesworth and George Liddell were unable to win Heaton by 1720 and were prosecuted by Mitford in the High Court for lost rent.

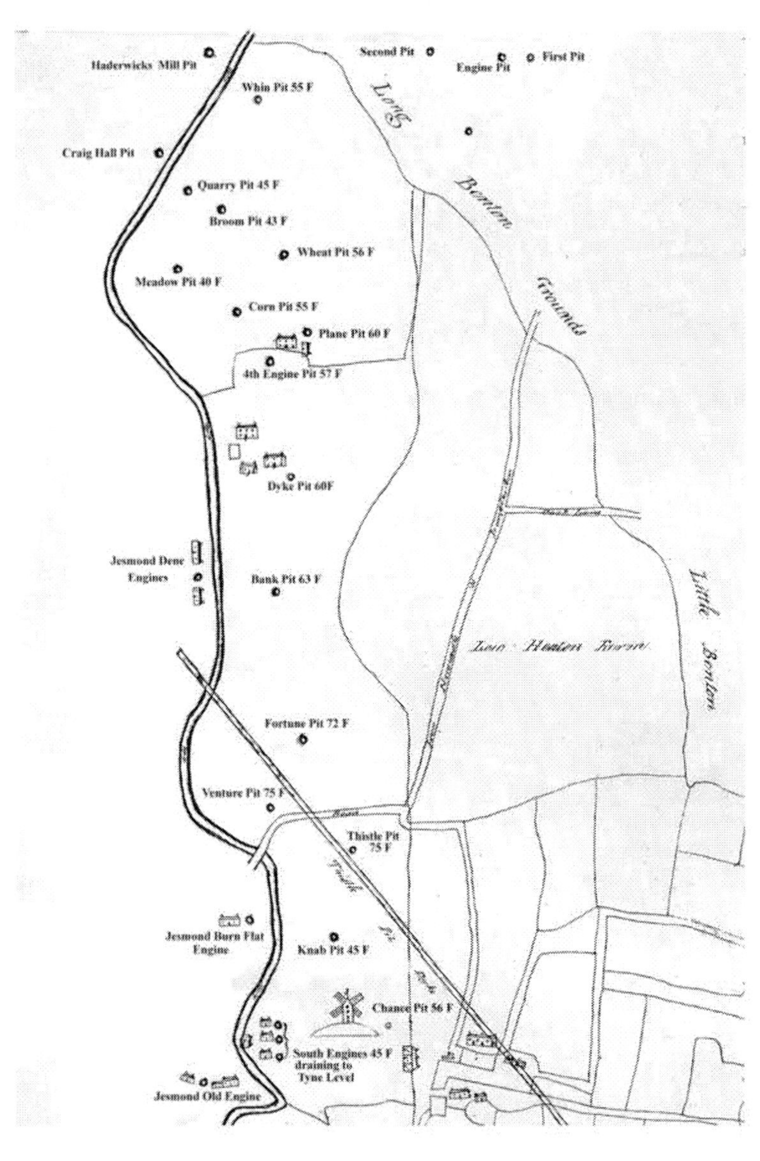

Heaton Banks Colliery

Liddell wrote to his partner Cotesworth 'I am sorry L.Cha. (Lord Chancellor) has ordered Mitford's money to be brought into court as it will straiten us; however let me know what you expect of me and I shall endeavour to prepare it'. Eventually, the lease was renegotiated and Heaton became one of the collieries of the Grand Allies. This was the largest partnership of coal owners in the region and included the Liddells, the Wortleys, the Bowes and the Ords. William Cotesworth, the driving force behind the partnership, had died in 1726 but his heir, his eldest son Robert Cotesworth, became a member - indeed the first meeting was held in Robert's house. The foundations had been laid for Heaton to become one of the great collieries of the mid eighteenth century.

The map of Heaton Banks Colliery is based upon an undated eighteenth century map in the Ridley papers and documents in the Mining Institute: it shows the geography of a large colliery at this period. There are eighteen pits spaced about 300 yards apart forming the colliery. All these shafts were necessary because of the limitations of the ventilation system in the mid eighteenth century which relied upon the use of convection currents created by a furnace in or near the shaft to draw the bad air out. The workings are to the west of a major geological fault, the Plain Pit Dyke, which is marked as a north - south line running up the centre of the map. Water was the major problem at Heaton and the colliery was exceptional in the number of Newcomen engines installed. The four pumping engines marked on the map were erected between 1729 and 1731 - three of them to the south west of the windmill which still stands in Heaton Park. These three engines were situated at the lowest point of the colliery. The fourth engine was about a mile to the north. The pumping engines for Jesmond Colliery and Longbenton Colliery are also marked since the water from these collieries drained into Heaton.

One of the lower engines is illustrated in the view book of the colliery engineer Amos Barnes on a plan dated 2nd February 1733/4 for draining the Knab Pit. This large engine had a 42" cylinder and a seven foot stroke. It was capable of ten strokes a minute and drew 220 hogsheads (11,550 galls) of water per hour. The rocking beam of the steam pumping engine is shown linked to three sections of pumps which raised water to the Tyne Level Drift. The shaft was sunk through the High Main seam past the

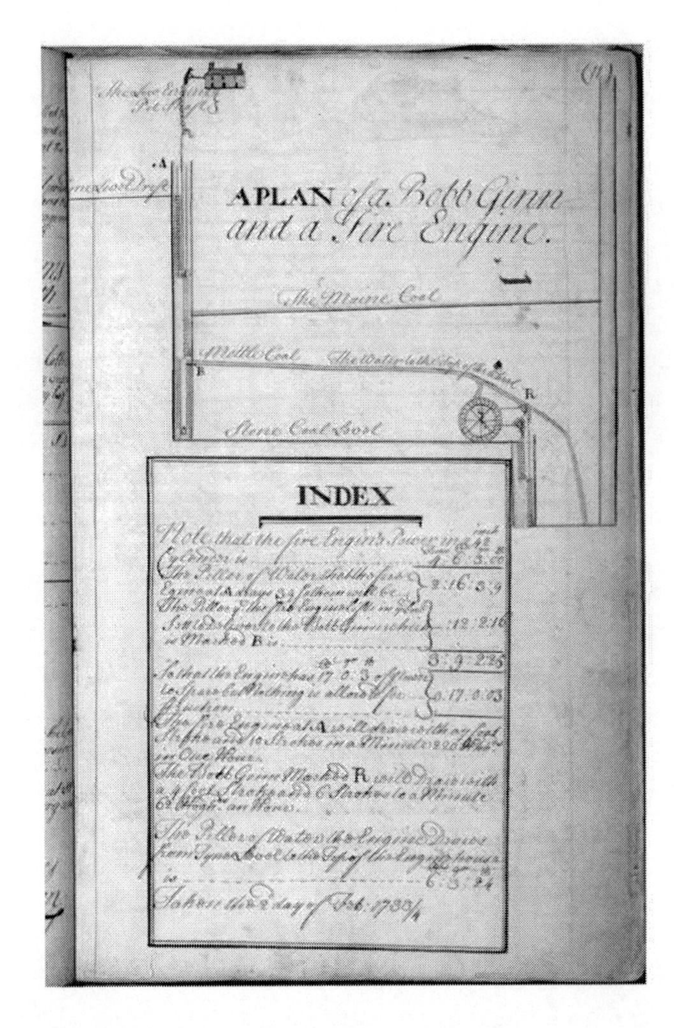

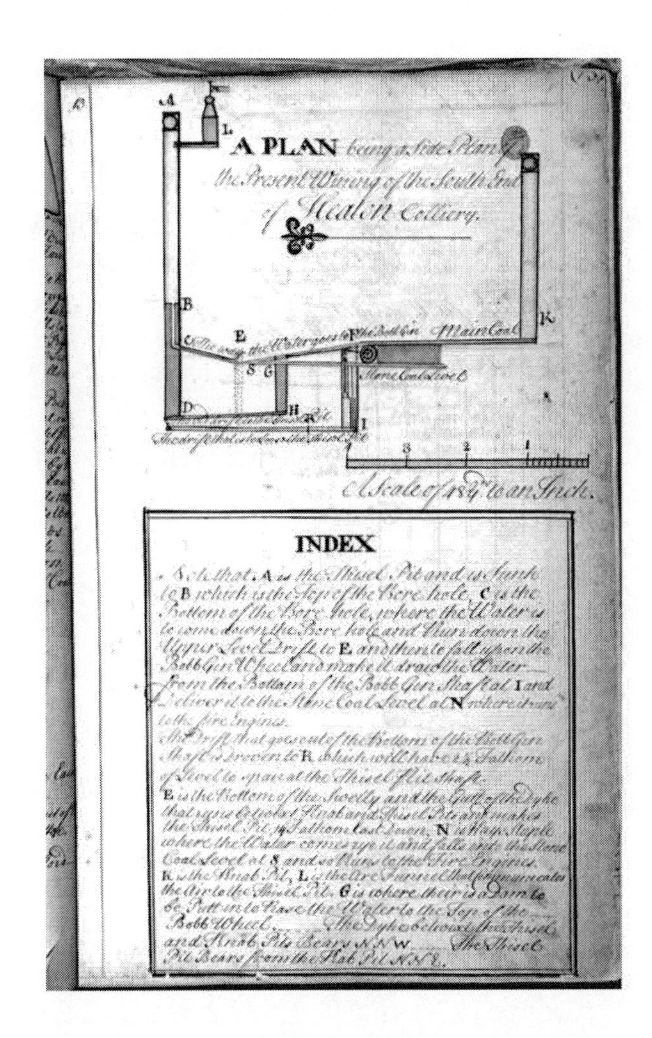

Metal Coal seam to the Stone Coal seam. Part of the water from the first lift is conducted down the Metal Coal Level to a waterwheel. This raised water from the Yard seam to the Stone Coal Level where it fell to the bottom of the Engine Shaft to be pumped out. The bob gin had a four foot stroke. It was capable of six strokes a minute and pumped 62 hogsheads (3,255 galls) each hour.

Another plan in the view book shows work in progress to win the Thistle Pit. The method of draining the Thistle Pit (A) from the Knab Pit (K) is with a bob gin (F). Because of the geological fault, known as the Thistle Pit Dyke, the High Main seam was fourteen fathoms (84 feet) deeper in the Thistle Pit. A drift from the bottom of the Bob Gin Shaft (I) was driven to the Thistle Pit. The water was pumped to the Stone Coal Level where it ran down to one of the three Newcomen pumping engines near the windmill. Water to drive the bob gin is conducted down the bore hole (B-C) to the upper level drift (E) and then to the bob gin wheel.

The structure marked L on the plan is described as an 'aire funnel that communicates aire to the Thistle Pit' and is a similar device to that described by Sir John Clerk on his visit to Byker Colliery in April 1724. The Swedish engineer at Byker, Mr.Denald, described 'the methode which he used to drain ill aire out of Alderman Ridley's works and likewise carry a mine a great way without the expense of letting down a shaft'. At the mouth of the shaft was a furnace. A timber pipe was carried down the shaft to the coal face at the far end of the mine. The bad air and any gas was drawn out by the convection currents. At a time when candles were the principal method of lighting down the pit the removal of explosive gases was crucial for the safety of the men. Later in the eighteenth century, the method of coursing the air around all the mine was developed: this was an improvement because pockets of gas which accumulated in the old

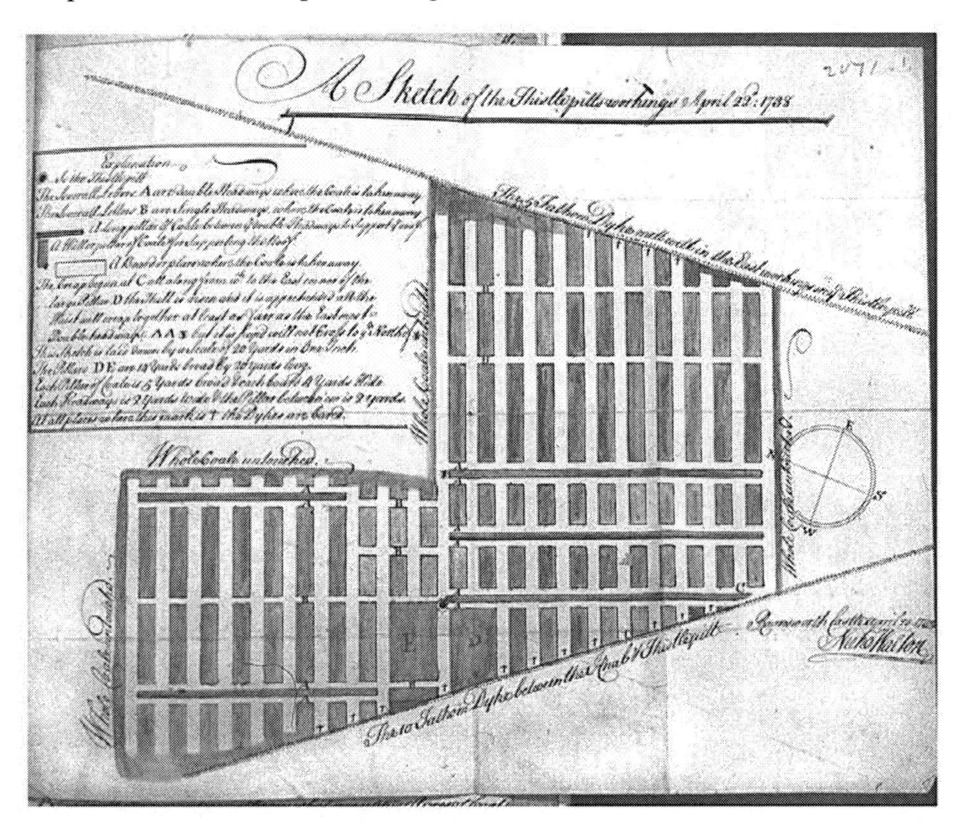

workings could be moved to the coal face by a change in atmospheric pressure. Partitions of brick and wood known as stoppings were built to direct the air up and down the workings. Trap doors were constructed where access was needed into an airway. The important job of opening and closing the door was the responsibility of children - the trapper boys. These were the youngest workers in the mine, often under the age of ten, and they were generally the children of miners.

The Thistle Pit was won in 1736 and a sketch of the workings dated April 1738 from the view book of Nicholas Walton, agent of the Grand Allies, is reproduced. It shows the pillar and stall (or bord and pillar) method of working which was common practice in Northumberland and Durham. From the shaft bottom headways, known as mothergates, which were two yards wide, were cut across the grain of the coal to give access to the seam. From these headways bords, four yards wide, were driven with the grain of the coal. Large pillars of coal, five yards wide, were left to support the roof. The sketch was drawn because the viewer, Nicholas Walton, was concerned about creep - that is when the pressure from the pillars forced the floor to rise endangering the mine. A century later, John Buddle giving testimony to Parliament, described how 'the first appearance was a little curvature in the bottom of each gallery... but we can generally hear it before we can perceive it. The next stage is when the pavement begins to open with a crack'.

The hewer working in his gallery or bord was the aristocrat of the workforce and his job was to excavate the coal. The miners drew lots for a bord at regular intervals to ensure a fair distribution of the easy and difficult workplaces. This was important because the men were paid by the number of corves they filled. The antiquarian John Brand writing in 1789 describes how 'the hewer first digs as far as he can into the bottom of the stratum; then he nooks or corners off the part measured out, and afterwards the great coals come away by a wedge or a mallet'. The hewer used a pick to undermine the coal for a distance of about two feet. An experienced hewer could tell where the vertical cleats in the coal occurred which greatly

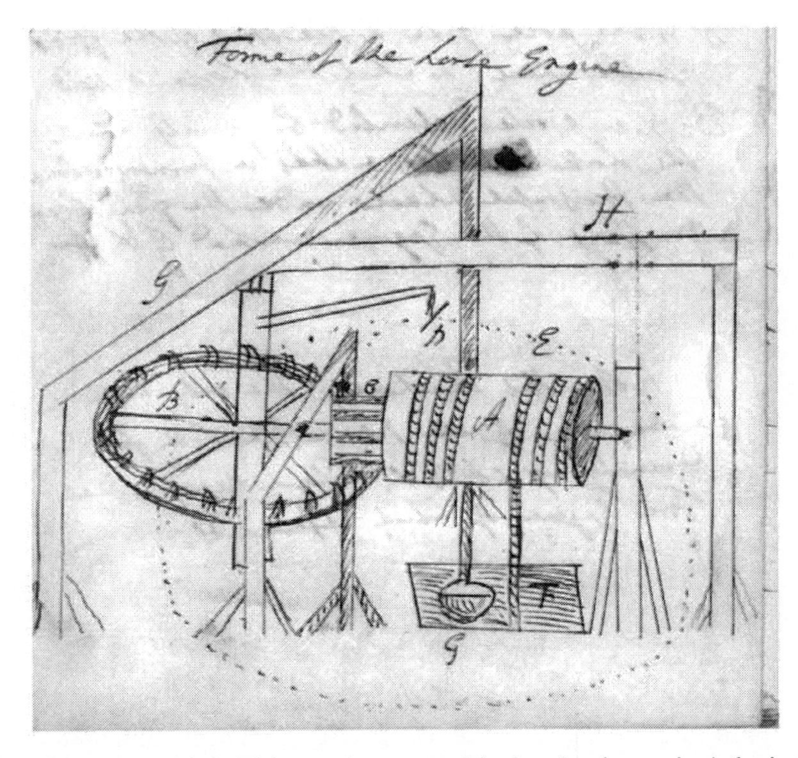

assisted the excavation. This was known as kirving (undercutting) the jud (the body of coal to be extracted). Next the hewer cut the vertical grooves on each side of the jud and then forced the coal down with a wedge. He often worked semi-naked because of the heat underground and used a cracket, a small stool, to sit or lie on. He then shovelled the coal into a corf or wicker basket which the putter moved on a sledge from the coal face to the bottom of the pit shaft.

In 1724, Sir John Clerk sketched a machine which 'is the only one made use of at Newcastle both for drawing up coals and water except the Fire Engine' and described its operation. This is illustrated above. 'A is the cylander upon which the rop turns which draws from the pit or shaft F. B is a horizontal wheel with cogs which turns the cylander by the spinnel C. D is the pole fixed to the Axis of the Horizontal wheel, to which the horse is tied. E is a circle described by points which the horse makes in turning about the Horizontal wheel under the great beams or stays of the Engine marked G & H'. It is likely that a similar device was used for winding at the pits in Heaton. The same rope was used by the men and boys to travel to and from their workplace sometimes by simply clinging to a loop on the rope, at other times travelling in a corf.

According to the evidence of George Cloughton to the House of Commons Committee on the Coal Trade in 1738, the Grand Allies had spent £40,000 in winning Heaton Colliery. The Minute Book of the Grand Allies Partnership provides details of the production at Heaton between 1728 and 1745 although there is reason to believe that production began before 1727. An entry for October 1727 records the resolution 'That Heaton Wagon Way be kept in ye Owners hands till further Order' implying it was a well established feature probably built in 1725. Heaton's contribution to the vend, the sale of coal from the River Tyne to the London market, is given below. The early output from Low Heaton was modest and was served by the waggonway mentioned in the minute which went to Walker Quay. However, after the pumping engines were installed between 1729 and 1731, the output was greatly increased making Heaton Banks Colliery one of the largest collieries of the period. For this colliery a new waggonway would be needed - hence the debate over the future of the first waggonway. In all probability, this would have involved only a realignment of the route of the waggonway in Heaton lands to link up with the original route through Walker to Wincomblee: branches from the new pits were built to link up with the old main line to the Tyne. Three proposals for a branch from the Venture Pit dated February 1737 survive. The branch line was to cross Benton Lane (the modern Coast Road) by means of a wooden bridge en route to James Lockey's house in Heaton village to 'Joyn ye Old waggonway'. The route of the waggonway through Walker is shown on Isaac Thompson's map of Walker estate dated 1745 and the place where it entered Heaton royalty is near the site of the Chillingham Hotel.

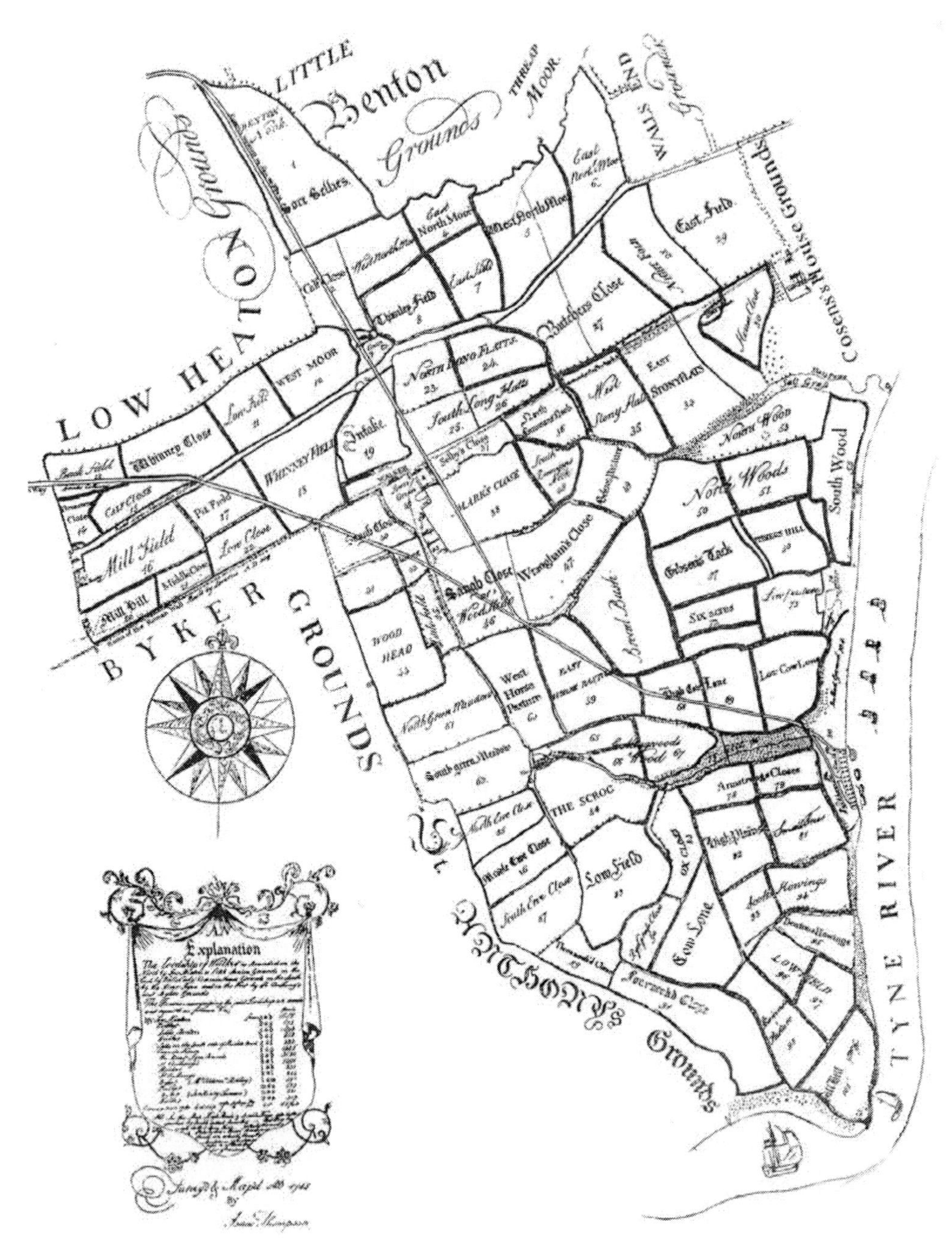

Production at Heaton 1728 - 37

1728	12,272 tons
1731	7,123 tons
1732	86,819 tons
1733	88,981 tons
1734	72,660 tons
1735	86,523 tons
1736	94,942 tons
1737	85,600 tons

From 1739 to the closure of the colliery in 1745, Heaton was allocated 84,800 tons as its share of the vend from the River Tyne but there is no confirmation that the colliery did achieve this target. Difficulties with water continued to trouble the viewers. The dip or lower part of the colliery was drowned and in an effort to keep the workings in the rise to the north operational, alterations were made to the pumping engines. The coal in the dip was abandoned and the lift of the pumps was changed from 44 to 22 fathoms to increase the amount of water being discharged. Simultaneously, the Grand Allies looked to develop Longbenton Colliery lying to the north between Heaton and the Ninety Fathom Fault.

Since at least November 1727, the Grand Allies had seen High Heaton as a means of gaining access to the coal in the neighbouring estates of Gosforth and Longbenton: when Heaton Banks Colliery was drowned out production was shifted to Longbenton. A map of Longbenton estate dated 1749 shows the Grand Allies' colliery with four fire engines in operation. Horses are seen hauling chaldron waggons along the main 'Waggon Road' which has branches leading to the individual pits as would have been the practice at Heaton. This main way can be traced on the early Ordnance Survey map heading for the south east corner of Longbenton royalty; it probably ran to the southern boundary of Benton Park and turned east to the north west tip of Walker royalty roughly on the line of the present Coast

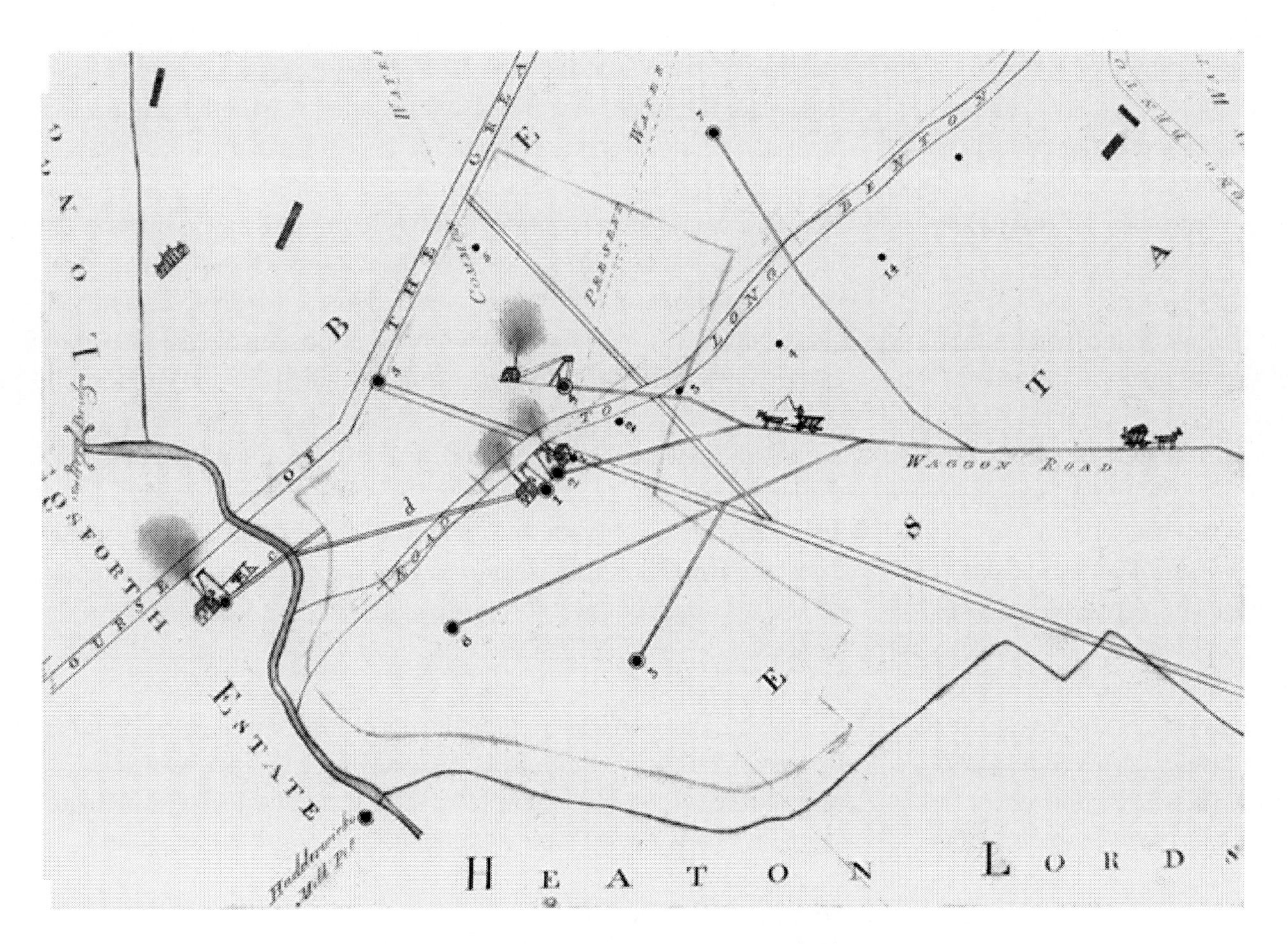

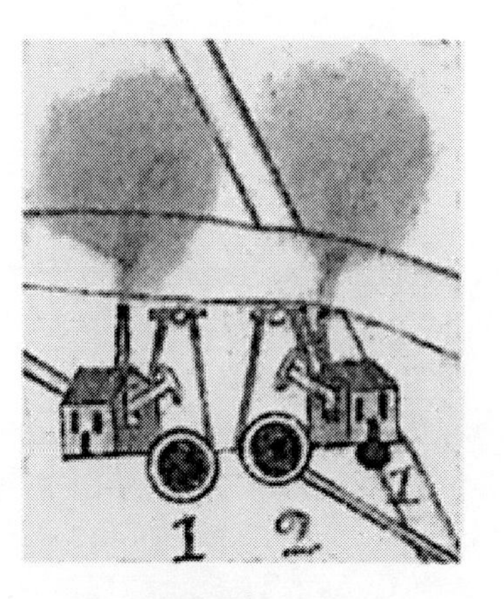

LONGBENTON COLLIERY 1749

Road to its junction with Benfield Road. It is clearly shown on Isaac Thompson's map of Walker following a gentle downhill gradient to link up with the route from Heaton to Wincomblee. Note that the waggonway from the Longbenton pits follows an entirely different course to the later nineteenth century Kenton and Coxlodge waggonway which still exists in this area as a pedestrian walkway.

It is worth looking closely at the detail of the drawings on the map for they illustrate aspects of colliery life in the mid eighteenth century. The loaded chaldron waggon heads for the staith with the driver standing at the rear next to the brake. The empty chaldron waggon returning to the pits is driven by a man sitting upfront next to the brake. The pumping engines, numbered 1 and 2, are shown with the rocking beam housed in a two-storied building next to the shaft. At shaft number 8, the 40 fathom Gosforth Pit, not only can the pumping engine be seen but a whim gin is also shown indicating that this shaft was also used for winding coal to the surface. The fourth illustration of a steam engine at the 58.5 fathom Lane Pit, numbered 4, is very different: instead of the pumping beam, ropes are shown emerging from the engine house to a pair of pulley wheels suspended over the shaft suggesting that it was being used for raising coal. This is exceptional because it is generally thought that steam power was not used for drawing coals until James Watt developed the rotary engine in 1780. The Lane Pit was opened in 1747 and during the next three years 45,000 tons of coal was raised annually. Longbenton Colliery was laid in about 1765 but was re-opened ten years later. In 1777, a fire engine was being used for pumping and the water was directed to drive a waterwheel which powered the coal gin at the Prosperous Pit. Something similar may have been employed in 1749.

An inspection of Heaton Colliery in February 1745 by a group of eight leading viewers, which included Amos Barnes and Nicholas Walton, concluded that 'all has been done to keep down the water to prevent the Colliery from drowning and at a very great expense not less than £1,200 p.a. upon so small a quantity as about 14 tens (700 tons) of coal per week' and they recommended closure. The coal owners issued a writ against the lessees for the loss of the mine. Giving evidence at the subsequent trial, Nicholas Walton argued in defence of the lessees that 'notwithstanding the Assistance wch the Engines of Jesmond gave to drawing of the Water of Heaton it would have required Seven Fire Engines at least to have drawn the Water of Heaton so as to prevent that Colliery from Drowning so great was the overpressure of Water'. The expense was too great. The viewers also examined the possibility of winning the coal in the eastern part of the estate, beyond the Plain Pit Dyke, and concluded that 'it is impossible not only from the great quantity of water at so great a depth but from the hazard of fire which will attend the same'. Consequently, Heaton Banks Colliery was abandoned in 1745 and the Grand Allies concentrated their attention on their neighbouring colliery at Longbenton. Despite being threatened by water from Heaton wastes, Longbenton Colliery remained productive for about twenty years because of the success of the pumping engines.

There are indications that mining did not cease completely in Heaton during the mid eighteenth century. A plan in the Mining Institute, which is reproduced on page 109 shows two landsale collieries in Low Heaton Hymers Pit and Fiery Pit but no other information has been found.

Heaton Main Colliery

The second half of the eighteenth century was a time when many engineers were striving to improve the Newcomen atmosheric engine. One of these engineers was William Brown of Throckley who supervised the construction of 22 pumping engines between 1756 and 1776 including one at Byker (1757), two at Walker (1758) and two at Willington (1775). The size of pumps increased as the technology to build larger cylinders was developed. Now one boiler was insufficient to supply the steam for these larger engines and the practice of using multiple boilers was developed. In 1763, William Brown received the largest cylinder ever made at that time (6 ft 2 in diameter and 10 ft 6 in long) from Darbys of Coalbrookdale for

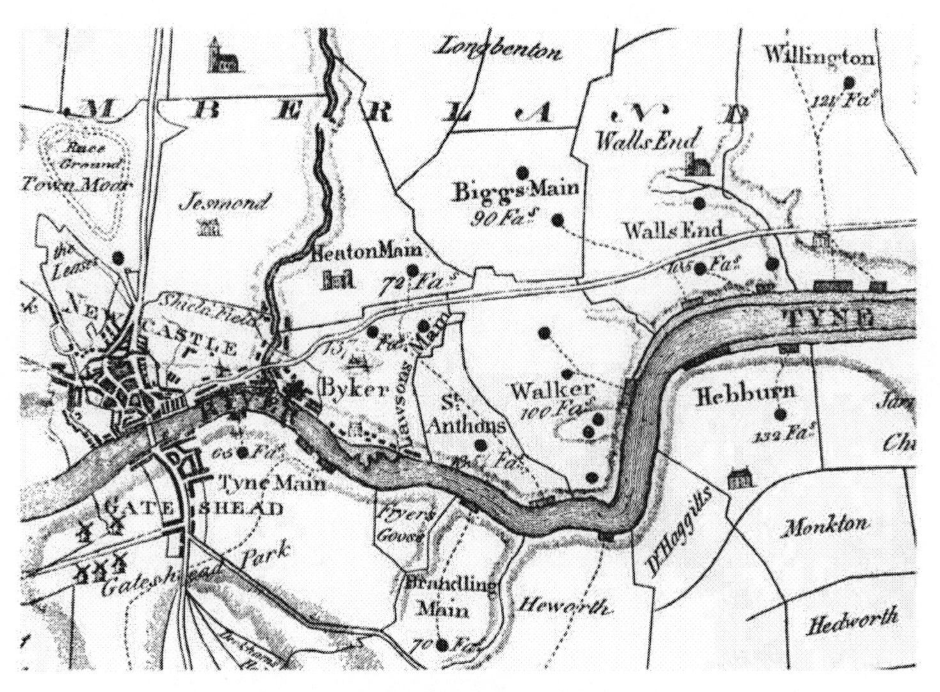

Casson's Map, 1801

Walker Colliery. The major breakthrough came in 1769 when James Watt separated the condenser from the cylinder and produced an engine driven by steam as distinct from atmospheric pressure. Once again the prospect for coal mining in Heaton changed with the development of more effective pumping machinery.

Engineers were also engaged with the problem of converting the linear motion of the pumping engine to circular motion for haulage. One method was to direct the water from the pump over an overshot waterwheel to drive winding gear; and, although there is no indication on the drawing, this may have been the system in operation at Longbenton Colliery in 1749. It was certainly in use at Longbenton by 1777. Keane FitzGerald built a machine for Walker Colliery in 1758 which worked two rotary mine ventilators and assisted in turning the winding gin. In 1763, Joseph Oxley took out a patent for raising coal by a fire engine and two machines were installed at Hartley Colliery. However, the motion was sluggish and irregular since the machine had no flywheel. James Watt, who visited Hartley in 1768, had solved the problem of obtaining direct rotary power from the steam engine by 1780. Later, in 1782, Watt obtained double power by applying steam alternately on both sides of the piston. This double-acting rotary engine was soon applied to colliery winding. In 1800, Phineas Crowther, owner of the Ouseburn works, patented a design for a vertical single cylinder engine which became the standard type of winding engine in the northern coalfield. One such engine in its distinctive tall engine house is preserved at Beamish Museum.

In the neighbourhood of Heaton, deep collieries had been won at Walker in 1763, Willington in 1775, Wallsend in 1781 and Bigges Main in 1784. The section from Casson's map of 1801 shows the location of these collieries, their depths in fathoms and the waggonways leading to the staiths. George Johnson, one of the leading viewers of the time, considered that it was now possible to win Heaton which still had 515 acres of whole coal left in the valuable High Main seam to the east of the Plain Pit Dyke. He calculated that the colliery could produce one and a quarter million tons of coal at 57,000 tons per annum over a period of 22 years and then a further 57,000 tons per annum for 7 years from robbing the pillars. In 1786 estimates were prepared for his partners of the capital and running costs of the mine which he calculated would take two and a half years to win assuming no major obstacles were encountered. These calculations provide interesting detail about what equipment and manpower was needed to win a major colliery at the end of the eighteenth century. The capital estimates seem to be arranged in the order that the work would be carried out. Firstly, the pumping engine to be used in the sinking of the shaft is erected; then the sinking of the first pit, the Engine Pit; then the erection of the second engine at the Engine Pit. A second shaft is sunk for coal winding which is linked to the Engine Pit underground. This shaft is provided with two machines for drawing coal. Finally, the waggonway and staiths are built.

(1)	For erecting Engine House for engines plus one Fire Engine with pumps	£2,100
(2)	For the sinking of the Engine Pit with an engine 86 fathoms deep and 11 feet in diameter with a Brattice down the middle including tubbing back water, finding all timber, deals, iron coals etc.	£3,805
(3)	For making an opencast for Engine delivery drift, making conduits, leading material during the winning and sundry jobbing work	£750
(4)	For erecting a second engine after the Engine Pit is sunk	£1,450
(5)	For sinking a coal pit 86 fathoms deep and 7 feet in diameter finding all timber, tubbing, boring etc	£1,100
(6)	Drifting between the Engine Pit and Coal Pit say 100 yards of stone and coal drifts. Levels for standage of water at the bottom underground, opening out the pit by drifting etc keeping the Fire Engine during this time with all necessary attendance	£548
(7)	Two machines for drawing coals complete	£2,000
(8)	Four gins	£160
(9)	Laying two miles of waggonway including sidings and branches, three keel births of staith with Ongate and Offgate	£1,560
(10)	Sixteen wagons and horses	£400
(11)	Twenty underground horses with stables, trappings etc	£260
(10)	Sinking gear underground hauls wedges and all other underground materials	£250
(11)	Staith and off putters houses, offices, granaries, stables, agents and workmens houses etc	£2,000
(12)	Agency during winning	£300
(13)	Binding pitmen for first year with sundry contingencies	£400

The total capital costs were £17,083 . The two shafts were to be sunk in the far south east corner of the manor which was where the fall of the drainage lay.

The plan of the new colliery in the east of the manor was very different from its predecessor - Heaton Banks Colliery in the west. The development by James Spedding, the viewer to the Lowther family's collieries in Whitehaven, of the technique of coursing the air around the workings removed the necessity for a large number of shafts. Steam engines were to be used not only for pumping but also for winding the coals to the surface although the horse gins were still retained. The estimate of running costs (below) reveals that an improvement in underground transport was planned by the introduction of underground waggonways using horses to pull the rolleys. This was necessary because of the greater distance from the coalface to the shaft. The estimate also reveals that it was planned to screen the coal (see 14 below). Snaps, a small flat pointed pick used at the screens to chip off pyrites and stone from the large coals, were to be bought; and wailing, the task, undertaken by boys, of picking out stone and pyrites which the screeners had missed, was budgeted for. However, it is not known whether the screening was to take place down the mine or at the surface or at both places. Candles were still the principal source of lighting.

George Johnson's estimates of the running costs were based upon an annual production of 20,000 chaldrons (53,000 tons), a Newcastle chaldron at this time being 53 cwt. These estimates provide some fascinating details about how it was proposed to operate the mine since they contain a comprehensive list of the jobs within the colliery. The men were paid per score (20 at Heaton) of corves mined and this is what the prices in the first section are based upon.

(1)	Hewing per score with 20 peck corf (a 20 peck corf weighed about 4.5 cwt and a score was therefore about 4.5 tons)	2s 3d
(2)	Putting	2s 0d
(3)	Overmen and deputies wages, propping, bratticing, laying barren ways, ridding falls in workings, cutting sumps, pumping water, oil wick and candles, lamp and	9d

	lamp lighters	
(4)	Onsetting	1.25d
(5)	Driving headways, holing walls, wet, double and narrow work turning and laying out boards, water levels and other drifts, setting over hitches and troubles (geological faults)	10d
(6)	Sinking and keeping pit shafts in repair	4d
(7)	Trap door keepers, attending forelamps underground, building stoppings including bricks, lime and shift work in the waste	6d
(8)	Planks, deals, props, barrowing stuff, brattish and other timber except for waggonway underground	1s 0d
(9)	Smith work - sharpening, sledge shoes, trams, waggons and waggonway plates, mauls, wedges, shovels, irons, hooks and chains , trace chains, underground corf cows and nails for every purpose.	3d
(10)	Wrightwork including timber, deals for waggons and waggonways, sledges, trams, shovel boards, maul shafts and hamesticks	2d
(11)	Drawing the coals with machines	1s 8d
(12)	Banking including man and horse	4.5d
(13)	Corving exclusive of corf cows (metal hooks)	4d
(14)	Wailing, shovelling screens, shovels, snaps and barrows	4d
(15)	Ropes	8d
(16)	Binding and removing pitmen, their fire coals etc	8d
(17)	Viewers and agents salaries	6d
(18)	Surgery and subsistence to maimed pitmen during their illness	1.5d
(19)	Contingencies	4.25d
	Total	**12s 10d**

(1)	Which will be per chaldron	6s 1.75d
(2)	Fire engines per chaldron	1s 0d
(3)	Leading on average	9d
(4)	Waggonway and waggons including everything	3.5d
(5)	Rent at 30s per Ten / 440 Bolls to a Ten (This was a measure upon which the landlord's rent - tentale rent - was based amounting to 51.7 tons)	1s 6d
(6)	Wayleave rent and staithroom at 4s per Ten with all other taxes and lesses etc	2.25d
(7)	Loss by small coals	7d
(8)	Repairing buildings including materials and leading for every purpose	1.5d
(9)	Staith charge including staithman, off putter, turnerout, wailers, trimmers, shovels, barrows, repairing and upholding staith and spout	3d
(10)	To replace the sum of £17,000 laid out in winning at 10% p.a.	1s 8.25d
(11)	Fittage and owners wages	1s 3.5d
	Total (exclusive of costs at London)	13s 11.25d

(NB - that the price of coal was expected to remain 17s per chaldron)

From these figures Johnson drew the following conclusions:

Value of coal that may be obtained	£498,666
Cost of laying on board ship	£410,666
Expenses at London	£29,333
Profit	**£58,667**

George Johnson warned that cost of winning the colliery could be much larger if difficulties were encountered and added 'that over and above the risk that attends the winning and working of all collieries, especially deep fiery collieries, there is that of being surrounded on the North and West and probably in a few years on the South also by very extensive drowned Wastes in which parts when the Colliery were working were found prodigious feeders of water'. Clearly, the winning of a mine was not for the faint hearted.

In 1791, George Johnson, viewer, of Byker; William Rowe, merchant, of Newcastle and Robert Smith, gentleman, of Plessey leased the colliery for a period of 31 years from the owners of the mineral rights for an annual fixed rent and an additional rent based upon the production of the colliery. One half of the rights were owned by the Grand Allies - Sir Thomas Liddell, Lord Wharncliffe and Lord Strathmore ; a quarter was owned by a Yorkshire gentleman, Colonel Henry Pulleine; while the remaining quarter was shared unevenly by seven others - four owning only 1%. Some families made fortunes from their ownership of the mineral rights such as the Liddells of Ravensworth, the Blacketts of Wylam, and the Ridleys of Blagdon. Not all were men: Lady Jane Clavering of Axwell Park was a formidable force in the Derwent valley. There were also lesser individuals who shared in this wealth as the list of the owners of mineral rights in Heaton illustrates. Indeed, Whellan's directory records that one of Sir Henry Babington's female descendants named Atkinson - 'a scullion at an inn' - received a share of Heaton Colliery in 1796. Although some made enormous fortunes from their estates, it should not be forgotten that many took great risks: a large investment of capital was needed to win a colliery and besides geological hazards to be overcome there was always the dangers of flooding, fire and explosions. Some ended their days in bankruptcy: Sir William Selby died insolvent in 1649 as a result of his mining ventures in the Winlaton area.

In January 1792, George Johnson and his partners also signed an agreement with Sir Mathew White Ridley, the owner of the surface rights, which gave them permission to sink three pits on Heaton estate, build a waggonway and to use the old waggon road through Ridley's estate in Byker. Four acres were set aside for the pithead and the partners were required 'not to erect any Pitmens or other Houses on any part of Heaton Estate; or any Smithshop, Wrights Shop, Warehouses, Agents or Engine Mens Houses on any other part of the Estate except in the aforesaid four acres'. This probably explains why no colliery village developed at Heaton. The census returns of the nineteenth century indicate that only about 20% of the workforce lived in the manor. Ridley claimed all the manure from the colliery and 'one hundred fothers of good….coal yearly for Heaton House - gratis'. The partners also had to pay wayleave rent to the other owners of land between Heaton and the River Tyne - Sir John Lawson, Henry Ibbotson, William Hargreave and the Mayor and Burgesses of Newcastle. Substantial wealth was acquired not only from the ownership of mineral rights but also from wayleave rights for the waggonways. For example, the glebe land of the rectors of Whickham lay between the River Tyne and the collieries to the south: the rectors were well aware that they controlled the access route to the market and exacted high wayleave rents. Consequently, the parish became one of the richest in the country.

On Thursday 23rd June 1796, the distinguished chemist and minerologist Charles Hackett 'breakfasted with Mr Johnston at Byker and afterwards went with him and his son to Heaton Colliery'. His diary records that 'the shaft here is divided into three parts; the coal is drawn by two of these divisions and the third is for the Engine Rods'.Matthias Dunn commented that Heaton 'was the first Treble Pit in the Trade comprising two Coal Pits and an Engine Pit and for several years each shaft went double shift'. Hackett noted that 'the coal here is raised in Basket Corves which contain 24 Pecks. The coal is conveyed to the water side by what they here call Waggons made of wood with small iron wheels which have a Rabbit which fit the wooden rail roads. The Basket Corves are fastened by a spring Woodcock eye Hook to the Rope by which it is raised from the Pit…. The waggons can contain about 8 Corves or 5300 lb. The Ropes are worked by a steam engine, common construction, the cylinder of which is 70 inches in diameter. The same raises the water out of the mines, 300 gallons each stroke'.

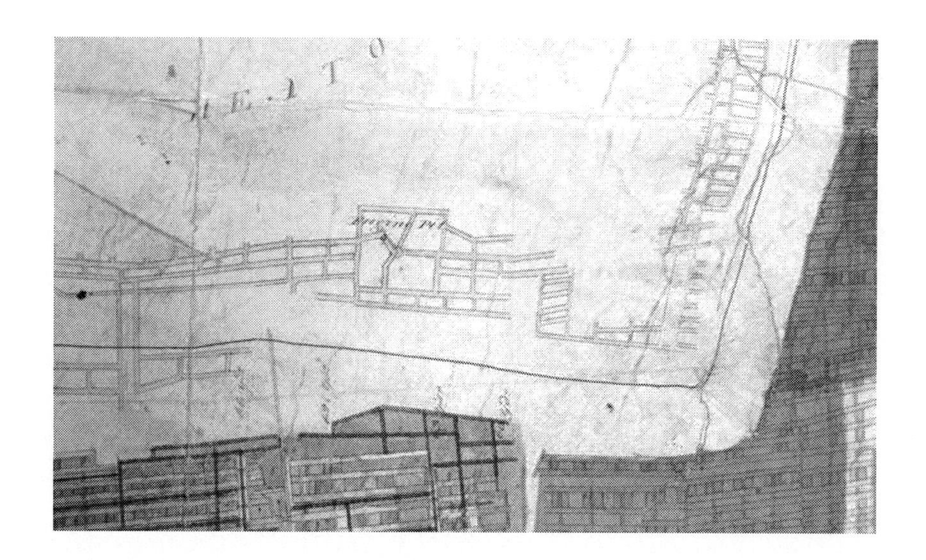

The colliery described by Charles Hackett is a modification of what was proposed by George Johnson. Note that the size of the corf, the measure upon which piece work rates of pay were based, had increased from 20 to 24 pecks (about 4.5cwt to about 5.4cwt). There is only one shaft known as the Engine Shaft which is divided into three parts which included two coal pits known as A and B pit. Part of an early nineteenth century plan of Heaton Colliery survives. This shows the Engine Pit shaft in the south east corner of the manor with the mothergates which opened up the mine leading off to the west and to the north. It was drawn to show the barrier of whole coal left to separate and protect Heaton Colliery from Walker Colliery. The thick dark line marks the boundary. Between 1801 and 1803 the Middle Pit (C and D pits) and the Far Pit (the E pit) were opened.

When Matthias Dunn was viewer at Hebburn Colliery in 1811-12 he wrote down the recollections of an old pitmen Sam Haggerston which he later presented to the North of England Institute of Mining Engineers as a manuscript entitled 'History of the Viewers'. The term viewer was the name given to mining engineers at this time and they were responsible to the owners for the strategic planning of the colliery. Sam Haggerston was about 70 years old and he was employed in keeping the furnaces at Hebburn Colliery. Sadly, he died in the workhouse at Heworth in 1812 but his recollections survive as an invaluable source of information about the early mining engineers including George Johnson.

The first mention of George Johnson is as under viewer to John Allen at Wallsend Colliery. When John Allen was killed in an explosion at St.Anthony's Colliery, Johnson became viewer at St. Anthony's and Wallsend. At the death of William Brown he also became viewer of Willington 'ranking at this time as the greatest viewer on both Tyne and Wear'. Sam Haggerston commented that George Johnson was 'well liked amongst the pitmen' and that the miners of Blyth had pulled his carriage around the town as a token of respect. Like Amos Barnes and John Buddle, George Johnson trained many apprentices including John Watson who served under Johnson at Bigges Main, Willington and Heaton. Watson later 'became the leading man on the River Tyne' and it is his collection of plans now housed within the Institute which illustrates much of this book. However, 'the winning of Heaton so easily over elevated George Johnson ...he got very rich ...and left off going down the pits'. With his riches from Heaton he purchased an estate at Wolverhampton where he developed another colliery. Unfortunately, the discovery that the workings of St. Anthony's had penetrated beneath the Tyne into Felling Colliery belonging to the powerful Brandling family and a similar trespass had taken place from Heaton into the royalty of the more powerful Grand Allies led 'to the great grief of Johnson'. George Johnson 'was called to London to attend the trials on those trespasses after which he retired to Wolverhampton where he died shortly afterwards'. His son, Major George Johnson, had inherited his father's share in Heaton Colliery by 1800.

John Buddle's View Book

In 1807, John Buddle Junior became the principal viewer at Heaton colliery - a position which he held until 1821. He also had a 9/96 share in the partnership. Three volumes of the view books of John Buddle Junior are preserved in the library of the Mining Institute and they record some interesting details of Heaton Colliery for the period 1807 and 1821. John Buddle Junior had first entered the pits at the age of six and had learnt his skill from his father, the viewer of the collieries of the Bishop and the Dean and Chapter of Durham. Besides being head viewer at Heaton, John Buddle was viewer at other collieries including Wallsend, Benwell, Walker, Percy Main, Backworth, Elswick and the Lambton collieries. He was regarded as one of the leading authorities on mining practices in the early nineteenth century and his advice was sought at several parliamentary inquiries. He was also secretary to the Northumberland and Durham Coal Owners' Association.

Buddle visited Heaton on a regular basis but the day to day management was in the hands of a resident viewer assisted by two overmen and six deputies. In his view book Buddle gives a list of the 262 pitmen signing the bond on Thursday 17th October 1807 to work at Heaton for the coming year. This included an overman and two deputies for each of the three pits forming the colliery. The main underground workforce comprised 90 hewers, 27 hewer drivers and 31 inby drivers. There were also 14 shifters signing the bond who did general work including storing stone and small coals underground; six wastemen who were responsible for the worked out area of the mine especially for checking for any accumulation of gas in the old workings; the two furnace keepers were essential to maintain the ventilation system; the four crane men assisted by the four crane-onsetters were responsible for loading corves onto a rolley for transport underground to the shaft where another four onsetters attached the corf to the rope for haulage to the surface. There were six banksmen enlisted. These were senior pitmen who received the coals at the surface and managed the screens and the pitheap. The seven waggonway men were responsible for maintaining the railway and the 49 waggon drivers were employed to lead the coal along the waggonway to the riverside staiths at St.Anthony's Byker. Buddles notes that there were 140 horses employed at Heaton - 103 underground - hence the need for nine horsekeepers. There is no mention of trappers (the boys who opened and closed trap doors to keep the ventilation system in operation) since these were not bound. They were usually the younger sons of the hewers. However, another entry in the view book noted that there were 20 trappers at the Middle Pit and 18 at the Far Pit in 1808. Young men employed at the screens or at other work above ground were also not required to sign the bond.

Like agricultural workers, pitmen signed a contract, the bond, which committed them to an employer for the following year. It laid down in detail the conditions of employment including the rates of pay and the penalties for neglect of duty - for example, absence without leave. At times of unemployment the men were entitled to a loan in addition to their house and free coals. Like the agricultural hiring fairs, the colliery bonding day was a time for celebration. In his assessment of the capital needed to win the colliery, Johnson had set aside £400 binding money - probably an average of about £1.50 per person, the equivalent of two weeks wages. Breaking the bond was a criminal offence as the following public notice shows:

'William Dial, 26 Years of Age, 5 feet 7 inches high, pimpled in the Face; and John Hills, 23 Years of Age, 5 feet 7 inches high, slender made, and round shouldered. Whoever will apprehend either of the above Men or give Information so that they may be apprehended shall receive a Reward of TWO GUINEAS for each Man, to be paid by the Owners of Heaton Colliery; And any Person employing either of the above Men after this Public Notice will be prosecuted as the Law directs. June 2nd 1803'.

It was generally accepted that it took about twelve years to train a boy to become a hewer and much of this training was familiarisation with the working of the colliery. Owners were anxious to retain experienced hewers upon which the entire production of the mine depended. The bond was a means of trying to hold on to experienced workmen. The miners were aware of their position and there was much bargaining before the bond was agreed. Originally, the bond ran from October to the following October but to avoid the threat of industrial action at the height of the coal trade the owners attempted to change the date of signing to January. This the miners resisted in the great strike of 1765. Eventually, a compromise was reached. After much unrest, including an unsuccessful strike by the Heaton pitmen in 1810, the date of binding was altered in 1812 to run from April to April. Originally, individual collieries had their own bond but in the early nineteenth century the bond became standardised. In an expanding market for their labour, the restrictions of the bond became a major grievance amongst the miners and it was one of the causes of the great strikes of 1831-32 and 1844. Much evocative language was used falsely describing this contract of employment as slavery because the men were bound for twelve months. Even a cursory knowledge of the miners of the North East would dispel this myth: the records suggest that they were independent and resourceful individuals not slaves. With the creation of trade unions in Northumberland and Durham the legality of the bond was challenged and it was finally abolished by the Coal Mines Regulation Act of 1872.

The rising cost of using horses led to improvements in the transport system both under and above ground. In 1798, Thomas Barnes used an inclined plane worked by a counterbalance weight in the pit shaft at Benwell Colliery to replace horses to transport coal to the staith. There was an inclined plane on the southern part of the Heaton waggonway where the ground fell steeply towards the Tyne. Furthermore, inclined planes had for many years been used underground. In May 1812, Buddle improved the inclined plane in the west mothergate of Heaton Main Colliery at a cost of £430 which enabled him to dispense with ten horses per shift. Wooden waggonways were used underground and sometimes these were plated with iron. Improvements were also made to the rolleys. On 12th October 1813 Buddle 'resolved to put a new set of double corf rollies with 18" wheels into the far way .... by this change we expect that one horse will draw six instead of four corves at a pull'.

A steam engine had been installed for pumping at Heaton but horses were still used to power chain pumps at the Middle and Far Pits. In July 1807, Buddle records that 'the new crank in the D Pit goes well - two horses will draw the water with ease working seven hours per day'. In May 1808, two horses were being used at the D Pit and two at the E Pit for drawing water. Buddle 'bought the Penshaw Engine of Mr. Lambton for £2,200' in July 1813 for pumping at the Middle Pit. Horses were an important and expensive part of the workforce and Buddle was concerned about their welfare: he suggested that the workload of the horsekeepers should be reduced from 12 to 10 horses to enable the men to better care for the animals. An estimate for the waggonway dated January 1820 revealed that the cost of maintaining a horse was £50 per annum - a waggonman cost £45 per annum. Another estimate indicates that most of the cost (47%) was in feed - oats and beans - while the cost of hay represented 25%. Like the men working underground, the horses were lowered into the pit by the rope and Buddle reckoned that the 'gin drew a horse in about ten minutes'. At this rate it took a whole day to put the horses into the mine and for that reason they were stabled underground.

In April 1809, Buddle 'ordered a Keeker to be placed over the men in the D Pit to make them work the broken fairly'. A keeker was an inspector (or spy to the men) and working the broken was robbing the pillars left in the initial working to support the roof. Generally, the hewers removed half of alternate pillars thus recovering 25% of the coal left after the first mining. In June 1810, Buddle records a meeting of the owners 'to investigate the conduct of Jonathon Taylor, the staithsman, and Robert Thompson, off putter, for giving over measure to the spout ships - after a long hearing, the fact being proved, they were dismissed'.

Just how precarious mining could be is shown by the following two examples. In January 1810, Buddle records that the E Pit caught fire and 'had the fire not gone out itself I do not think it could have been extinguished by the engine or any other means that could have been devised without drowning up the Colliery which from the fire being situated so much to the rise would have taken 9 or 10 months to accomplish and in the meantime the pit must have been torn to pieces by repeated explosions'. On 6th December 1814, Buddle records that 'the timber at the quicksand broke completely in the old Engine shaft this morning and the pit is in danger of being lost...as there is now no other prospect than a long interruption of coal work set about distributing the men and boys to the neighbouring collieries'. He made a sketch in his view book showing the bed of sand and the damage caused by the collapse. There is also a plan of the triple shaft in pencil. 'William Gardner, Ralph Witherington and his two sons were so alarmed at the idea of giving up the pit that they volunteered to attempt to put her thro' the sand by short lengths of timber; and offered to give their labour if the owners would find the timber etc. This I consented to subject to the approbation of the owners and promised if they succeeded in securing the shaft thro' the sand - 8 or 9 feet in diameter- that they should have a present of £50 over and above their wages'. They did succeed and on Friday 6th January 1815 Buddle 'put the horses down the old pit again, finished the heapstead and got all in readiness for drawing the coals tomorrow so that we may be ready for coal work on Monday morning'.

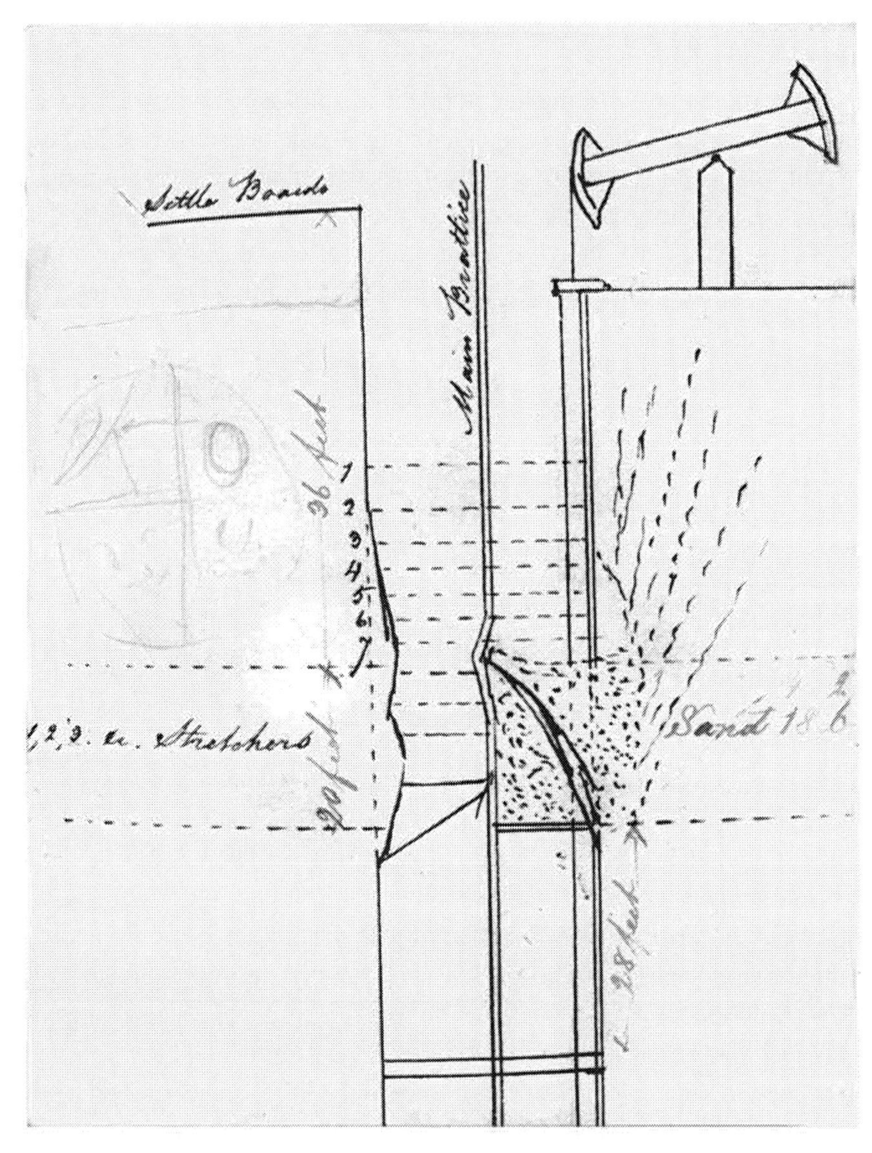

There are many references to the problem of water in the colliery. Matthias Dunn, who regularly visited Heaton Colliery in 1812, noted that the water was ten feet up the Old Engine Pit shaft on 21st August and 'the engine ...goes most dreadfully'. On 25th May 1813 Buddle 'decided to purchase a powerful engine for the Middle Pit without delay ...the object of erecting this engine is not only to ensure the working of the whole coal in the west of the old pit but also to attempt the draining of old Benton or Heaton Wastes or perhaps both'. Unfortunately, on 15th April 1814 the 'boiler of the new engine at D Pit burst killing Jas.Young and Geo. Shelaw - putter. Walter Blacket the fireman was severely scalded'. Many other accidents are recorded. On Sunday 14th November 1813 'Tim Dodgson, overman, and Geo.Robson, deputy, burnt this morning in the north exploring drift of the old pit.....In going their rounds Dodgson and Robson went into the drift without looking at their candles and when near the face were fired upon unawares ...Robson was severely burnt but Dodgson received little injury. The fire happened entirely through the carelessness of the parties themselves'. In February 1814 an explosion in the drift killed three trappers - 'Hall, Richardson and Short had wandered up the drift despite warnings of gas'. The following year, on the morning of 3rd May 1815, a major accident took place - the colliery flooded, killing 75 men and boys when the men broke into the old workings of the abandoned Heaton Banks Colliery. The story of this inundation - the most serious accident in the colliery's history - is told in detail in Chapter Three.

Production Figures

The measurements used in the coal trade upon which wages and rents were based can be confusing because they were based upon volume not upon weight. The miners filled corves which were either 20 pecks or 24 pecks in size at Heaton and the hewers were paid by the score of corves filled. A score was 20 on the Tyne, 21 on the Wear and between 20 and 26 on the Tees. The corves were loaded into chaldron waggons and a score of 24 peck corves filled 2.125 chaldron waggons. Eight chaldron waggons were needed to fill a keel boat and between ten and twelve keel loads to fill the average collier boat of 200 - 300 tons burden. A chaldron waggon contained about 53cwt of coal but as the entry in Buddle's diary for 25th May 1816 indicates this could vary: 'As Heaton measure is proved to be worse than any of the other Collieries, fixed with Mr. Potts to put ledges upon the waggons by nailing an Inch Deal upon the fore and side overings - tapering them off at the hind end. By this small addition it is to be expected that the measure will give content'. From an assortment of records surviving in the Mining Institute, it is possible to provide production figures for forty four years of the sixty years of Heaton Main Colliery's existence. These records are usually expressed in chaldrons but have been converted into tons to aid understanding.

On 30th March 1802 three colliery engineers - John Bedlington, George Dormand and William Casson - conducted a detailed examination of Heaton Colliery. Part of their report notes the production from the colliery between 9th April 1792 and 21st April 1802 . During the first ten years of its life a total of 349,457 chaldrons (925,704 tons) was mined which was disposed of in the following manner:

Seacole	316,417	(838,505 tons)
Landsale	5,605	(14,853 tons)
Furnaces underground	1,620	(4,293 tons)
Pit fires/ smiths	2,500	(6,625 tons)
Machines for drawing coals	4,850	(12,853 tons)
Pitman's coals	8,130	(21,545 tons)
Total	339,122	(898,673 tons)

(N.B. There is a discrepancy of 10,335 chaldrons. The figure for seacoal sales is confirmed from other sources - therefore the discrepancy occurs in the other modes of disposal).
The average yearly production was 34,946 chaldrons (92,570 tons) more than the target of 30,000 chaldrons (79,500 tons). The vast majority of the coal was for the very important - and lucrative - seacoal trade (90.5%). Only 1.6% was landsale and this was likely to be small coals for local use perhaps by the glassmakers and potteries at the mouth of the Ouseburn. A fair proportion - 5,080 tons per annum (5.5%) - was used by the mine itself: 2,703 tons for the steam engines hauling the coal from the mine; 1,285 tons for the pumping engines; 622 tons for the smiths fires and other pit fires; and 429 tons for the underground furnaces driving the ventilation system of the mine. The traditional free coals for the pitmen amounted to 2,154 tons per annum - about seven ton per miner based on a workforce of 300 men.

Several records of the number of chaldrons of coal led along the waggonway to the staiths at St. Anthony's survive as half yearly accounts. These have been used to produce the table below. This seacoal amounted to about 90% of the production from the colliery and the figures on the right have been added to show the probable yearly production in tons for the period April 1802 to April 1806.

5th May to 3rd November	1802	21,564	104,802 tons
3rd November to 11th May	1803	17,984	
11th May to 9th November	1803	18,948	97,390 tons
9th November to 9th May	1804	17,803	
9th May to 7th November	1804	16,975	93,010 tons
7th November to 8th May	1805	18,123	
8th May to 6th November	1805	18,179	103,928 tons
6th November to 7th May	1806	21,039	

A more comprehensive list of accounts for the period 1806 to 1836 survive amongst the Watson Collection in the Mining Institute. This represents half of the lifetime of Heaton Colliery. These accounts also show that most of the coal - generally over 90% - was shipped from the River Tyne and only a small proportion was for landsale at the pithead. The accounts are summarised in the table below and the figures have been converted into tons. In most years the colliery produced its target of 30,000 Newcastle chaldrons (79,500 tons) making it one of the largest in the coalfield. The accounts also show when each pit was in production.

HEATON COLLIERY PRODUCTION 1806-36

Year	Old Pit	Middle Pit	Far Pit	H.M.	New Pit	Total
1806-7	-	44,838	81,395	-	-	126,233
1807-8	-	45,402	58,217	-	-	103,619
1808-9	-	22,488	33,565	-	-	56,053
1809-10	-	30,327	57,778	-	-	88,105
1810-11	5,663	2,547	88,653	-	-	96,863
1811-12	27,232	-	54,356	-	-	81,590
1812-13	42,233	-	16,091	-	-	58,324
1813-14	55,509	-	2,957	-	-	58,466
1814-15	24,004	-	2,645	-	-	26,961 *
1815-16	46,273	318	13,416	-	-	60,007
1816-17	47,708	693	20,215	5,636	-	74,252
1817-18	37,496	3,877	30,125	-	-	71,498
1818-19	36,270	16,253	30,298	3,640	-	86,461
1819-20	39,725	19,443	36,062	3,988	-	99,218
1820-21	7,902	2,515	20,580	3,719	-	34,721 **
1821-22	32	23,155	46,968	-	-	70,155
1822-23	-	28,316	41,645	-	-	75,284
1823-24	-	35,364	38,724	-	-	74,088
1824-25	-	37,853	40,751	-	-	78,604
1825-26	-	36,132	29,113	-	14,424	79,669
1826-27	-	39,341	11,107	-	31,440	81,888
1827-28	-	34,764	-	-	40,891	75,655
1828-29	-	43,690	-	-	43,103	86,793
1829-30	-	58,795	-	-	28,883	87,678
1830-31	-	67,908	-	-	12,635	80,543
1831-32	-	48,179	-	-	45,384	93,563
1832-33	-	44,623	-	-	55,834	100,457
1833-34	-	65,755	-	-	19,472	85,208
1834-35	-	68,755	-	-	24,848	93,603
1835-36	-	43,675	-	-	55,869	99,544

The figures represent the coal sold or the vend not the coal mined. There was a limited market for the small coals: most of this small coal was left in the pit, used as ballast on the waggonway, or burnt at the surface.

Howard's Main (HM) was Benton Colliery on the land of the Earls of Carlisle, the Howards. This colliery was connected underground to the Far Pit. The New Pit, sunk nearby in 1825 to give better access to Benton coal, was regarded as part of Heaton Colliery. Indeed, it was the last part of the colliery to survive and became known as Heaton Colliery (it is marked as such on Bell's map) despite being in Benton.

* The low figure is explained by the flooding of the colliery in May 1815. It graphically shows the economic impact of a major mining accident - production was cut by half.

** The low figure is explained by a change in the accounting system which ran from November to November until 1820. In 1821 it changed to May to May and this is associated with the new lease. Thus 1820-21 is a short year.

The Middle Pit connected with Bigges Main Colliery and from 1831 Bigges Main coal was mined from Heaton. Earlier, in 1802, coal in Bigges Main royalty had been mined from the Engine Pit.

There was a change of ownership and a radical re-organisation of the colliery in 1836 which undoubtedly explains why the detailed production figures end in that year. In April 1835, an advertisement in the press announced that 'this extensive and valuable colliery is now to be let containing unwrought all the seams of coal excepting the High Main'. Another advertisement in the local press dated 7th September 1836 offered three sets of pumps and 'about 180 tons of cast-iron waggon-way rails and chairs of different patterns' for sale which could be seen 'at Heaton Colliery Office, Bigges Main'. It would appear that the new owners had abandoned the Engine Pit and the dip part of the colliery, lifted the waggonway, apart from the link with the Coxlodge line, and moved the administration to Bigges Main. Coal from Heaton royalty was now mined from the Middle Pit and the New Pit in Benton. The lifting of the waggonway would suggest that the Middle Pit became a landsale pit and the New Pit, which was linked to the Coxlodge waggonway, remained a seasale pit.

Comprehensive production figures do not survive for the new enterprise. However, a report by George Johnson shows the market for Heaton coals in 1836-37.

	Tons sold	Price per ton
Seacole 1st class	55,491	10s 6d
Seacole 2nd class	7,582	8s 3d
Oversea 1st class	———	
Oversea 2nd class	1,484	6s 10d
Home 1st class	———	
Home 2nd class	8,668	6s 10d
Nuts	11,302	2s 3d
Small	36,477	1s 10.5d
Total	121,004	

Seacoal was still the most important part of the business and all the top quality coal was sold to this market; but the proportion of seacoal in the total coal being marketed had fallen from 90.5% to 52% and the landsale coal had risen from 1.6% to 46.6%. This probably reflected the fact that much of the mining was now from the pillars. The prices for the different products of the mine emphasize the importance of the seacole trade. Although seacole now represented only 52% of the output from the mine, this generated 80% of the value of the sales. George Johnson also recorded that the vend in 1844 was 127,266 tons and again this included a large proportion of small coals.

Work underground

The miners at Heaton Main Colliery like their predecessors at Heaton

Banks Colliery worked by the pillar and stall system. However, by the end of the eighteenth century it was common practise to rob the pillars at a second working of the colliery and Buddle's view books record the stages by which the old Heaton Banks and Benton Collieries were reworked. The physical graft of hewing the coal varied in different areas of the mine which was why the hewers drew lots for working places. In some parts the coal 'is course and strong to work and the hewers complain much of the hardness of the work'. Buddle 'agreed to allow them gunpowder'. The sentiments of the hewer in Thomas Wilson's poem 'The Pitman's Pay' spring to mind:

> I've bray'd for hours at woody coal,
> Wi' airms myest droppin' frae the shouther
> But now they just pop in a hole,
> And flap her down at yence wi' pouther.

Down the pit candles were generally used for lighting even after the invention of the safety lamp in 1815 - indeed at many collieries they were

LIGHTING DOWN THE PIT

CANDLES, DAVY LAMP, ELECTRIC HEAD LAMP

used until the twentieth century as in the photograph of a hewer at Brancepeth Colliery. The engraving from the *London Illustrated News* of 1849 shows a miner with a Davy lamp of the period. Buddle records the use of the Davy lamp at Heaton in March 1816 during the attempt to recover the colliery after the flooding of 1815. Heaton was one of the first collieries to be equipped with the Davy lamps and in 1819 Buddle notes that 'the Far Pit work entirely with Davy's'. However, sometimes 'from the weakness of the air course, the styth (foul air) will not allow the Davy's to burn; but the steel mills play very well'. A steel wheel strapped to a boy was turned at speed. A piece of flint held against the wheel produced a shower of sparks which was sufficient to enable a group of about six miners to work.

Each year, prior to the binding of the pitmen, Buddle calculated the manpower needed to reach the colliery's production target: an example is shown from his view book:

'Estimate of the number of hewers required for the ensuring year.
Supposing the vend to be 36,000 chaldrons
Have in hand 2,000 chaldrons
Reqd. to be wrought 34,000 chaldrons
Supposing a score of 24 peck corves to yield 2.125 chaldrons
Then 34,000 chaldrons = 16,000 scores
Which is 615 scores per fortnight or 307.5 for two shifts
Which at 11 days per fortnight will be 28 score per day each nearly.

This will require 28 men per shift, or 56 in all, but to cover sickness and Casualties say 60'.

According to this calculation, Buddle expected each hewer to fill a score of corves each shift or 11 score each fortnight. A score was equal to 2.125 chaldrons or about 5.63 tons - 11 score about 62 tons.

The men were paid fortnightly. The bond which the men signed annually designated the rates of pay. No bonds survive for Heaton but George Johnson noted that the average earnings of hewers in the year 1842-3 was £44-13-0d per annum or an average of 17s10d per week. The hewers were on piece work and were paid by the amount of coal hewed. At Heaton the hewers worked on average 4.25 days a week. The wages of some of the other men at the pit are mentioned in the view books: Thomas Suthering, an under viewer was paid £78 p.a.; a wasteman, £65 p.a. and a banksman £72 p.a. The highest wages in the kingdom at this time were earned by the Staffordshire potters (£2 for a 72 hour week) according to Samuel Scriven's report to Parliament

Profits

Although there were considerable financial risks to developing a coal mine, and the financial output was large before the colliery produced coal, if the mine was successful like Heaton Colliery, the rewards could be considerable.

Only one statement of the profits made from Heaton is recorded in Buddle's view books and that may appear because the year, 1807, was a year of record production. The statement reads:

Actual Profit		£16,316 - 3 - 1.5d
Mr Row's share of the above	46/96	7,818 - 3 - 0
W. Johnson's share	18/96	3,059 - 5 - 9
Geo. Fenwick's share	6/96	1,019 - 15 - 2.5
Th. Crudace's share	6/96	1,019 - 15 - 2.5
Exs of M. Featherstonehaugh	6/96	1,019 - 15 - 2.5
Jn. Buddle	9/96	1,529 - 12 - 9
Jas. Potts	5/96	849 - 16 - 0

These are the colliery owner's profit. In addition, the owners of the mineral rights received their certain and tentale rents; and the owners of the wayleaves for the waggonway also received an income from the colliery.

The waggonway

The landsale coals, which amounted to about 1.5% of the colliery's production, were carried by cart down the burn road which still exists by the side of the Ouseburn. The cart contained a fother, a third of a chaldron, which was the weight which an average good horse could pull. However, the bulk of the production was transported by the waggonway to the River Tyne for seasale. A plan of the Heaton waggonway dated January 1805 shows the line running from the High or E Pit to the Middle Pit (C and D Pits) and on to the Old Engine Pit (A and B Pits); it then crossed Shields Road heading in a south westerly direction to Lawson's Main Colliery; from here it followed the Lawson's Main waggonway to the staiths at St. Anthony's. The total distance was 3 miles 258.5 yards. The plan was drawn because two realignments of the waggonway from the Engine Pit were being considered. Both the new routes proposed went directly to St. Anthony's staiths avoiding Lawson's Main and the climb up Walker Hill.

Sections of the plan have been reproduced to show the holding sidings at the Far Pit and Middle Pit; the climb up to Lawson's Main (where an earlier waggonway serving the Byker colliery is marked heading in the direction of Walker); and also the staiths at the riverfront.

A detailed account of the traffic on the waggonway survives for the year 1814-15. The document reveals that the trade was no longer seasonal as it had been in previous centuries. There was a peak period between June and November and a dip in traffic during December and January when the Christmas holidays and the worst winter weather affected trade; but traffic continued throughout the year. Significantly, 530 chaldrons (1,405 tons) was moved during early May 1815, when the colliery was closed because of the flooding, indicating that the coal was stockpiled on the surface at the pitheads. A total of 21,861 waggons travelled the line in year 1814-15. The effect of the accident in economic terms is shown by the fall in traffic: in the following year, 1815-16, only 5,535 waggons are recorded travelling along the waggonway.

The Heaton waggonway was at the forefront of technical experiments. Although Thomas Brumell had considered using iron rails for the Byermoor waggonway as early as 1710, the engineer Nicholas Wood claimed that the Lawson's Main waggonway was the first iron railway in the North of England. The wooden rails attached to wooden sleepers were replaced by cast iron rails and stone sleepers in 1797 according to the viewer Thomas Barnes. However, when in 1811, the owners of the neighbouring Felling Colliery stopped pumping from the High Main seam, Lawson's Main (also known as South Heaton) was flooded. The owners were declared bankrupt in 1811 and an advert appeared in the local press for the sale of '1,500 yards of cast iron railway with chairs and stone sleepers ... lately used for leading coal from South Heaton Colliery to the River Tyne' together with 'a Cast Iron Wheel and Brake for the use of the inclined Plane'. The land over which this waggonway ran was restored in 1811. Clearly, one of the realignments proposed in 1805 had been adopted for Heaton Colliery.

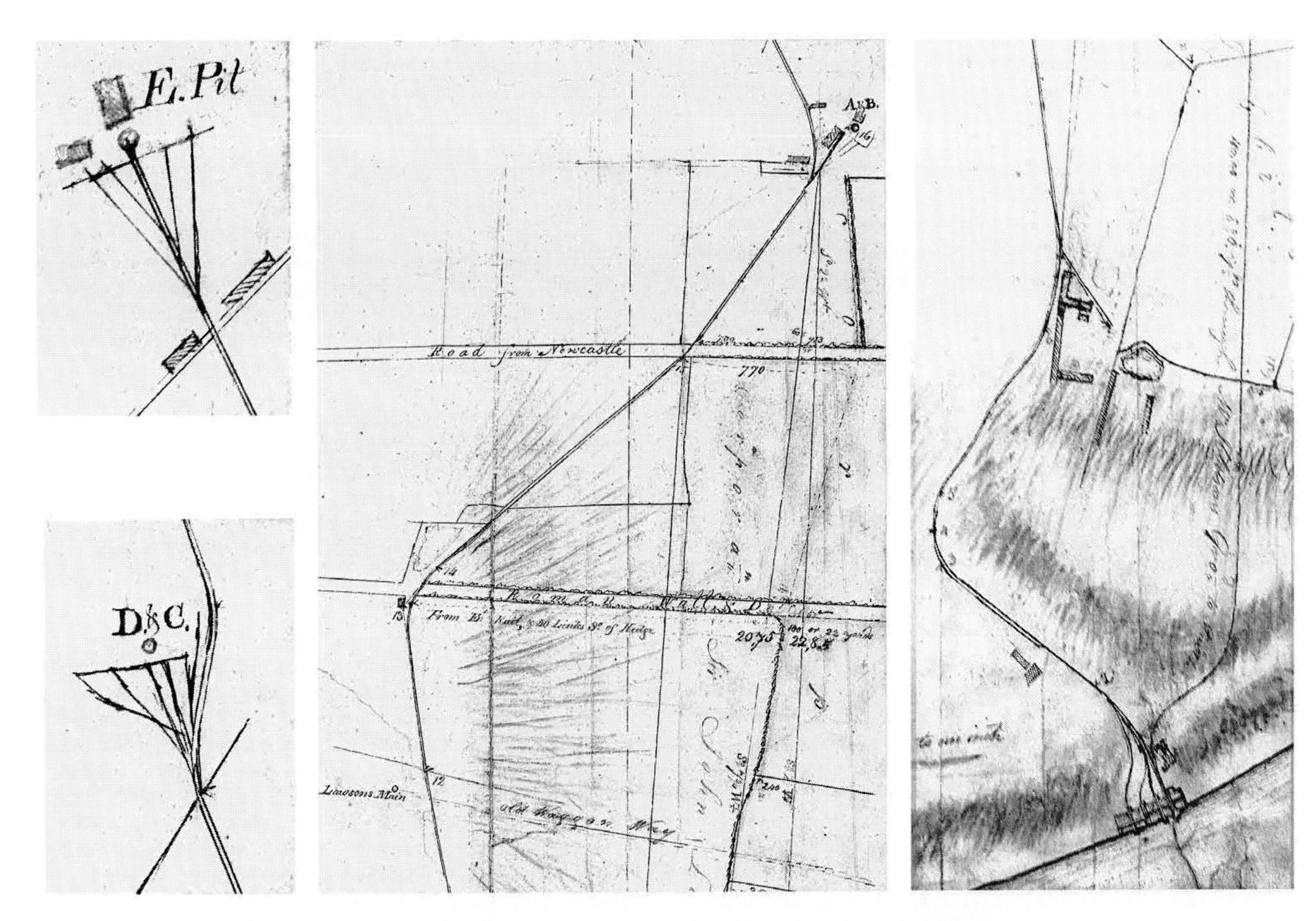

SECTIONS FROM THE HEATON WAGGONWAY MAP DATED 1805

The shortage of horses and the high cost of both horses and fodder during the period of the Napoleonic Wars was one factor which led colliery engineers to experiment with steam locomotives which they called 'travelling engines'. The first steam locomotive had been built by the Cornishman Richard Trevithick in 1803. In 1805, a similar engine was built at John Whinfield's foundry in Gateshead to Trevithick's design for the Wylam waggonway but it was considered too heavy for the route and never left the workshops. Trevithick's engines had proved that the weight of the locomotive was sufficient to enable smooth wheels to run on smooth rails but not all engineers accepted the point. In 1813, John Blenkinsopp of Walker experimented with a rack engine on the Coxlodge waggonway and, at nearby Heaton, William Chapman conducted trials with a locomotive which pulled itself along by means of a chain. Included in Chapman's patent for the chain driven locomotive was the design of a bogie to spread the weight of the locomotive and enable it to move freely round curves. A second Chapman locomotive was built in 1814 for the Lambton collieries (where Buddle was also the viewer) by Phineas Crowther at the Ouseburn foundry. The chain locomotive was not a success at Heaton since the chain frequently broke. However, the bogie - first tried at Heaton - became a standard feature of the steam locomotive. The experiment had cost the owners of Heaton Colliery nearly £3,000. The travelling engine was subsequently used for pumping and haulage at the Middle Pit, the Far Pit and Benton Pit.

In the same year, 1813, William Hedley, the viewer of Wylam Colliery, and George Stephenson, the enginewright at Killingworth Colliery, were also experimenting with steam locomotives. Hedley demonstrated conclusively that the weight of the engine provided sufficient adhesion for the locomotive to pull waggons in all weathers - rack rails and chains were unnecessary. He built 'Puffing Billy' for the Wylam waggonway and a replica of this engine can be seen at Beamish Museum. Stephenson built the engine 'Blucher' (named after the Northumbrian word meaning a huge animal) which on 25th June 1814 drew a load of eight loaded waggons at four miles per hour up a gradient of 1:450 on the Killingworth waggonway. By 1822, there were five engines working on the Killingworth line. In the same year, George Stephenson built the Hetton Railway which used a mixture of locomotives, self-acting inclined planes and stationary steam engines to convey coal to the River Wear. Steam haulage was becoming a feature of the large colliery.

The flooding which caused the disaster of on 3rd May 1815 at Heaton Colliery drained the old workings of Benton Colliery. Heaton Far Pit linked up with these old workings in Benton. Buddle decided to repair the No.3 shaft of Benton Pit and to rework the colliery as part of the Heaton enterprise. He proposed to build a branch from the pit, 121 yards long, to the Kenton and Coxlodge waggonway. He sought permission to use this established route for 3,300 yards and the adjoining Bigges Main waggonway for 1,166 yards. Then he proposed to build another new branch, 1,276 yards in length, from the Bigges Main way, past Wallsend Colliery, to the new staith at Wallsend called Howard's Main staith. Two sidings each 25 yards long were planned for the pit and the line was to be doubled for the first 220 yards from the staith to facilitate turn around. Cast iron rails were ordered from the Glasgow foundries at £9 per ton because the local foundries were charging £12. The rails were to be fixed onto stone pedestals with four wooden pins and laid on ballast.

In addition, on 8th April 1817 Buddle 'measured the distance from the A or old Pit, through Walker Estate to Coxlodge Waggonway to ascertain the distance to the intended new staith in case it should be thought right to relinquish the present line of W.way to St.Anthony's'. The proposed new way ran from the Old Engine Pit for 88 yards to the Corporation's lands in Walker; it travelled 1,302 yards through Walker to the Dean and Chapter of Durham's lands in Wallsend; and on a further 359 yards to the Coxlodge way: a total of 1,749 yards of new waggonway to lay. The route used the Coxlodge way for 363 yards before reaching the new branch leading to the Howards Main staith and thereby enabling all Heaton coal to be shipped from Wallsend.

By May 29th 1817, Buddle had obtained permission from the owners of Willington Colliery to use one of their staiths for shipping Benton coals until the new Heaton staith was ready and began to make 'the heapstead, banks, skreen etc at the 3rd Pit'. He noted that 'all the spare waggons must also be put to repair and made to fit the Kenton Way which is 2" narrower than Heaton way' which was 4 feet 9.5 inches. (There was not a standard gauge for railways at this time.) However all was not progress, for 'the boiler of the travelling Engine seems too small for drawing a considerable quantity of coals at the 3rd Pit. The engine has power enough; but the boiler cannot keep up a regular supply of steam'.

By the end of June the winding engine was ready at Benton No.3 Pit and on 22nd July they began leading coal to a 'seven keel ship freighted and laid under Bigges Main spout' at Wallsend. Then waggonway politics intervened. The following day 'Mr. W. Brandling stopped the Benton waggons from going along Coxlodge Waggonway in Benton ground which he purchased from Ld.Carlisle ... because we have not asked their leave'. This involved the first 300 yards of the route. Buddle believed that 'the stopping of the waggons is merely a scheme to bring us to an arrangement about the Barrier' i.e. the working of the barrier of coal between Heaton and Benton. However, the matter was resolved by the end of the month.

The diary for October records that 'Thomas Atkinson a skreener at the 3rd Pit was killed ...by falling down the Pit'; that 'Wm Carrick deputy overman was killed in the High Pit by a fall of stone when drawing props'; and that 'the waggonway and new staith at Wallsend were finished yesterday and the first Howards Main - Wallsend coals were shipped this morning 28th October 1817'. Wallsend coals was a general term for coal from the High Main seam - the best domestic coal on the market.

On Thursday 26th February 1818 Buddle 'set out the main branch of Waggonway from the E Pit to join the Coxlodge Way. When this branch is joined any proportion of the Far Pit coals that may be thought right may be taken to Howard Main spout'. The work was undertaken by John Wilkinson at 2s 0d per yard.

On 23rd January 1819 Buddle met with the owners of Heaton Colliery - now Mr. Pearson, Mr.Potts, and Major George Johnson - to discuss the state of the colliery and they 'agreed to endeavour to renew the leases of the Spanish Closes and Heaton and to obtain a lease from T.H.Liddle for part of Longbenton'. The major's son, also called George Johnson, was at this meeting. He was appointed resident viewer at Heaton in June 1819. Applications were made for the renewal of the leases and also for a change in the line of the waggonway to bring all the coals to Wallsend in January 1820. Estimates were submitted for the new line from the old Engine Pit to Howard Main staith - the route surveyed in April 1817. These provide interesting information about the method of operating the waggonway and cost of the workforce. The estimate states that '12 waggon horses will lead 26,000 chaldrons annually reckoning each horse to take 3 waggons and to go four gates per day and 240 working days in the year'. It then lists the workforce of 34 men and horses required to run the waggonway and their costs. Interestingly, the horses are the most expensive item.

12 horses keeping at £50 per annum	£600
12 waggoners at £45 per annum	£540
4 men to assist the waggoners to fill at £40 p.a	£160
One staithmans wages	£80
One off putter	£54-12-0
One turn rail £39, one boy £20-15-0	£59-15-0
2 waggonway wrights at 16/- per week	£85- 4-0

While these negotiations were underway, it became evident that the life of the Engine Pit was limited and the decision was made to pursue a more direct route from the Middle Pit to the Kenton Way. Negotiations with Sir Mathew White Ridley were acerbated by his belief that the cracks in the ceilings of Heaton Hall were caused by miners robbing the pillars of coal beneath the building. Ridley wanted to 'confine us to keep the present line from the Pits to join the new line'. Ultimately, agreement was reached with Ridley's agent on the route of the new way and on 12th July Buddle 'let the laying of the way to Forster at 8 pence a yard. They prepare the ground, lay the way and make foot-gangs and gutters; but where the cuts or batteries exceed one foot in height they are to be paid 6 pence per cubic yard'. Buddle records on September 19th 1820 'the new waggonway to join the Kenton Way will all be laid this week after which it will only be to ballast'. This was a cast iron waggonway. In November he noted that 'the waggonway from the Far to the Middle Pit ought to be laid with cast iron immediately' but 'considering the short time which the Old Pit may continue to work, it will hardly be worth while to lay the waggonway up to the Middle Pit with cast iron'. The old Engine Pit ceased drawing coals in summer 1821. The waggonway between the Middle Pit and St. Anthony's was abandoned and by 11th December 1821 'the whole of waggonway to St. Anthony's is now taken up ... and the staith has been taken down'.

Buddle bought 'a travelling engine from Lambton to fit up for the new way'. This was the other Chapman engine built at the Ouseburn foundry in 1814 and it had arrived by November 24th 1820. On December 19th Buddle records that he 'decided to attach the chain apparatus to the travelling engine to enable her to take the empty waggons up to the Far Pit'. The fact that on 9th January 1821 he 'sold off the waggonway horses by auction' would suggest that this second locomotive was successful. On 21st March he wrote 'the travelling engine has been tried several times on the way from the Far Pit to the Kenton way and goes very well but the steam cannot be kept up so as to drive the engine at sufficient speed. Nothing but a larger boiler can remedy this inconvenience'. Buddle 'decided to lengthen the boiler of the travelling Engine three foot, to put a single tube into it and to mount the engine on a single tram with four wheels to be connected by an endless chain'. In April the engine was 'dismantled preparatory to the proposed alterations' and by May 7th 1821 it had 'started to lead coals from the Far and Middle Pits to the Kenton way near Carville Gate'. Chapman's locomotives hauled themselves along by means of a chain laid along the way. The chain ended at Carville Gate where the Heaton line joined the Bigges Main waggonway. For the remaining distance of about a mile to the staiths the waggons would have been pulled by horses.

The waggonway remained in operation until 1836 when the new owners routed all seacole traffic down the Kenton and Coxlodge waggonway from Benton Pit. However, it does appear to have experienced some changes. A map of the Tyne Collieries dated circa 1825 shows the route from the Middle Pit to Wallsend and also another line to Walker. Curiously, the Benton Pit and the link with the Kenton and Coxlodge waggonway are not marked which casts doubt on the accuracy of the document. Greenwood's map of 1828 shows the link with Walker severed - see page 102.

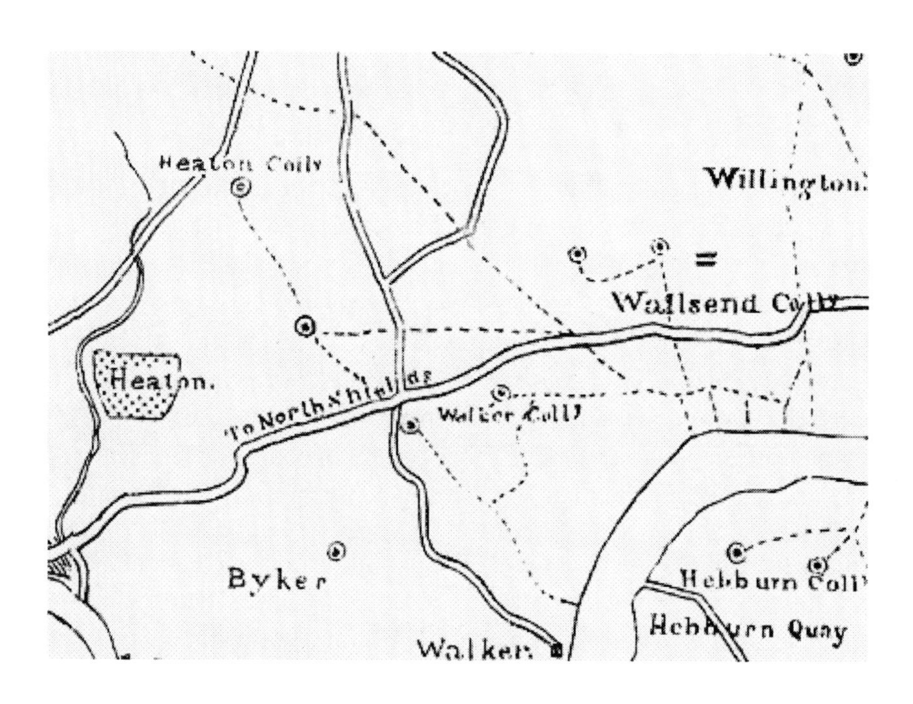

Railways and the steam locomotive developed from the colliery waggonways. It could be argued that this development was the North East's greatest technological achievement since the region created and exported to the world this new form of public transport. The Heaton waggonway made a modest contribution towards this achievement through the experiments with Chapman's travelling engines.

The Workforce in 1842

After John Buddle left Heaton in December 1821, George Johnson, the grandson of the man who had won the colliery at the end of the eighteenth century, was elevated from resident to principal viewer. He held the same position at Willington and Burdon Main collieries in Wallsend. Although the records are less extensive than for the earlier period, his papers provide some interesting information about the later history of the colliery before it was abandoned in 1852 at the end of the second 31 year lease. For example, Johnson recorded details of the condensing engines used for pumping and hauling in 1835. There were two pumping engines one of 104 horse power, the other of 140 horsepower; and three engines for drawing coals of 25, 35 and 45 horsepower. He also provided some interesting detail about the workforce: he noted that in 1828 there were 389 men and boys employed - 269 below and 120 above ground; and in 1844, there were 452 - 305 below and 147 above. In 1842, he provided a breakdown of the workforce giving a comprehensive list of all the jobs below and above ground at the Heaton Colliery.

WORKFORCE AT HEATON COLLIERY 1842

Underground workers 315		Surface workers 176	
108	Hewers	6	Banksmen
52	Putters	4	Brakesmen
54	Drivers	4	Enginement
15	Trappers	8	Firemen
		2	Heapkeepers
2	Overmen	30	Wailers
8	Deputies	32	Screeners
		12	Waggonwaymen
2	Wastemen	14	Wrights
26	Shifters	13	Smiths
8	Rolleywaymen	5	Masons
		3	Corvers
4	Onsetters	1	Horsekeeper
9	Cranemen	13	Cartmen
7	Sinkers	24	persons employed in leading and shipping including staithmen, off putters, trimmers etc
2	Platelayers		
4	Woodleader		
4	Furnacemen	2	assisting carts up Benton Bank
5	Horsekeepers		
5	Greasers (for the rolleys)		

The number of cartmen (13) and their two assistants providing banking assistance on the steep climb up Benton Bank to Jesmond reflects the growing importance of the landsale market for Heaton's coal which from 1836 amounted to almost half of the production.This traffic was probably from the Middle Pit.

No illustrations survive of the men and boys working at Heaton Colliery but it is possible through engravings and later photographs to illustrate the working conditions of the men and boys. Although the photographs were taken in the early twentieth century, the pitman at Heaton would have worn similar clothing and would have been familiar with most of the equipment illustrated.

The hewers were the largest section of the workforce. The two engravings dating from the mid nineteenth century show hewers dressed in flannel shirts, short jackets and trousers. They carry the tools of their trade: the pick (a hewer needed four sharp picks for each shift), the shovel and the cracket or small stool. Their heads are protected by a cloth cap - deputies wore leather caps. In general, helmets were not worn until well into the twentieth century.

The following photographs show the hewers in action. Left, a hewer from Emma Colliery, Ryton has brought his tools to the surface at the beginning of the General Strike of 1926. Behind, his boy clutches a midgy lamp. They are wearing a collarless flannel shirt, waistcoat and jacket, trousers cut off at the knees, heavy boots and woollen stockings – and a cloth cap. Right, a hewer is shown kirving or undercutting the coal with a short pick; another uses a hand drill, resting on a support known as a monkey, to make a hole for the shot. Below, a hewer is working on his side in a narrow seam undercutting the coal; another working by candlelight is preparing the shot for firing using a copper prick to prevent the sparks prematurely igniting the shot. On the following page a hewer works on his knees in a narrow seam with a pneumatic drill known locally as a windy pick. Pneumatic drills were not used at Heaton Main Colliery and nor were the narrow seams worked unlike other parts of the coalfield.

WORKING UNDERGROUND

Almost half of the underground workforce was made up of teenage boys who worked as putters, drivers and trappers. From the middle of the nineteenth century wheeled tubs replaced rolleys and corves and the next series of photographs show a putter bent double pushing tubs at Dunston colliery in 1893; a boy riding 'limmers' as his pony leads the tubs to the shaft; and a trapper boy at Ashington Colliery in 1911 opening the trap door for the tubs to pass through.

The Children's Employment Commission

Presenting evidence to the Children's Employment Commission in 1841, the viewer Matthias Dunn noted that in the collieries of Northumberland and North Durham hewers earned from four to five shillings a day; putters earned from 2s 6d to 4s for a twelve hour day; drivers earned 1s 3d for twelve hours. Boys from 10 to 16 years of age were also employed underground at helping the putters, leading wood, assisting at the cranes where the corves were transferred onto rolleys, keeping the lamps, assisting the overmen, cleaning the tramways etc at wages varying from 1s 3d to 2s 3d for twelve hours work. There was also 'various jobs at the top of the pit, such as taking out stones, carrying the picks, tramming out from the screens, firing the engine, assisting the banksmen etc' earning from 1s to 1s 6d a day.

Heaton was visited by the Children's Employment Commissioners in April 1841 and the evidence of George Johnson and several workers at Heaton was published in the commissioner's report of 1842. Johnson commented that he did 'not allow children under 9 or 10 years old to be trappers, although a strong desire for earlier employment exists both amongst parents and children..... Thinks the employment of a boy as a trapper is not at all injurious provided the lad is in ordinary health. It is quite certain that the drivers meet with more accidents than any other persons in the pit, mainly owing to their own carelessness, or to the horses turning restive and kicking and plunging'. Regarding educating the young, Johnson noted that there was 'a very good lending library and an excellent Sunday school' at Heaton Colliery and 'three fourths of the lads in the colliery go and those who are well inclined make every effort at night schools to make up for want of education'. (These facilities were probably at Bigges Main were Heaton Colliery Office was since 1836). However, he felt that 'even a promise to educate free of expense would not induce parents to send their children to school after 9 or 10. They would much rather see them uneducated than unemployed'.

The views of several workers are recorded including Edward Wright, aged 19, who 'kept a door at first for two years; next drove rolleys for four years; next put for a half-marrow for three years; next was a wood-leader and is now. Goes in the day-shift at half-past 3 o'clock a.m. and comes out at half-past 3 p.m. There are three of them in the C pit (Middle Pit). Woodleaders have to run about for the deputies and hewers. Has both to carry and prop up the wood. Has 2s 4d per day fixed wages'.

Another witness, Joshua Stephenson, aged about eight years, lived in the thatched houses near Benton. He went down the Middle Pit before he was six years old as a trapper. 'Gets up out of bed at 3 o'clock and down the pit at 4 o'clock a.m. The pit louses (finishes) at 4 and he gets up and home about 5 o'clock; then he washes himself and gets his dinner, meat and potatoes. After dinner he goes to bed almost directly; he never plays about first. Goes down the pit in the cage. Takes bait down with him; mostly bread and cheese, sometimes beef; always as much as he wants. Some of the putter-boys bray him but not to hurt him. Cannot read at all. Never was at school in his life'.

George Beresford was aged almost thirteen. 'Has been down Benton Pit for four years and a half. Kept a door for a bit, then went to cleaning the way, then went to driving. Gets up at half past two every morning because he lives a good way off at Ouseburn which is two to three miles off. Gets to the pit and goes down at 4 o'clock. Drives all day. Gets home to Ouseburn about 5 o'clock. Then gets his dinner, potatoes and meat; then washes himself after dinner and then goes to bed directly, perhaps about 7 or 8 o'clock. Never has any time for play'.

Joseph Peel, aged 14, 'has been down seven years and more in this colliery. Kept a door at first for a year; cleaned the way for half a year; next drove for two years; next helped up for three or four months; next hoisted the crane for ten months; next put and is now putting. Worked at keeping a door for four shifts of 12 hours each, at one time, that is, was 48 hours down the pit without coming up at all. He got into the wrong shift and stopped to get into his right shift. The overman told him to stop as they wanted boys. His bates were then sent down to him. Has often worked three shifts following. Besides this has been down many double shifts of 24 hours'.

Amazingly, Ralph Hall, aged 77, had worked 70 years in the pits and 'he now goes down the pit every day and works for 8 hours for which he gets 2s 6d and house and firing'. However, his feats were surpassed by Thomas Batty, aged 93 who had worked until his 85th year and 'has always had good health and good fortune'.

Over fifty interviews were recorded. Most of the boys worked a twelve hour shift underground and on occasions, when requested by the overman, a double shift of twenty four hours. Some experienced physical punishment from their fellow workmen mainly to retain discipline. Many received minor injuries particularly the drivers and several suffered from the bad air down the pit. However, like Michael Jobling, several 'would not like to come out of the pit (for surface work) because they are warmer in the winter'. Many of the boys could read and a few could write. Most attended chapel. Although the working conditions at Heaton were draconian by today's standards, the commissioners reported far worse conditions for children working in the coal mines elsewhere - for example in Fifeshire and Lancashire. Furthermore, there were worst jobs on Tyneside - such as in the large chemical works along the banks of the River Tyne.

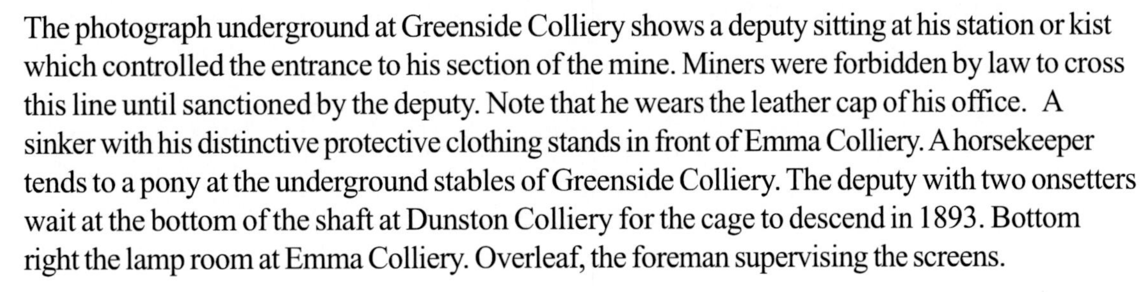

The photograph underground at Greenside Colliery shows a deputy sitting at his station or kist which controlled the entrance to his section of the mine. Miners were forbidden by law to cross this line until sanctioned by the deputy. Note that he wears the leather cap of his office. A sinker with his distinctive protective clothing stands in front of Emma Colliery. A horsekeeper tends to a pony at the underground stables of Greenside Colliery. The deputy with two onsetters wait at the bottom of the shaft at Dunston Colliery for the cage to descend in 1893. Bottom right the lamp room at Emma Colliery. Overleaf, the foreman supervising the screens.

Another Landsale Colliery

Besides the major seacoal colliery operated by George Johnson in the northern and western parts of the Heaton, there was also a landsale colliery in the south eastern part. This was advertised to be let in September 1844. It is described as 'the current-going landsale colliery at Heaton Banks near the Ouseburn with the fireclay mines and quarry'. The Royalty consisted of 'so much of the High Main Seam as is unwrought under about 240 acres and of the Metal Seam of the same extent, now first won, and found of excellent quality'. The fire clay, which was found about 6o feet below the surface, was 'well adapted for the use of potteries and for the making fire bricks and draining tiles'. There was a ready market for building bricks in the developing township of Byker. It is interesting that 'the working of the whole is carried on by a drift without an engine being required'. The first edition of the Ordnance Survey map surveyed in 1858 shows a small landsale colliery on Heaton Park Road near the railway. By the second edition of 1895, it had closed and been replaced by a school but West Heaton Brick Works was a prominent feature on Newington Road.

At the main colliery George Johnson's lease was running out. With the exhaustion of the High Main seam attempts were made to develop the Low Main seam which had proved to contain excellent coal at neighbouring collieries such as St. Lawrence Colliery in Byker. The enterprise was not successful. However, it is likely that it was the problem of draining Heaton that once again determined its future. In 1823 a new pumping engine had been built at Friar's Goose in Gateshead to alleviate the problem of water in the mines of the Tyne Basin. The 180 horse power steam engine was capable of drawing water from the High Main seam at the rate of 1,444,800 gallons a day. In 1841, a 70 horse power engine was erected to drain the Low Main seam. A consortium of collieries (including Tyne Main, Felling, Walker, Wallsend, Willington and Heaton) contributed towards the cost of pumping at Friar's Goose until 1851. The breakup of the consortium and the ending of pumping in 1851 was followed by a general flooding of the basin and the closure of the major collieries: Heaton in 1852, Wallsend in 1854, Willington in 1856 and Bigges Main in 1857. The ruins of the Friar's Goose engine house remain on the banks of the Tyne near Gateshead International Stadium as a reminder of the mining engineer's struggle against the great enemy - water.

Important changes had taken place during the sixty years Heaton Colliery had been in operation. Steam engines for winding and pumping had been improved. The safety lamp had been invented and it was extensively used at Heaton for lighting underground. Tubs may have begun to replace corves for carrying coal underground at Heaton as early as 1807. By 1842, cages had been introduced at Heaton to carry coal and men from the pit. Experiments with steam locomotives had taken place on the Heaton

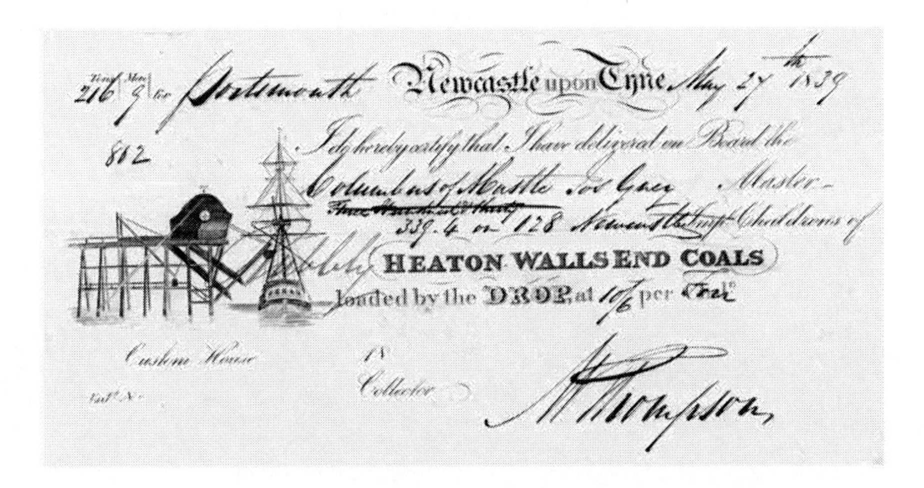
Tons Mts 216 | 9 for Portsmouth Newcastle upon Tyne, May 27th 1839
812
I do hereby certify that I have delivered on Board the
Columbus of Seattle Jos Grey Master
339. 4 or 128 Newcastle Chaldrons of
HEATON WALLS END COALS
loaded by the DROP at 10/6 per Chal.
Custom House
Collector
W Thompson

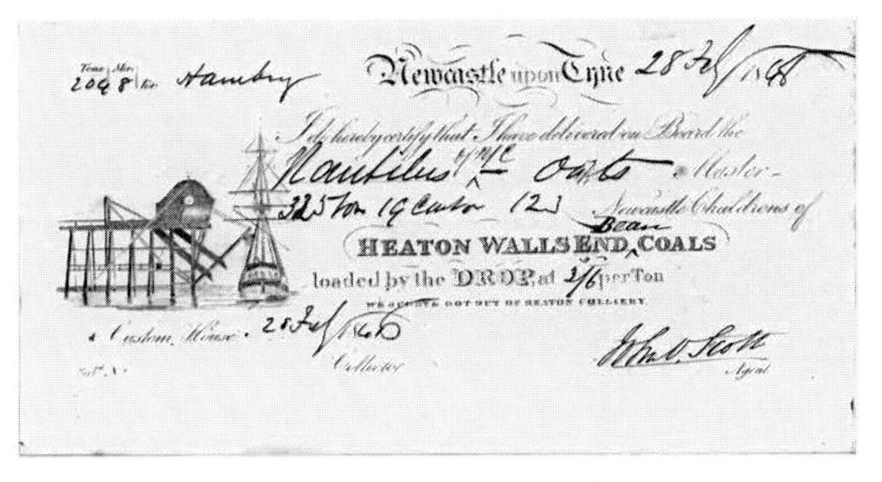
Tons Mts 2048 for Hamburg Newcastle upon Tyne 28 Feb/1848
I do hereby certify that I have delivered on Board the
Nautilus Oats Master
325 Ton 19 Cwt (123) Newcastle Chaldrons of
HEATON WALLS END Bean COALS
loaded by the DROP at 2/6 per Ton
Custom House 28 Feb/1848
Collector
Wm. Scott
Agent

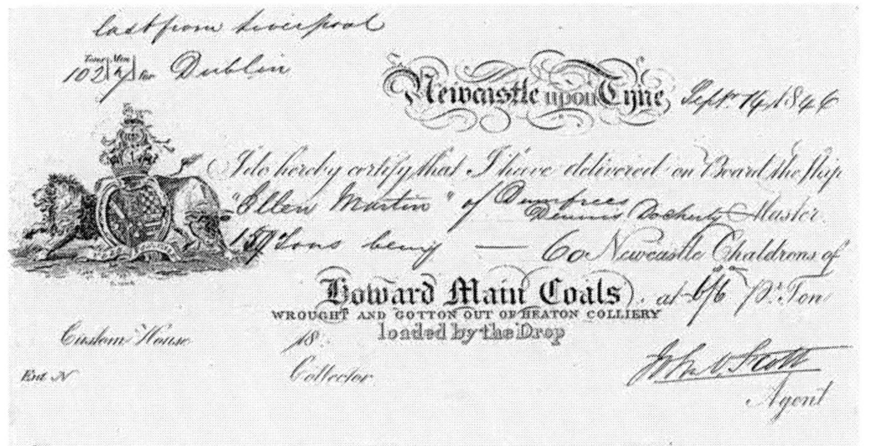
last from Liverpool
Tons Mts 102 | 4 for Dublin Newcastle upon Tyne, Sept. 14 1844
I do hereby certify that I have delivered on Board the Ship
"Ellen Martin" of Dumfries Dennis Docherty Master
159 tons being — 60 Newcastle Chaldrons of
Howard Main Coals at 6/6 per Ton
WROUGHT AND GOTTON OUT OF HEATON COLLIERY
loaded by the Drop
Custom House 18
Collector
Wm Scott
Agent

waggonway and the spout had been replaced by the coal drop to reduce breakages when loading the colliers at the staith. For sixty years Heaton Colliery seems to have provided a steady income to the owners of the mineral and surface rights, a good profit for the owners of the colliery and a high standard of living for the workforce.

The Coal Trade

At Heaton's major colliery some of the coal was sold locally. However, the lucrative market was in seacole and all of the top quality coal from Heaton was shipped from staiths at St. Anthony's until 1821and then afterwards at Wallsend. After loading at the staith, the captain of the collier ship received a certificate (such as the loading bills reproduced below) which was a guarantee of the quality of his cargo. One records that Joseph Grey, the master of the *Columbus,* loaded 128 Newcastle chaldrons (339 tons 4 cwt) of Heaton Wallsend coals for Portsmouth on 27th May 1839; the second that Captain Oats of the *Nautilus* loaded 123 Newcastle chaldrons (325tons 19 cwt) of Heaton Wallsend coals for Hamburg on 28th February 1848; the third that Captain Docherty of the *Ellen Martin* loaded 60 Newcastle chaldron (159 tons) of Howard Main coals for Dublin on September 14th 1844. On arrival at his destination the captain would present the certificate at the coal market as a guarantee of the quality of his cargo.

Wallsend was the brand leader and many collieries adopted the prefix 'Walls End' to enhance the value of their product. An account of coals at the London market in Billingsgate for 17th August 1835 shows twenty collieries shipping from Newcastle, eight from Sunderland and eleven from Stockton using 'Walls End' to advertise their coal. The Wallsend coals were the grand cru of the trade and commanded the highest price. In 1826, a parliamentary enquiry recorded the price in shillings of a Newcastle Chaldron for 75 collieries shipping from the River Tyne. Percy Main Walls End (34s), Wallsend (33s), Coxlodge Walls End (32s) and Heaton Wallsend (31s) were the most expensive coals. The cheapest at 16s per chaldron was from Elswick, Team and Whitley Main collieries. The loading bill below from Haswell Coal Company shows 'Wallsend' coals being shipped from the River Wear. In the engraving an early locomotive hauls a rake of chaldron waggons presided over by Britannia.

Sunderland 18

For

I have shipped on board the

Tons of the

Haswell Coal Company's

Haswell Wallsend Coals

At per TON.

Custom House, Sunderland

The bills of lading acted as advertisements for the collieries and they are frequently adorned with engravings of pithead scenes and views of the river. Even allowing for artistic licence they provide invaluable illustrations of the collieries and the coal trade during the mid nineteenth century before photography was widely available. The top illustration shows Derwent colliery a small enterprise in the Derwent Valley. A rare view of Radcliffe Colliery with the castle in the right background is shown on a bill of lading for Warkworth Harbour (later known as Amble). The engraving of Buddle's West Cramlington Colliery shows the engine house, the screens and a rake of chaldron waggons. These were typical colliery scenes of the period.

The Final Winning

The last phase of coal mining in the manor of Heaton belongs to the twentieth century when the coal reserves from the lower seams were mined from Walker Colliery until 1918 and later from the Rising Sun Colliery, Wallsend, some two miles away. Heaton became part of a large, highly mechanised operation, mining multiple seams over many square miles. The Rising Sun Colliery differed from Heaton Colliery not only in the scale of its operations but also in the extensive use of machinery for cutting, loading and transporting the coal underground particularly after 1947. Electricity was now used for lighting and power throughout the colliery. The massive extractor fan to ventilate the mine was very different from the convection system used in the nineteenth century collieries. The coal treatment plant, the mines rescue station, the laboratory and the pithead baths were also innovations.

Work began on sinking number one shaft at the Rising Sun Colliery in February 1906 in an attempt to alleviate the drainage problems at Wallsend Church Pit and by February 1908 the Bensham seam had been reached. A second shaft was sunk between 1912 and 1915. In 1934, this shaft was deepened to reach the Brockwell seam and a new coal preparation plant was built. After nationalisation in 1947, the Rising Sun was selected by the National Coal Board for major reconstruction costing £2.9 million. A third shaft, 22 feet in diameter and sunk 1,400 feet to the Beaumont seam, was opened in 1960 to improve access and ventilation. The underground roadways were altered and all winding was directed to number three shaft which was dominated by a massive winding tower 115 feet high. Power cutting and loading were introduced and electric locos hauled two ton cars to move the coal underground. The surface operations were also mechanised. The pithead baths were centrally heated. In 1958, the *Wallsend News* reported upon the 'vast untapped resources amounting to about 60 million tons which at a conservative estimate will provide full employment for at least another 60 years'.

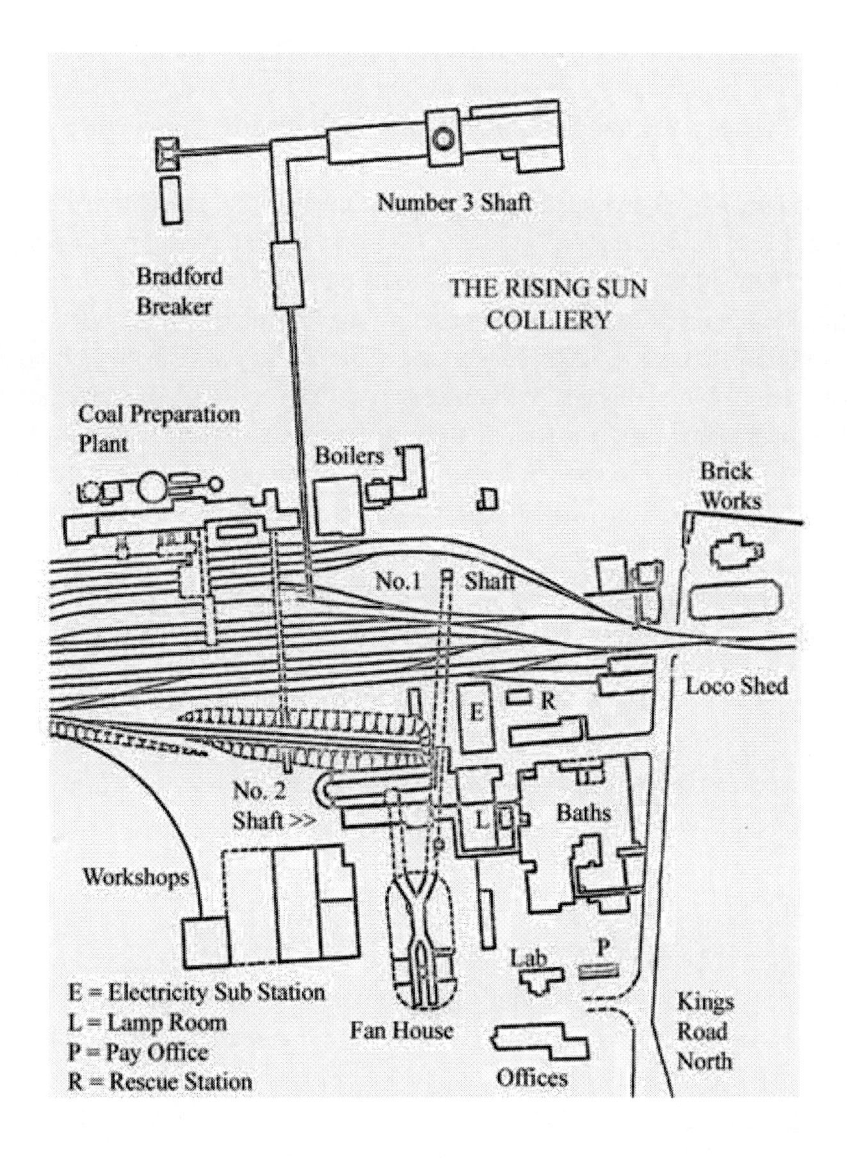

The rebuilding was completed by 1961 and production rose from 1,800 tons per day to 3,000. The annual target of half a million tons was exceeded in 1964 when the 1,750 men employed at the colliery produced

650,000 tons of coal. However, as at Heaton and Wallsend in previous centuries, water was the great enemy. For every ton of coal raised seven tons of water were pumped from the mine. This recurrent problem, together with the difficult geological conditions which were encountered, caused the N.C.B. to question the future of the colliery. In February 1968, the *Newcastle Journal* reported that 'a super face capable of producing more than 1,000 tons of coal a day is to be opened at the Rising Sun, a consistent money-loser over the past few years'. The report added ominously that 'the 1,500 men working at the colliery have been warned by their manager that this year will make or break the colliery'. The production shifts were increased from two to three to make maximum use of the new machinery which included bi-directional Anderton shearer loaders. To no avail. The Rising Sun Colliery was closed in April 1969 ending the long and illustrious history of mining in Wallsend and Heaton. The N.C.B. offered the men jobs in the Yorkshire and Nottinghamshire coalfields which many accepted. The 26 pit ponies were retired to the N.C.B. farm at Seaton Delaval. The pithead winding tower - barely ten years old - was demolished in January 1970. A reclamation scheme costing £400,000 transformed the pitheap and much of the surrounding area of the colliery into a nature reserve. The *Newcastle Chronicle* proclaimed that 'the ugly muck heap will soon be a perfumed garden'.

Conclusion

The history of coal mining in Heaton begins modestly with medieval miners toiling at the outcrop in the south west corner of the manor. By the reign of James II a large colliery was supplying the London market until the battle against water was lost and the flooded colliery had to be abandoned. The development of the atmospheric pump or the 'fire engine' by Newcomen enabled Heaton Banks Colliery to be won by the largest mining consortium of the time - the Grand Allies. However, this colliery also had to be abandoned as the water overpowered the pumps. Towards the end of the eighteenth century, the invention by James Watt of the more powerful steam pump enabled George Johnson to win Heaton Main Colliery which became one of the great collieries of Tyneside: for sixty years Heaton produced top quality coal primarily for the London market. The colliery owners experimented with Chapman's 'travelling engine' and thereby Heaton played a role in the development of the locomotive. This colliery closed in 1852 and the lower seams of coal were mined from Walker Colliery and later from the neighbouring Wallsend Rising Sun Colliery - one of the major collieries of the twentieth century.

The history of mining in Heaton clearly demonstrates the relationship between the development of technology and the exploitation of the coal reserves. It represents in microcosm the story of the Great Northern Coalfield as a whole and demonstrates how the coal mine changed as new technology was developed to deal with the constant problems of lighting, ventilating and draining the mine; extracting the coal, winding it to the surface and transporting it to market. The mining engineers of the North East - men such as William Brown of Throckley, John Buddle of Wallsend, William Chapman of Willington and George Stephenson of Killingworth - played a major part in solving these problems. These men helped to promote the reputation of the North East of England as the leading centre of mining expertise in the world. Fortunes were made by the landowners, the owners of the mineral rights and the colliery owners. Nor should it be forgotten that the workforce, especially the hewers, enjoyed a higher standard of living than many of their contemporaries. However, at Heaton as elsewhere in the coalfield, there was a cost in human terms as the frequent fatal accidents, culminating in the disaster of May 1815, sadly demonstrated. As Sid Chaplin, himself a miner, commented:

> 'Twenty lads, so hearty, went down the pit
> Today.
> Twenty lads, once hearty, will never again draw
> Pay'

Chapter Three – Mining Accidents

Let us not think of tomorrow,
Lest we disappointed be;
All our joys may turn to sorrow,
As we may daily see.
Today we may be strong and healthy,
But how soon there comes a change,
As we may learn from the explosion,
That has been at Trimdon Grange.

The opening verse of Tommy Armstrong's song about the Trimdon Grange explosion of 1882 captures the daily uncertainty that miners and their families faced because of the hazardous nature of pit work. Mining was - and still is - a dangerous job and injuries at work, some of which resulted in death, are part of the miner's lot. One exhibit at the Woodhorn Colliery Museum is a book listing the men killed at the collieries of the Ashington Coal Company, one of the former mining companies in Northumberland. This company had a good safety record: there were no major accidents at any of the five collieries which would have made the national news. The greatest loss of life occurred at Woodhorn Colliery on 13th August 1916 when 13 men were killed in an explosion. However, during the lifetime of the five collieries, between the opening of the first pit at Ashington in 1867 and the closing of the last at Ellington 138 years later, 509 men were killed. This persistent loss of life – although rarely recorded in the newspapers or history books – is more typical of work in the coal mines than the great disasters which interested the media. This opinion was expressed by the eminent viewer John Buddle: writing in 1814 he commented 'that the ordinary and unavoidable casualties in collieries occasion more calamities than explosions'.

A detailed examination of the records reveals the causes of these fatal accidents in the collieries of the Ashington Coal Company: fell down the shaft, crushed by the cage, jammed against the roof, caught by the cutter,

Hartley Colliery soon after the disaster

struck by shot debris, buried in the coal hopper, kicked by a pony, struck by the engine rope, killed by the boiler, burned by beeswax, run over by the engine, electrocuted. For a surprising number (10%) the cause was unknown. Another 10% were killed as a result of accidents with the tubs below ground or the waggons above ground. However, the major cause of death at all the five collieries was roof falls which accounted for 36% of the total casualties. The case of Isaac Grint, a hewer at the Carl Pit Ashington, is typical: he was killed by a fall of stone on 7th November 1923. The sad consequences of these deaths generally go unrecorded: Isaac Grint was the breadwinner for his family and left a pregnant wife and three young boys aged 2, 3 and 5 to fend for themselves.

The first recorded major disaster in the North East was an explosion at old Gateshead in 1700 which killed over 100 miners and the second was another explosion at Bensham in 1709 which resulted in 75 deaths. For the next century records are scanty because of an agreement with the newspapers not to record mining tragedies for fear of discouraging men from entering the pits. With deeper mines and increased output there was an alarming rise in major accidents during the late eighteenth and early nineteenth century which led to public concern about safety in the mines. These disasters have become part of local folklore and to point out that the continuous loss of life in the pits was more typical of the miners' experience is not intended to detract from the tragedy of the major accidents but to put them into perspective. Moreover, it is also worth remembering that the miners did not have the monopoly of dangerous working conditions. For example, some would argue that the seamen transporting coal from the North East ports faced equal dangers: between 1830 and 1900, 70% of all the sailing ships carrying coal from the Tyne were lost at sea. Nonetheless, major tragedies are an important element in the history of the Great Northern Coalfield and this chapter is concerned with three accidents which were of more than local significance. The entombment of the miners at New Hartley in 1862 resulted in legislation requiring two shafts at a mine; the explosion at Felling Colliery in 1812 led to the development of the miner's safety lamp; and the flooding of Heaton Colliery in 1815 added to the pressure for old mining plans to be kept for future reference.

The Hartley Colliery Disaster

Perhaps the best known of the three disasters was the accident at the Hester Pit, New Hartley, on January 16th 1862 because it resulted in the largest loss of life. The entombment of 199 men in the pit, when the 42 ton beam of the pumping engine snapped in half and crashed down the shaft sealing the only entrance into the mine, attracted national attention. Not only did *The Times* and *The London Illustrated News* report upon the progress of the rescue operations and the subsequent funerals but even Queen Victoria herself was moved to write to Mr Carr, the owner, asking him to convey her sympathy to the widows.

Old Hartley Colliery was flooded in 1844 and work began in the following year sinking the shaft of the Hester Pit at New Hartley. The sinkers were led by William Coulson, one of the most experienced men in the coalfield, and in 1845 the Low Main seam was reached at hundred fathoms. The mine worked three seams – the High Main, the Yard or Main and the Low Main. Water was always a problem and on 14th February 1852 a torrent burst into the Low Main seam and rose 70 fathoms up the shaft drowning the mine. In 1855, a massive new pumping engine was installed: it was 300 horse power and capable of drawing 1,500 gallons a minute. The engine, built at Walker Iron Wroks, was believed to be the most powerful in the north of England.

The miners working the bottom seam (the Low Main) were so concerned about the threat of flooding that they wrote to the government inspector Matthias Dunn asking for an inspection. As was the usual practice, a barrier of coal separated their colliery from the surrounding pits which were flooded. Trial borings were made on a regular basis as mining progressed to assess the strength of the barrier. Nonetheless, the men feared that the water would break through trapping them as had happened at Heaton Colliery in 1815. For the shift of about a hundred men, the only means of escape was a single shaft with a cage capable of carrying eight men at a time. On July 23rd 1861, the inspector recommended that a ladder be placed in an auxiliary shaft linking the Low Main with the Yard seam fourteen fathoms above. The owners immediately carried out this suggestion. However, there was no link between the Yard seam and the High Main seam and this was to prove fatal for the men entombed six months later.

About 2.30 a.m. on Thursday 16th January, the foreshift went down the pit. About ten in the morning the backshift descended to relieve these men. Thus, at 10.30 a.m., when the beam snapped and 21 tons of cast iron crashed down the only shaft to the surface, most of the two shifts were down the mine. The diagram reproduced from *The London Illustrated News* shows the main shaft divided into two by a wooden brattice: the cage is on the left, the downcast section; and the pumps on the right, the upcast section. A furnace in the Yard seam drove the ventilation system. The beam broke at point 'A' and because the shaft was protected by a brick wall for only a short distance, the beam tore the backing deals and debris from the sides of the shaft as it fell. The mass of timbers, piping, earth and machinery blocked the shaft. Eight men were riding the cage to the surface when the beam fell. John Short, the enginewright at New Hartley, immediately began the rescue of the men trapped in the damaged cage. Four had been thrown out and fell to the shaft bottom mortally wounded and, although the cage was wrecked as the illustration shows, incredibly the four others survived. The rescuers reached the wrecked cage shortly before midnight. A rope was attached to the injured George Sharp but on being hauled to the surface he was struck by hanging timbers and fell to his death. William Sharp, Ralph Robinson and Thomas Watson were rescued. The other 199 were trapped. Unfortunately, the blockage occurred between the Yard and High Main seams sealing both the escape routes for the men working below in the Low Main seam.

By the next day, Friday 17th, William Coulson had arrived with a team of sinkers to begin the main rescue. Coulson was a man of 48 years experience and was widely regarded as the most capable sinker in the region. A photograph survives of William Coulson in his sinker's gear at the Hester Pit and it is one of the earliest photographs of a North East miner. The sinkers' task was a formidable one which was made more dangerous by debris falling from the open sides of the wrecked shaft. Progress in such treacherous conditions was necessarily slow.

The accident had been caused by the fracture of the cast iron beam of the pumping engine which may have been damaged while undergoing maintenance the previous week. If the engine had been built of wrought iron, which is more malleable, it is unlikely to have broken. Several factors contributed to turning the fracture of the beam into a major disaster. The timing of the disaster when both shifts were underground was unfortunate. The place where the wreckage blocked the shaft was also unfortunate for had it fallen a little further below the Yard seam escape would have been possible by means of the ladder recently installed. However, it was the fact that the colliery was a single shaft mine that was the principal cause of the total loss of the 199 men trapped underground. For not only did the wreckage block both the escape routes but, because Hartley was a single shaft mine, it also destroyed the ventilation system of the colliery. With the pumps out of action the Low Main seam began to fill with water. The 43 horses underground were drowned but the 199 men escaped to the Yard seam by means of the new ladder. However, without any system of ventilation they were poisoned by foul air. It was not all bad luck: the main inclined plane had broken stopping the supply of coal to the shaft. Therefore, the onsetter had been sending the men to the surface who

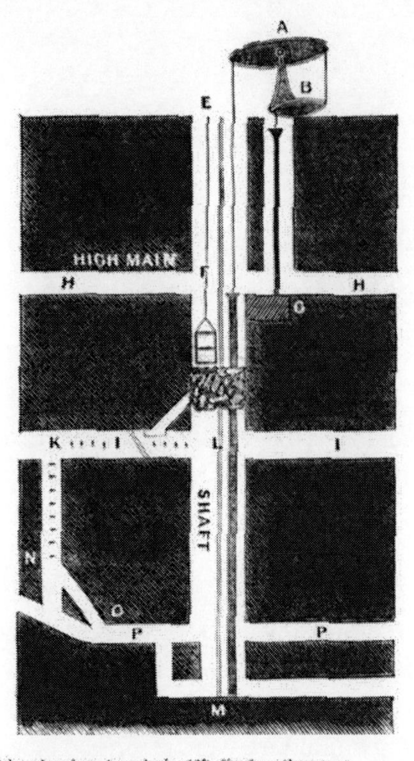

A. Point where large beam broke, 16ft. 6in. from the spears.
B. *Lower beam for top set of pumps in small shaft* to 7 fathoms below High Main Seam, making the high set of pumps up to surface 45 fathoms.
E. Top of pit, or Main Shaft, 12ft. diameter, and 105 fathoms to the bottom of the sump (M), where the third set of pumps rest.
E to F. 38 fathoms to High Main Seam.
F to L and M, as shown by blank line, are two sets of pumps, of about 30 fathoms each.
G. Bottom of staple for high set of pumps, showing the sump, 7 fathoms below High Main.
H H. High Main Coal Seam, not working.
I I. Yard Coal Seam, not working.
K. Top of staple, up which the men ascended by a wire rope ladder from the top of the slope drift, *10 fathoms*.
N to O. Slope drift.
P. P. Low Main, where the principal workings were in progress.

Hartley Disaster - the cage before and after

would normally have had to wait until the coal was removed. Undoubtedly, the death toll was reduced by this mechanical failure.

Almost a week later, on Wednesday 22nd January, the first bodies were found. In the subsequent days the remaining men were found lying four abreast along the rollyway where they had been suffocated. It took seventeen and a half hours to bring the bodies to the surface where they were placed in coffins and taken to their homes. The local reporter of the *Newcastle Daily Journal,* Wemyss Reid, noted that Hartley was an unpicturesque village comprising two long rows of houses standing at right angles in the form of a letter 'L'. In every house there were coffins to be seen and 'coming to the end house we were appalled to see a perfect pile of them.... and looking around we were informed that seven dead bodies lay in this cottage.' This was the home of the Liddle family who lost nine members.

The mass funeral was held on Sunday 26th January at the parish church at Earsdon village some four miles away. The old church yard could not cope with such numbers partly because some of the 76 victims of the explosion at the neighbouring colliery at Burradon in March 1860 had been buried there. Additional land for the burials was granted by the Duke of Northumberland adjacent to the church. The funeral was a major attraction and *The London Illustrated News* estimated that a crowd of 60,000 descended upon Hartley for the funeral mainly travelling by rail. One local miner, Robert Turnbull, who had acted as the men's leader during the rescue, had the enterprising idea of charging visitors six pence to see the shaft. Over one thousand people took up his offer and by so doing he raised £30 for the disaster fund. Such was the public interest in the disaster, that the relief fund reached £80,000 which included a contribution of £200 from Queen Victoria. Today, a monument to the men stands in shade amongst the trees of the beautiful churchyard at Earsdon.

At the inquest into the accident the distinguished mining engineer T.E.Forster commented 'such an accident never occurred before and will probably never occur again'. A staple drift which would have enabled the

William Coulson

Robert Turnbull - pitmen's deputy

men to climb from the Yard to the High Main seam 'was not made because the idea of such a staple being needful or even useful never entered the contemplations of the owners and was never thought of by either the inspector or the workmen'. However, following the inquest there was considerable public pressure that all mines should have two shafts. *The Times* thundered that 'the expedient of a second shaft is so obvious that very good reason indeed must be shown against it if its absence is to be further tolerated'. On 7th August a special Act of Parliament made it compulsory for every mine to have two shafts. This was the lasting memorial to the miners of New Hartley.

The men who had bravely attempted a rescue and later worked to recover the bodies and open up the mine were directed by William Coulson and supervised by the master sinkers George Emmerson, William Shield and David Wilkinson. A list of the 45 sinkers who had worked at the rescue survives with the interesting comment that 'the names ticked in red are those of the men who left or ran way – so says Coulson'. As would be expected, not all the men were heroes. However, those who escaped Coulson's red pen were presented with a medallion to acknowledge their bravery.

The story of the New Hartley disaster illustrates several features which were common elements in accidents within the industry. The bravery and self-sacrifice of the men and officials who tried to save the trapped miners; the pithead vigils and the refusal of the relatives to give up even after all reasonable hope of rescue had passed; the concern of the owners and the community at large for the future welfare of the widows and orphans; the public outcry for better safety in the mines; and the perverse hand of chance.

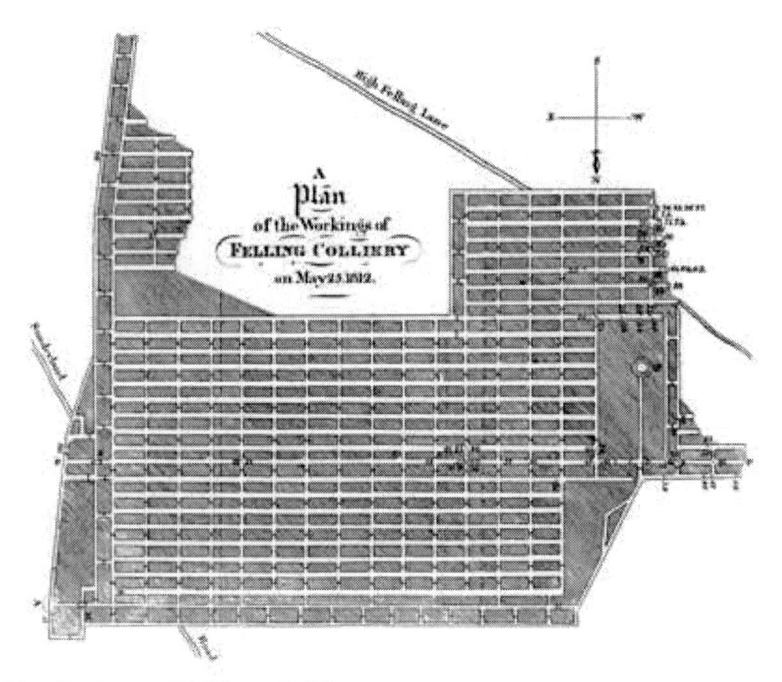

The Explosion at Felling Colliery

Felling Colliery was situated to the north of the present Metro station. It was owned by the Brandling family of Gosforth. The colliery was in the parish of Heworth and the vicar, the influential Rev. John Hodgson, wrote a detailed description of the mine following the explosion on 25th May 1812. This included a plan of the pillar and stall workings showing how the ventilation system operated and where the bodies of the miners were found.

He records that the High Main seam was largely excavated when in October 1810 work started on the Low Main. There were two shafts, the downcast shaft called the John Pit (A) and the William Pit (B), the upcast shaft. Hodgson commented that 'this mine was considered by the workmen a model of perfection in the purity of its air'. A furnace in the William Pit shaft provided an upward draft. Air was drawn down the John Pit and guided throughout the workings to the William Pit shaft where the foul air was emitted. Two shifts of men were constantly employed except on Sundays. The first shift entered the mine at four in the morning and was relieved by the second shift at eleven in the morning. About 128 men and boys were employed and in the first fortnight of May 1812 they had produced 3,500 tons of coal.

At 11.30 am on 25th May 1812, at the very time when the foreshift was being relieved underground by the backshift, an explosion of methane gas occurred killing three quarters of the workforce – 92 men and boys. Hodgson commented graphically that 'the explosion drives before it a roaring whirlwind of flaming air, which tears up every thing in its progress, scorching some of the miners to a cinder, burying others under enormous heaps of ruins shaken from the roof, and, thundering to the shafts, wastes its volcanic fury in a discharge of thick clouds of dust, stones, timber and not infrequently limbs of men and horses'. The explosion destroyed the ventilation system in the mine and this meant that many of those who survived the initial explosion were suffocated by the carbon monoxide gas produced by the explosion. Thirty two men were rescued but six died later from the injuries they had received. Volunteers attempted to enter the mine to search for other survivors but they were prevented by the foul air and the fire. Matthias Dunn described how during the rescue attempt 'the pit showed symptoms of exploding and Haswell, the overman, immediately ordered the men coming down and those beside him to get to bank as fast as they could.... When the last loop full was near at bank and only a single man and himself left she exploded...... He threw himself down and folded his arms about a standing prop which fortunately held him ....The people in the loop, though dreadfully shaken, yet were saved'.

Matthias Dunn 'went to the colliery in the afternoon when Mr Buddle and Easton – two giants – attended to give their advice....It was resolved to let the pits remain open (rather than seal them to extinguish the fire) not with the hope of saving any lives .... but for the satisfaction of the friends of the unfortunate sufferers'. After three days, confident that nobody could have survived, the owners decided to seal off the mine to extinguish the fire. The colliery engineer Straker was greatly disliked by the local men for this act.

On 8th July Straker re-entered the mine and the process of removing the 86 bodies began. This gruesome task was not completed until 1st September. A memorial to those who lost their lives in the mine still stands at the entrance to Heworth Church.

The publication of the Rev. John Hodgson's account of the accident was a radical act. Previously, there had been a 'gentleman's agreement' between the coal owners, the local magistrates and the newspaper owners, whereby accidents in the mines were not reported. The mine owners argued that the publicity would add to their difficulties in recruiting sufficient labour which was a major problem when the industry was expanding. Even the law making it necessary to hold an inquest following a death had been ignored for deaths in the pits. As a result of Hodgson's publicity, accidents were now reported and inquests carried out. Also, in October 1813, the publicity led to the formation of the Society for the Prevention of Accidents in Coal Mines, comprising professional people who were concerned about the increasing death toll in the region's collieries during the early nineteenth century.

Before the accident at Felling, a Sunderland doctor, William Clanny, had been experimenting with a safety lamp which he demonstrated to the Royal Society in May 1813. Perhaps because it was cumbersome and needed a second operator, viewers and owners were not keen to use Dr. Clanny's lamp. In 1815, the Society for the Prevention of Accidents invited the eminent scientist Sir Humphrey Davy to conduct experiments with methane gas. He met with Dr. Clanny and the leading colliery engineer of the time, John Buddle, in August and the first models of the safety lamp were shown to the Royal Society on 9th November 1815. The lamp was successfully demonstrated at Hebburn Colliery in January 1816. Meanwhile, George Stephenson had experimented with lamps at Killingworth Colliery and demonstrated a successful model on 30th November 1815. Thus, two lamps were developed simultaneously, one in London by the great scientist Davy, the other in Killingworth by the local colliery engineer Stephenson. Charges of plagiarism were levelled at Stephenson and the coal owners were divided in their support – the Brandlings and Liddells supporting Stephenson while the Lambtons championed Davy.

This was only the beginning of the process of developing a safety lamp for the pits and both lamps were modified in later years. In spite of these inventions accidents continued in the mines because of the ignorance of the miners and the cupidity of the owners. The men sometimes refused to use the lamp properly. In 1817, an explosion occurred at Harraton which killed 38 men because a hewer, dissatisfied with the light from the safety lamp, lit a candle. For their part, the owners saw the invention as a means of opening up old pits formerly condemned as inaccessible because of the presence of large quantities of methane gas. Nonetheless, the safety lamp is a fitting memorial to the men and boys who lost their lives at Felling. The rate of deaths from explosions fell in the collieries of the North East after the introduction of the lamp.

Part of the Felling Memorial

The Flooding of Heaton Colliery

In 1815, Heaton Colliery was one of the foremost coal mines on Tyneside under the supervision of the eminent colliery engineer John Buddle. His view books which record his inspections of the colliery survive and they contain a detailed description of the accident which occurred on 3rd May 1815. For several years the workings had been approaching the flooded waste of old Heaton Banks Colliery which had been abandoned in 1745. Because no detailed plan of the old colliery had survived, a series of trial bores had been made from drifts since 1812 to determine the position of the flooded waste and the amount of coal which it was safe to mine from the barrier. Once the bore found the waste of the old mine the holes were plugged which was standard mining practice.

On Wednesday 3rd May 1815, Jonathan Bell and Andrew Cadwell were working with their putter boy William McCoy in an exploratory drift. This was driven in stone upwards from the north west mothergate of the Engine Pit in a northerly direction to locate the High Main seam beyond an upcast dyke. The face of the drift was 180 yards south from the shaft of the old Chance Pit which was situated due east of the windmill which still stands in Heaton Park. In today's geography, the men were working about 330 feet beneath St.Theresa's Roman Catholic Church on Heaton Road. During the previous week, the drifters had reached the bottom of the coal seam and the men were now pushing the drift forward to give full access to the seam. About 4.40 a.m. the overman, William Miller, visited the men at their workplace. They pointed out to him that there was a greater bleeding of water than usual coming from a weak point in the coals on the western side of the drift. Miller was not unduly alarmed and ordered another two feet of coal to be taken out after which the nine o'clock shift would make a trial bore.

After leaving the drift Miller met Tim Dodgson, another overman, who asked him to ride to the surface with him. Miller replied that he was going to stay underground awhile since the other wastemen were waiting to go into the old waste with him. About fifteen minutes later a discharge of water 'like the spout of a garden pot' took place 'with a loud hissing noise' about two yards from the face of the drift. This did not alarm the men who continued at their work.

However, when the coal broke away and the feeder increased in size with a noise louder than a steam engine, Bell and Caldwell came out of the drift and sent their putter boy to warn the people at the cranes. They waited at the old crane which was about 110 yards from the face of the drift. After a short time John Bell decided to go back to see the state of the drift; but, just as he reached the door into the drift, the water broke in with a noise of thunder and the wind blew him down. He returned to Andrew Cadwell and they scrambled to the shaft with their putter boy and William Holt, the rolleyman, as quickly as they could in the dark for the wind had also extinguished their candles. They were followed by fifteen rolley drivers and trappers, by John Pratt, the onsetter, and by the rolleyway men, William Rutter, Thomas Carr and Thomas Wilkinson. The coal seam dipped to the east and therefore the water rushed downhill towards the Engine Pit shaft. The hewers Thomas Curtis and Joseph Harrison were the last to escape before the rising waters sealed off their escape route. Seventy five men and boys were trapped to the west in the upper part of the mine.

Almost immediately after the accident had happened, the Chance, Old Engine, Thistle, Bank, Knab and Venture pits fell in. These were all part of the former Heaton Banks Colliery and had been sealed after the closure of the mine. The Chance Pit, which was nearest to the trapped men, appeared to be open nearly to the bottom. Balks were laid across and preparations made for securing the top of the shaft in order to get down the pit. However, about 5.00 p.m. the large bed of sand about thirty feet down broke away and by 8.00 p.m. it had filled the pit up and closed the nearest point of rescue.

By Thursday afternoon the water had risen 183 feet up the Engine Pit shaft after which it began to fall. The water also cut off access to the men from the Middle Pit and Far Pit where the pumps could not cope. From various calculations that were made it appeared that the water could rise 240 feet or half way up the Engine Pit shaft before it reached the face of the workings in the rise part of the mine where the men were before the inundation.

Attempts were made on Friday by boring several holes to find the Mathew Pit which had been part of old Byker Colliery. It was situated near the southern boundary of Heaton and may have provided access to the south west mothergate. These attempts were unsuccessful. However, in the evening a pit was found which Buddle believed to be Kenton Pit. Immediately work began to clean out this old pit but the air was so bad that William Patterson, one of the rescuers, was nearly suffocated. On Tuesday 9th air boxes were put into Kenton Pit to improve the ventilation and by Wednesday the wind was blowing so strongly from the west that air in the shaft could be kept fresh. A small air pump was brought from Wallsend to apply to the boxes in calm weather. By Saturday 13th John Buddle was able to get down the Kenton Pit and advance 52 yards along the north headway. A further 40 yards progress was made on Sunday and the following day the men got to the most northern part of the old workings which were almost under the boundary line between Byker and Heaton. This was calculated to be 97 yards from the nearest point in the waste of the Engine Pit. However, on Saturday 20th a great discharge of foul air compelled the men to abandon their work. By now it was realised that there was no chance of finding the men alive. The rescue attempt was suspended: the men were sent to work at Wallsend Colliery while two deputies were left at Heaton.

Buddle had incorrectly referred to the scene of these operations as the Kenton Pit which was much further to the west. He later noted that 'the proper name of this pit appears by an old plan to be the Moor Pit' described as 'an ancient pit in front of Heaton Hall'. The Moor Pit was a short distance south of the old Matthew Pit of Byker Colliery which Buddle's men had failed to find.

John Buddle's view book records the daily struggle to keep the pumping engines in action in the prolonged attempt to win back the colliery. One typical example is the entry for the 15th July which records that 'the Far Pit Engine has gone very little this week on account of the badness of the boilers; but the thorough repair of the middle one being completed and the other two being cleaned and repaired in a temporary way, the engine got to work again last night. The Middle Pit engine has also gone indifferently all week from the bad state of the boilers'. There are frequent references to borrowing parts from other collieries in the neighbourhood. There are many examples of the engineer's ability to improvise when confronted with an emergency. On Thursday and Friday the 5th and 6th of October, for example, he was 'occupied these two days in adapting the travelling Engine (Chapman's railway locomotive) to draw the rubbish with chains at the Middle Pit – got it to answer completely'. Two weeks earlier he had been able to enter the Middle Pit where ' all about the shaft was a complete scene of ruin'.

Gradually, the water subsided. On Tuesday 19th October, Buddle was 'down the Far Pit and was able to take candles all round'. The following Thursday, he 'lighted the Far Pit furnace without difficulty', a task which was necessary to secure the proper ventilation of that part of the colliery. By this time work was well advanced in ridding out the west mothergate in the Middle Pit. The final entry in the view book for 1815 records that 'the water was so low in the Old Pit this morning as to allow a sight of the tops of the full corves standing on the rolleys near the shaft'.

By 1st January 1816 'the water had lowered 2 feet in the old pit this morning which left only about a foot on the rolleyway. Jas. Smith and Jobe – enginewrights – went up the west mothergate to the entrance of the stables and found good air going. Saw two horses in the rollies at the shaft siding – they were entirely reduced to skeletons without any offensive smell, except when the sleek near them is disturbed'.The following morning the water was down to the level of the rolleyway and Buddle went down to examine the state of the pit with six miners. They were able to travel about ninety yards up the west mothergate where a large fall stopped their progress. They attempted to by-pass the fall by using the stable board to the south. Here the rolleyway seemed to be clear but Buddle decided that no attempt should be made to access the workings until the debris around the shaft was cleared.

On Saturday 6th January the body of William Stott was found in the stoneway linking the Middle and Engine Pits about 200 yards from the Middle Pit shaft. 'The body was found under a fall with nothing but the head out; the features were visible but the head had a chalky appearance and the body was reduced to a mere skeleton, the bones being held together by cloths'. The following day William Stott was buried at Wallsend. By the 19th January the debris from the fall in the west mothergate had been cleared. The next day the body of the overman, William Miller, was found in the west mothergate two yards west of the stoneway end. One of his feet was fast between a plank and the top of a corf and his body was entangled amongst the corves. 'The head was towards the pit and he appears to have been entangled in the act of escaping'.

The bodies of the wastemen, Robert Richardson, Henry Dixon and Arthur Dixon, were found on Tuesday 23rd lying four or five yards west of Miller's body in the west mothergate. Beyond this point the mothergate was blocked and it took until Sunday 4th February to clear the fall. The body of George Laws was found that day at the bottom of the inclined plane. Near to this spot, on Tuesday 6th February, Lancelot Nicholson's body was found covered with rubbish – his cloths had been torn off and his body severely mangled. The bottom of the inclined plane was covered with rubbish several feet thick and the plates were torn up in the upper part of it – all evidence that an immense torrent of water had run down the inclined plane.

The men were employed for the next week cleaning and securing the rollyway from the old Engine shaft to the bottom of the inclined plane. On Wednesday 14th February Richard Hepple and Thomas Smith led a group of men into the workings and discovered fifty five bodies at Gibson's crane. 'They had evidently survived the accident for some time as they had killed a horse and cut the flesh out of his hams – it had been divided amongst them; but little of it had been eaten as portions of it – seemingly the share of individuals – was found lying near to the bodies in caps and bags'.
The position of the bodies found near Gibson's crane at the top of the inclined plane are marked with a cross in a sketch from Buddle's view book reproduced opposite. The horse which was killed for food is drawn at 'a'; and the crane hole 'hh'.

On Monday 19th February the rollyway had been cleared sufficiently to get the bodies out from Gibson's crane. 'They were not so much decayed as might have been supposed – those which lay amongst any water were the worst. The body of a boy which was covered with water in the crane hole was a mere skeleton. They had evidently died of suffocation'. As there was free communication of air between the old Moor Pit and Gibson's crane, it is probable that the rescue attempt on May 5th 'put a period to their existence by letting the air which was highly compressed escape'. The pit was closed on Tuesday and Wednesday for the funerals of these victims who were buried in the south east corner of Wallsend parish church. Although the graves do not survive, a plaque in the church records the burial.

Meanwhile, on Thursday 15th February, the body of old Edward Gibson had been found in the first stable board just on going into the stables. It was lying upon some timbers nearly at the roof with the clothes mostly torn off. The following Thursday, 22nd February, Shipley Mitchinson's was found nearby. 'It was above a horse near to the roof and …the clothes were nearly all torn off. From this it is clear that the four wastemen and Miller, together with old Gibson had been altogether. Robert Richardson as well as Gibson were feeble old men and it is probable that Miller and the other wastemen had perished in consequence of assisting them out – they were all within 100 yards of the shaft'.

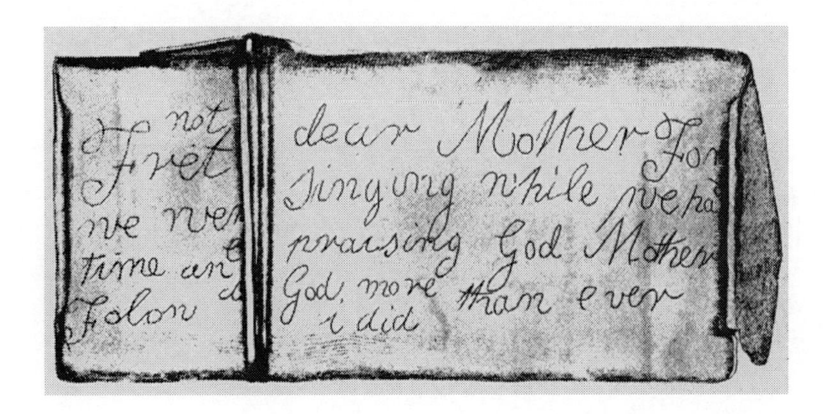

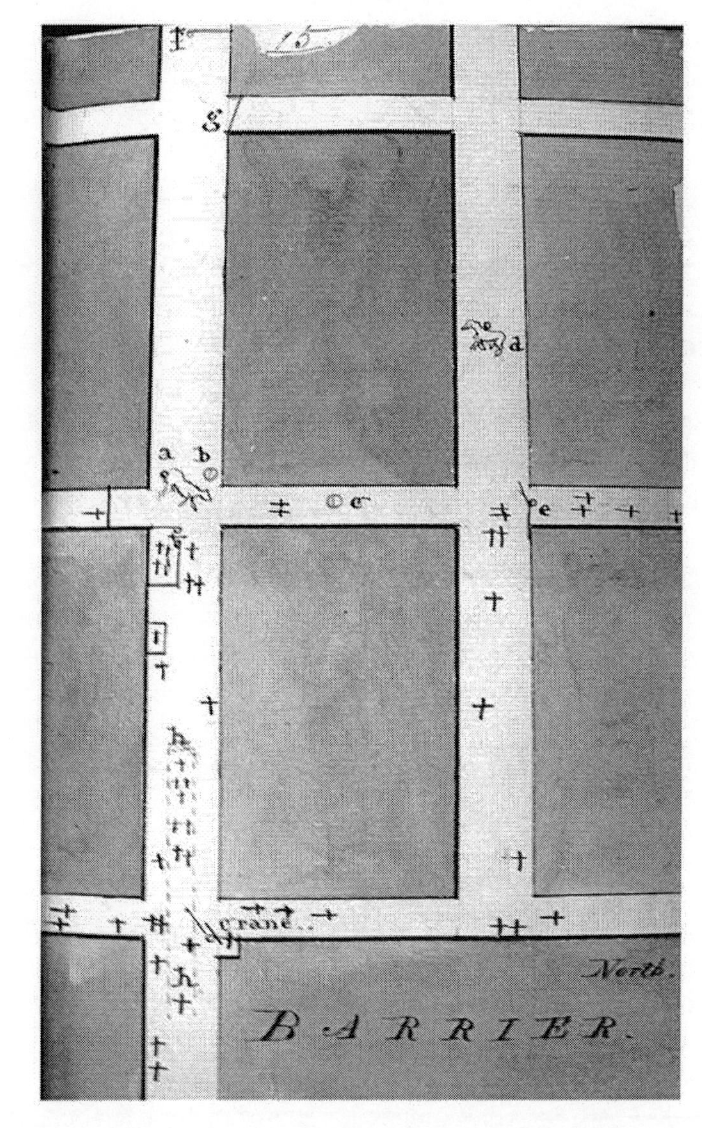

The final eight bodies were discovered in the face of the far south west board on Wednesday 6th March. These were the hewers William Southern, Edward Robson, Simon Dodds, John Reay and Matthew Johnson; their putters Anthony Southern and William Hall; and the craneman Thomas Miller. On March 7th Buddle records in his view book: 'nothing done underground today on account of the Coroner's inquest on the bodies and the funerals'.Unusually, the relatives were permitted to go down the pit to identify their husbands and sons. The bodies were so decayed that moving them to the surface would have destroyed the evidence. Elizabeth Thew was looking for her husband, her eldest son George and her middle son William. Her youngest son John had survived the flooding. She recognised William by his auburn hair and found his tin candle box in one of his pockets. On it was inscribed his last message: 'Fret not, dear mother, for we were singing while we had time, and praising God. Mother follow God more than ever I did'. On the other side was a message from her husband: 'If Johnny is saved, be a good lad to God, and thy mother'.

Buddle records that on March 8th, Richard Heppell and Thomas Smith travelled all around the Engine Pit with candles and were able eventually 'to enter the drift where the waste burst in with a lamp of Sir H. Davy'. This indicates that Heaton was at the forefront of technological development since the lamp had only arrived in the North East in January. 'They saw the feeder of water which seemed small'. The drift had struck the corner of a pillar which had given way under pressure from the water. Buddle reckoned that if the exploratory drift had been four feet further east the accident would not have happened: chance once again played a part.

Meanwhile preparations were in hand for re-opening the colliery. The stables had been cleaned and whitewashed and on March 9th sixteen horses were sent down the Engine Pit. Coal working began on the morning of the 11th March 1816. Two days later the bodies of Ralph Widderington and his son were discovered – these were the last victims of the flooding recorded in Buddle's view book. However, other minor accidents continued to happen: Tim Dodgson, the overman, was killed when drawing props on 21st August and on 18th December Arthur Wilson, the rolleyway keeper, was crushed to death.

As was customary in an age before state benefits, a public subscription was launched through the press to raise funds for the widows and orphans of the disaster. On 30th May 1815, *The Times* published an appeal on behalf the 41 men and 34 boys killed who had left behind 110 dependant relatives. Contributions were received not only from coal owners and workmen in the locality but many donations were sent from further afield including members of the Coal Exchange in London. Pamphlets describing the accident in detail and eulogies in verse were published to raise additional funds.

Conclusion

The entombment at Hartley, the explosion at Felling and the inundation at Heaton are but three of the many accidents which took place throughout the coalfield and serve as a reminder of the dangers inherent in mining. The heroic rescue attempts at the three collieries show the key role the local colliery management and engineers played in trying to save the men often at great risk to their own lives. The pernicious nature of chance is an element in all three disasters. So is the compassion shown to those left behind by the mine owners and the community at large. Water and gas continued to be the great enemies of the miner. In 1925, the View Pit at Montague Colliery in Scotswood was flooded and 38 men were drowned when the miners broke into old workings; while in 1951 the explosion of methane gas at Easington Colliery killed 83 miners. Dust became a new problem as the size of the collieries increased. It was suspected to be the cause of several explosions in the late nineteenth century although this was not proved scientifically until the early twentieth century. Dust was believed to have been the cause of the explosion at Stanley in 1909 which claimed 168 lives. Besides these major accidents, there were numerous minor ones such as those recorded for the Ashington Collieries. Furthermore, not all accidents resulted in immediate death: many more men were injured, disabled for life or died prematurely - especially as a result of respiratory diseases caused by working in dusty conditions. Buddle had commented in 1830 to the Select Committee of the House of Lords that 'there are not only a great number killed but a great number wounded and injured for life'.

'Tis Coal that makes our Britain Great, upholds our Commerce and our State', the popular rhyme proudly proclaimed. However, the coal which powered the industrial revolution and made Britain the leading industrial nation in the world during Victoria's reign was won at a high cost in terms of human suffering. It has been estimated that 1,000 coalminer's lives were lost every year in Britain during the late nineteenth century; and even today, with all the technology available to the mining industry, major accidents occur. In 2005, a gas explosion at the Sunjiawan Pit in China killed 214 miners; and in November 2007 *The Times* carried the headline '100 feared dead in mine blast' after an explosion at the Zasyadko mine in the Ukrainian Donbass coalfield. The words of the Durham miner Sid Chaplin in his poem 'The Weeping Widow', which was written underground at the Dean and Chapter Colliery, Ferryhill, still have resonance in 2008:

> When they carried my comrade
> Out of the pit
> Cold, silent and crushed,
> We knew that the price was paid.

Chapter Four - The Colliery Village

'Pitmen by their employments, their living in separate villages, and their inter-marriages, are a peculiar people; child like in many things they frequently needed to be humoured like children'.

Colliery Guardian 15th Feb.1862

The rapid development of the coalfield from the mid nineteenth century led to the colonisation of large areas of Northumberland and Durham and creation of new colliery villages. Families came from other parts of England and from Scotland, Wales and Ireland attracted by the possibility of permanent employment and the offer of good accommodation in the new colliery houses. This mixture of people was assimilated very quickly because they had one thing in common – they all worked at the pit. The neighbourliness of mining communities is a common theme of the literature of the region in, for example, the writings of Sid Chaplin. This community spirit sprang from the fact that the villages were almost entirely peopled by mining families. It was strengthened by the nature of pit work: when underground the miners depended upon each other for their lives. Often geographically isolated, the colliery villages were close-knit communities with a strong corporate spirit. The Wesleyan and Primitive Methodist Chapels were the centres of religious life within the villages. They were also the venue for many of the cultural activities within the community such as the male voice choirs and the brass bands. The colliery institute provided recreational and educational activities for the men.

The brotherhood, forged at work underground, was also expressed in the strong trade unionism of the miners, their support for the co-operative movement and their political loyalty to the labour party. The union played an important part in the running of the colliery particularly in the drawing of the cavils which determined where the men worked in the mine. The co-operative store was not only the most important shop in the village but it was also a centre of social life, including adult education. The Labour Party was the dominant political force in the twentieth century. In 2006, for

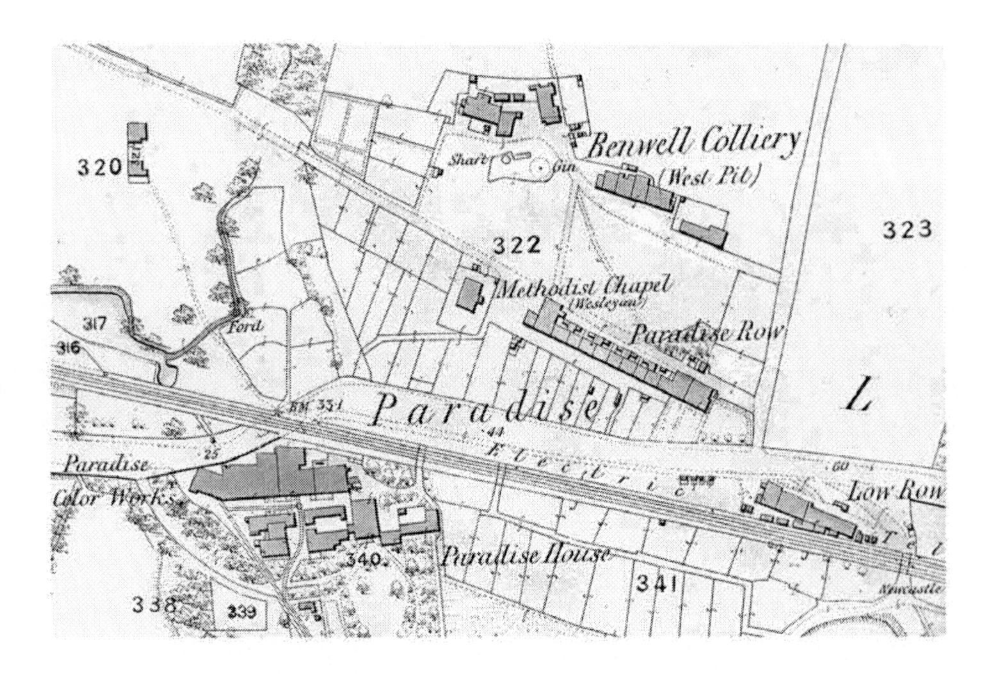

example, Chester-le-Street celebrated one hundred years of being represented continuously by a Labour candidate and Durham County Council has remained solidly Labour since 1919.

Paradise, on Scotswood Road in Benwell, is a typical colliery village of the mid nineteenth century comprising the pit, a large Methodist chapel and two rows of cottages – Paradise Row and Low Row. The village achieved fame because it is mentioned in the popular Tyneside song 'The Blaydon Races'. The 1861 Ordnance Survey map shows the village set in rural surroundings to the north of the Newcastle to Carlisle railway line overlooking the River Tyne suggesting that Paradise was not an inappropriate name. Nor was this the only Paradise Row in the coalfield for between 1804 and 1822 George Stephenson lived at Dial Cottage, Paradise Row, West Moor, when employed as the engineer for Killingworth Colliery. The cottage still stands on the north side of Great Lime Road in a setting quite different from the rural idyll of Stephenson's time.

Some colliery villages, like Chopwell in County Durham, were a development of existing agricultural communities; others, like Bigges Main in North Tyneside, were entirely new creations being built with the winning of the pit. Many of the villages, such as Chopwell, still exist but the nature of the community has changed with the closure of the colliery; others have disappeared, like Bigges Main, which is now beneath Wallsend municipal golf course. A colliery village has been recreated within Beamish Museum where it is possible to experience the lifestyle of the mining communities. The miners' cottages, warmed by a blazing coal fire within, are dominated by the colliery with its winding engine, workshops, spoil heap and railway sidings. The Methodist chapel, the schoolroom, the quoits pitches and the gardens with their pigeon crees and leek trenches are reminders of the social life within the village.

Bigges Main

Bigges Main Colliery was established in 1784 by Matthew Bell and William Brown the owners of the nearby Willington Colliery. From 1836 the offices of Heaton Colliery were at Bigges Main and the two pits were linked underground. The colliery mined the High Main seam at a depth of 95 fathoms until August 1857 when it was abandoned owing to the flooding of the Tyne basin. The village remained in existence until after the First World War but it is now lost beneath the greens of Wallsend municipal golf course.

In the mid nineteenth century the Ordnance Survey produced it first set of maps of the region and this is often a useful starting point for the study of a mining village. The map of the lost village of Bigges Main shows the colliery at the centre of the community. The 'A' shaft is named at the west end of High Row and the other is marked behind West Row. A large area is taken up by spoil heaps in the vicinity of each shaft. The waggonway from 'C' pit runs north-south through the village. This was an inclined plane – the loaded wagons descending the slight gradient by gravity, the force of this weight descending being used to return the empty wagons to the 'C' pit popularly known as Redhill. It joins the Coxlodge waggonway at the end of Low Row and heads southwards to the staiths at Wallsend. The Wesleyan Methodist Chapel is also in the centre of the village next to the stables. In addition to the houses at the pithead (95) and the adjacent stables, there are four rows of colliery houses. Blue Row, with the agent's house at the west end, High Row, West Row and Low Row. Next to the houses are the allotments which provided recreation for the miners who not only grew vegetables but also kept poultry and pigs to supplement the family food supply. The village is surrounded by farmland.

The enumerator's returns for the census, which was conducted every ten years from 1801, provide detailed information about the families living in the village and these are a second useful source for the study of mining communities. For example, the 1851 census reveals that on 4th April 1851 Ralph Robertson, a coal miner aged 47, lived with his wife Jane, aged 41, in High Row. They had three sons, Michael (20) and the twins Benjamin and William (18) who all worked in the pit. They also had two young daughters Jane (7) and Anne (4) and an infant son George (2). Jane Chambers (20) was employed as their servant. Their neighbours included John Jobling (62) the overman, William Hunter the colliery engineman and the widow Catherine Wilson (40) who was supported by her three sons Charles (24), James (18) and Hugh (15) - all coal miners. All the adult men living at High Row worked at the pit except Samuel Holmes, aged 84, who was a retired agricultural labourer.

By collating this detailed information it is possible to build up a picture of the community at Bigges Main in 1851. There were 136 households providing accommodation for 623 people. All the men were employed in coal mining except three agricultural labourers, Cuthbert Wilkinson the carrier, Peter James the grocer, a miller Edward Brown, Thomas Charlton a shoemaker and a solicitor's clerk, John Youill, aged 14. There were 123 coal miners living in the village together with 17 colliery labourers, 18 waggonmen, 9 blacksmiths and two trapper boys, Thomas Jackson and Robert Hall, both aged 11. There were 3 firemen, 3 enginewrights and 3

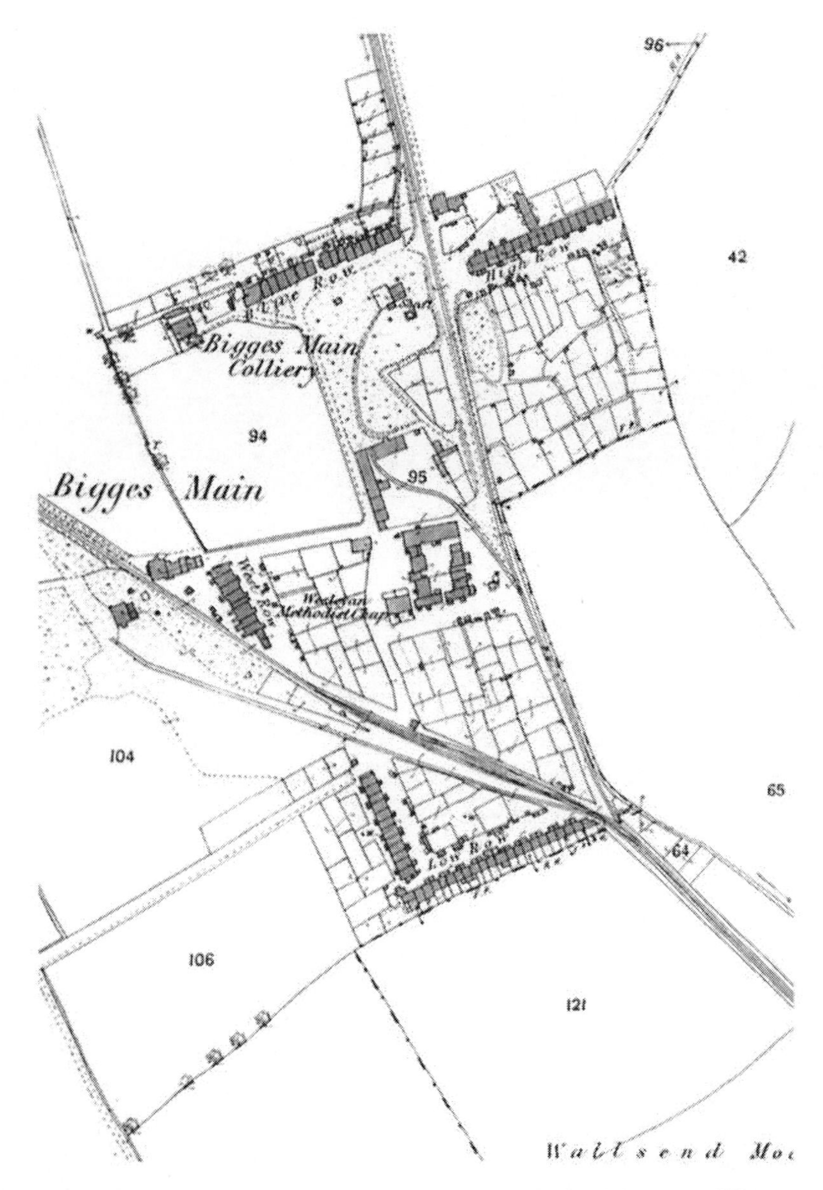

enginemen; 3 horsekeepers, a sadler , 2 grooms and 2 drivers. William Beggow the lampkeeper, John Graham the colliery waste heap keeper, John Brown the platelayer and William Ellerington the banksman, also living in the village. In addition there were 2 stonemasons, 2 sawyers and 3joiners. Women's work, outside the onerous task of running the home, was very restricted. Mary Hunter and Elizabeth Hunter worked as dressmakers, Jane Chambers and Hannah Scott were servants and the schoolmistress was Ann Hall. Half of the workforce was aged under 30 years while 92% were under 50 years – Bigges Main was a young persons' community. Both the Ordnance Survey maps and the Census Returns are available within the regional record offices and it is an easy task to use these primary sources to investigate other colliery villages.

Gosforth Colliery

Between October 1872 and April 1874 the *Newcastle Weekly Chronicle* published a series of articles entitled 'Our Colliery Villages' with the intention of bringing 'the weight of public opinion to bear upon some of the wealthy coal-owners of this district who have the men who produce their wealth living in hovels'. These articles reveal a diversity of living conditions from the hovels at Seghill to the model accommodation being built at Gosforth some of which is still occupied in 2008. The writer commented that 'we are sometimes tempted when passing some of our pit villages at a distance to envy the pitman his snug rent-free house, his unlimited coal and his useful kitchen garden: all is not gold which glitters'. There were places recorded where the living conditions were intolerable such as at Wylam where 'in one house of three small rooms there are three different families numbering in all eleven members..... there is not the slightest provision for social or sanitary decency'. However, 'among the new villages springing up ... care has been taken that the comfort of the miners and their families shall be provided for'. The articles note the inadequate provision for water supply and sanitary arrangements, a common complaint about houses for the working classes in general. They also emphasise the importance of the co-operative stores and Methodist chapels in catering for the bodily and spiritual needs of the community.

In November 1873, the newspaper featured Gosforth Colliery which was won in 1829 and the Brandling family held a grand ball 1,000 feet underground for the local gentry and the workforce to celebrate the

Gosforth Colliery

opening. The author writes in that in 1873 'the residences of the men are very much scattered … and the bulk of the houses are away at Gosforth Long Row which is situated half way between the colliery and Longbenton and here we find the worst evils of the old fashioned system in full force. Gosforth Long Row is a lengthy row of back to back cottages one room on, or in some cases below, the ground level. They are of the usual stamp; the uneven brick floor needs no description, nor do the pantries, the unceiled garret, the offensive drains and sinks or the noisesome ash heaps – receptacles of all the garbage and filth of the village'. The nearest water supply and co-operative store were in Longbenton village a half a mile to the east. There 'is a neat Wesleyan Chapel and a furlong further on is another back-to-back row known as Benton Row which consists of some 40 or 50 houses. Here a slight concession to the demands of sanitary reformers has been made and Benton Row boasts four small privies which seem to be considered sufficient by the owners for the use of the entire community. Leaving the somewhat insalubrious neighbourhood of the Long Row we cross over by the pit heap to have a look at the new stone faced houses in the course of erection. One row faces the Blyth and Tyne Railway. These new colliery houses contain on the ground floor a back kitchen in which the cooking and the washing may be done; a larger room the front which may be used as a parlour and out of which a staircase springs to the floor above. Upstairs we have two snug bedrooms. The windows are large and made after the large pane fashion now in vogue. Nearly fifty of these model houses will soon be completed'. Thus there was a wide variety of housing provided for the Gosforth miners and this was true of the coalfield as a whole. In the late nineteenth century, the colliery villages contained some of the worst and some of the best living conditions for the working classes in the region. The section of the First Edition Ordnance Survey map of 1858 shows the scattered nature of the community. The Coxlodge waggonway runs diagonally across the section and the other railway line is the Blyth and Tyne Railway - now the Metro. The new houses of the 1870's were built in the field to the south of the colliery and north of Gosforth station. Most of these houses survive but the only part of the rest of the community remaining is the Methodist Chapel, now used as a garage.

Derwent Street, Chopwell, circa 1914

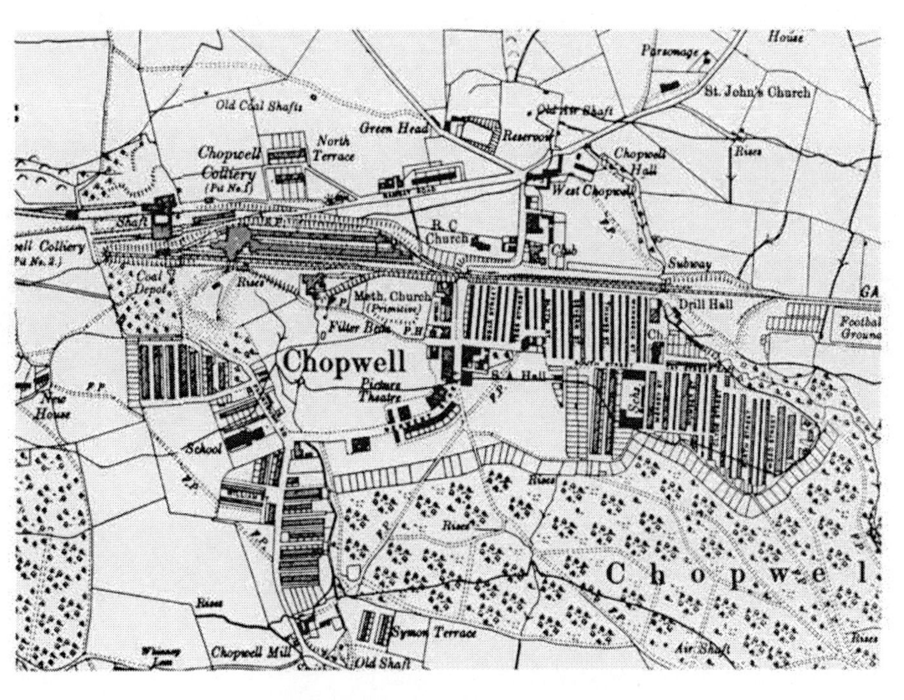

Ordnanace Survey Map, 1919

Village Life in Chopwell

Although the Ordnance Survey map, the Census statistics, and the newspapers provide very valuable information, it is the personal recollections of people who lived in the colliery villages which add the flesh to these bones. For much of the academic year 1977-78, I met on Friday afternoons with a group of senior citizens (Bill Charlton, Ernie Jacques, Andy Lawther, Jack Lawther and George Brown) from Chopwell and recorded the group discussing their life and work in the village.
The following text on village life is written from the transcripts in their own language and describes their domestic and working life during the first half of the twentieth century. Their experiences at Chopwell were typical of life in mining communities throughout the North East.

Childhood

Chopwell was a healthy place for children to be brought up in compared to the cities: we never knew the squalor and poverty of the slum districts of Tyneside. Our fathers worked very hard and wages could have been better but the women weren't good managers if the kids had no shoes. Children suffered from many diseases such as diphtheria, scarlet fever and tuberculosis which are almost unknown now. However, rickets was exceptional at Chopwell because children got plenty of milk and vegetables. Nonetheless, infant mortality was higher then and children were brought into contact with death at a very early age. We had a little girl who died and one of the things I still remember from childhood is seeing her in her coffin. In the bigger houses, such as Trent Street, you had a front room

which gave some privacy but in an ordinary house this was not possible. Many is the time as a child when I've called at such a house and in the far corner of the kitchen was the corpse. We once called upon a friend whose mother had died and a relative took us all in to see the corpse which was a regular thing in those days.

Before the First World War Chopwell was a wonderful place to spend your childhood for most families were large with six or more children and there was plenty of kids to play with. Many of the games we played such as duck-stone, monte kitty, Jack shine the maggie and kitty-kat are no longer seen in the village. In spring time marbles were very popular. We generally played with clay marbles since our glass alleys were reserved for special occasions. The lemonade bottles in those days had glass balls in the neck as a stopper and we used them for marbles. On dark nights we played 'knocky nine doors' and we always picked upon a person who would chase us. In the rows the doors were grouped in pairs with about eighteen inches between the two doors. We used to pinch a clothes line and tie the two door knobs together leaving a little play on the rope. We rattled at both doors. When one opened the other pulled back which caused some people to go wild and run after us. Some time we used to pinch a poss tub or any barrel which would hold water. Two or three of us would carry it down the street always to the person's door we disliked the most. Quietly we would half fill the tub with water and lean it against the door so that it was just balanced. Then we would knock on the door and run. When they opened the door … woosh.

Every two or three streets had a football team. There were dozens of teams and we used to run things on a league system. This was probably why our school was always the best in the Derwent Valley. There was a bit of trouble when we played the Catholics; in fact many street games ended in a battle. If two lads fell out over dirty play we would form a ring, they would have a go and that was that. Nobody interfered. Almost everynight there was a fight amongst the schoolboys. Crowds of lads would be watching the two contestants, striped off to their bare buffs, having a go – mind they were vicious. As likely or not they would get another hiding when they got home.

There were two schools in the village, the east school for juniors and senior girls and the west school for juniors and senior boys. Most children were educated in the village until they left to work at the pit. Although many pupils passed for the grammar school at Blaydon lots of really good scholars had to decline the offer of a place. This was because their parents could not afford to pay the train fares from Westwood Station to Swalwell each day: nor could they afford to buy the school uniform. Schooldays were happy days: although discipline was very strict it was always fair. If you were sent to the headmaster it was the end of the road. You were given three of the best on each hand if you had done something drastic. You took it and there was never any animosity shown. When you went home you got another hiding if your parents had found out.

People used to make a lot of their own entertainment in those days before the radio and television were invented. After chapel on a Sunday people would often get around a piano and have a bit of a sing song. Every Saturday night the whole of our family met in my grandparents' home. The piano would be going, or the old squeeze box, and we would have a right old jig. Birthdays were a great time for children, especially if you had jelly at the party. At Christmas most people had a party at their grannie's and you would be satisfied if you got one toy, an apple, an orange and a few nuts in your stocking. All sorts of games were played, such as snakes and ladders, dominoes, tiddlywinks and snapcards. The family, like the village itself, was a closely knit unit.

Children did a variety of jobs to earn a little extra money. Some lads did paper rounds and most people helped to harvest the potato crop. When the fruiterer came around the village the first one there got the job of helping him dish out the fruit. It was the same with the grocers. If you could get pally with the delivery man you could always earn a copper or two. Children were expected to help with the home. Lads mostly helped their dad with the garden. Most people kept a few hens and many people also kept a pig. It all depended on what shift your father was on at the pit. If he was at work you would have to get up early to take fresh water and crowdy to the hens and collect the eggs before going to school. It was the same with the pigs. Almost every one had a two-wheel barrow and you were forever out collecting horse muck for the garden.

Almost every child went to Sunday School which played an important part in our upbringing. The highlights of the Sunday School year were the trip to the seaside and the field day. We usually walked to Westgate Station and got the train to Whitley Bay or Tynemouth and had a great time. On the Friday before the field day, the Sunday School teachers would get the colliery rolley to come and collect the seats and the food. Everybody tried to make the sports day and picnic a great success. These were special occasions to look forward to for in those days not many people had the opportunity to take a holiday away from the village.

Washing day in the backyard. The lady on the left is working with a poss-stick in a poss-tub while her companion is rinsing clothes in the rinsing bath. A scrubbing board, wooden bucket and clothes basket are in the foreground.

Women's Work

Andy Lawther (brother of the miners' leader Will Lawther) recalls the work of his mother managing the home of a mining family.

Women had a very difficult life in mining villages especially those like Chopwell which worked a multiple shift system whereby men were coming and going, sleeping and eating all the day because of the demands of the pit. My mother's daily round was typical of the miner's wife. She would be up at three in the morning to prepare breakfast and a bait for my eldest brother, a hewer, who started at four o'clock. When he went to work she would try and snatch an hour's sleep before going through the same routine for one of my younger brothers who was a datal worker whose shift started at six. Meanwhile, father, who had started his night shift the previous evening at ten, would be coming out of the pit at six and going home for his breakfast and bath in front of the fire.

The photo opposite shows the fireplace of a miners house circa 1890. Notice the brass candlesticks on the mantelpiece and the tea caddies on either end. The brass rail beneath is for drying clothes. At the right hand side is a shoe horn. Below is the oven, open fire and set pot for keeping food warm. On the floor are the kettle, the kettlestand, the fender, tongs and poker.

By the time father had finished, it would be time for the three younger children to get ready for school. Even when they had been packed off to school mother had no time to rest. The hewers only worked a six and a half to seven hour shift and she had to prepare a dinner for my eldest brother returning from early shift. The children would be home from school for their mid-day meal before he had finished washing in front of the fire. In all probability father would get up and have something with the children at mid-day and then go to the local for a pint. When the children went back to school, mother had to prepare for the afternoon shift at 2.00 pm when me and my two brothers went down the pit. By the time we were off she had to prepare for her younger son returning from the 6 to 2 shift. By the time we were off she had to prepare for her younger son returning from the 6 to 2 shift. By the time his bath was off the kitchen floor it was nearly time for the schoolchildren to be home for tea.

Father would be back from the pub by tea-time and he would try to get a couple of hours sleep before night shift started at ten. Mother's work was not finished yet – in fact the biggest job of the day was yet to come. After 10 pm the three brothers who had gone to work at 2 pm would be home and mother not only had to prepare their dinner but she also had to boil water in the pan and kettle on the fire for their baths. Altogether, it would take anything up to two hours before they were finished. Consequently, it was always after midnight before mother got to bed at the end of a normal day – and the alarm clock would be ringing at three o'clock for the start of the next.

On top of this continual round there was all the washing and baking to do for a large family. It was slave's work – a housewife doesn't know she's born compared to those days. Washing day was generally a Monday – never a Sunday – and preparations began at six in the morning. If it was a rainy day it was a hell of a day because you couldn't get stirred in the kitchen because of the lines of clothes. The devil's birthday we called it. If washday was fine and the clothes could be hung in the lane everyone was happy. It was very strenuous work – all the carrying of water, the heavy poss-stick, the scrubbing and the large mangle to wring the clothes. And the work went on all day, for it was generally nighttime when it was finished. With big families, every day was a baking day. There was no bread bought – people baked their own. This somehow had to be fitted in. Not surprisingly, women aged quicker in those days – a woman over fifty looked like a grandmother.

The communal oven at the colliery village of Emma Vale near Ryton.

Unlike today, no married women worked. Their place was at home looking after the family. The odd spinster had a career such as teaching. Girls generally went into service on leaving school. There were several unofficial agencies which used to recruit girls when they were fifteen for domestic service either in far off places like London or nearer home in the large houses in Jesmond or Whitley Bay. They were usually given their keep and paid four shillings for a six day week. Many stayed at home to assist their mothers. Seasonal work was also available for women on the neighbouring farms picking wickens or potatoes and the like.

There was a rigid line drawn about what were the responsibilities of women in the colliery villages. They were responsible for the running of the home and matters like shopping and the family accounts were entirely their domain. It was a very serious matter when mother was ill – then you needed to rely on neighbours. There was always elderly women available when help was needed to serve as unofficial nurses, mid-wives, layers out and what have you. They did it gladly without thought of reward. Even in an enlightened place like Chopwell women were excluded from most social activities. There were no activities exclusively for women, run by women, until the Co-op Guild was started in the 1920's.

Women had an intense pride about their house almost to the point of it being a religion keeping the home neat and tidy. They would scrub the steps with a sandy stone, wash the front path and clean the back lane; even the wall under the fireplace would be whitewashed. Everything had to be kept clean and polished. The steel fender had to be made to shine, the ovens had to be black-leaded, all the brasses had to be polished. Knives were made of ordinary steel, not stainless steel, and they all had to be cleaned on a knife board. Younger members of the family used to be given different jobs – cleaning the knives, polishing the fender, greasing the pit boots, black-leading the old fireplace. Miners' homes on the whole were spotlessly clean and comfortable places thanks to the women. The thing that was most outstanding was the happy family life in the home itself where you made your own pleasure and happiness.

Emily Lawther cleaning the fireplace at 17 Lenin Terrace Chopwell.

Item		
2 stone flour	4/-	20
2lbs butter	2/10	14
½lb Cheshire cheese	5	2
1lb margarine	8	3
4lbs sugar	1/2	6
1lb bacon	11	5
1lb currants	4	2
1lb towel soap	2½	1½
1 tin Nestle's milk	5	2
1 stone potatoes	6	2½
2 dozen boxes matches	5	2
2 lbs candles	6	2½
2 tins boot polish	4	1½
1lb rice	3	1½
1lb sago	4	1½
2 ozs. tobacco	7	3
1lb lard	7½	3
	14/6	73p

The Chopwell Tay Street branch of Robinson's grocery store in 1909. An extract from the order book shows Mrs Hunter's bill for the week of 24th December 1914. Opposite, the Colliery Institute and Primitive Methodist Church in Derwent Street.

Village Social Life

Every workman at the colliery was compelled to pay one penny a week to the Miners' Institute as a condition of employment. The Institute above was owned by the Consett Iron Company and run jointly by the men and the management. The colliery manager acted as chairman. The library was a massive room and old Harbottle, who had been injured at the pit, seemed to make a full-time job of librarian. Every socialist publication was there from Marx to all the old anarchist writers. The old socialist insisted upon this and they were all avid readers. All the standard English novels were there – Dickens, Hardy, Thackeray – it was a wonderful library. Different speakers were paid to come to Chopwell including many of the early socialists. It is often said that Mr. Imrie, the colliery manager and chairman of the Institute, was to blame for the headway that had been made with socialist ideas in Chopwell. Although not a socialist himself, he was very liberal minded and democratic. There was also a well-stocked reading room with all sorts of periodicals – *The Sphere, The Graphic, The London Illustrated News, Punch,* engineering journals and sporting publications. It was a comfortable place well patronised and well conducted.

There were dominoes, draughts and chess played in the reading room. The unwritten rule was that you had to be quiet. The same was true in the billiard room which had eight large tables. The caretaker was in charge and if he raised his finger you were out. The company also provided the field for the village football team.

At the present time people have radio, television, cars and all kinds of distractions but at the beginning of the twentieth century there were none of these things. The chapels filled the gap. Not everyone who went to chapel was an out and out Christian but at that time the chapel was an important meeting house and a social centre in the village. There were two chapels, one belonging to the Wesleyans and another belonging to the Primitives. You would get anything from three to four hundred people at an ordinary service and twice that number at a special service.

Gala Day

The Durham miners' gala day was one of the greatest days of the year for the villagers of Chopwell. Whether you were connected with the pit or not you still went to Durham because you belonged to the community. Before six o'clock in the morning people would congregate beside the pit and march through the village behind the brass band. We marched all the way to High Westwood Station picking people up all along the way. Then we boarded the train for Durham. The railways claimed that the big meet at Durham was the largest single annual gathering in the world. Trains were coming into Durham all the time and you had to take your turn to march through the city to the racecourse. Everyone connected with the village would fall in behind the band when their turn came. We would march through the streets lined by thousands of people and you could bet that the contingent had doubled its size before reaching the racecourse. Some would never get out of the market – for them it was a proper beer day.

Besides the official speeches by leaders of the Labour Party and the unions, which were important because people were much more politically

The Chopwell brassband which played on important role in village life especially on Gala Day when it led the parade of the village through Durham City.

conscious in those days, the gala was a great social occasion. Durham was a meeting place for all your relations and friends from other villages who you only saw once a year. After the official speeches the platform was taken by various societies such as the Labour College and the Good Templars. Traders were banned. If you wanted a cup of teea you had to buy it from the different chapels in the area who set up tents to serve the miners and to raise funds. There were sad times also for if there had been an accident in the colliery the banner would be draped in black in memory of anyone killed during the previous twelve months and the band would play a hymn on the racecourse. There was also a service in the cathedral. After a great day at Durham the train would arrive back at High Westwood about seven at night and we would march back to the Miners' Hall. Not all the band got back at once but most managed the same month.

(The Northumberland Miners held a similar event generally at Bedlington)

The Union

All the men at the colliery belonged to a union, either the enginemen's union, the mechanics' union or the miners' lodge. The union was such an integral part of the life of the pit that you took it for granted but the actual running of the union was left to a handful of men. The miners' lodge was responsible for negotiating wages and working conditions at the pit. A regular feature of the lodge's business was the drawing of the cavils (lots) each quarter. Cavilling was the only fair means of deciding where men were to work in the pit where conditions could vary a great deal. The management would submit a list of the cavils to be drawn and, apart from providing the list, they had nothing to do with the system. We couldn't challenge them on wages but we could challenge them if the manager was introducing any oddity into the cavilling system. Everybody could be at the actual draw which at Chopwell took place in the pay office. All the names of the men were put into a box and we always had a very junior boy – a driver – to make the draw. He got a shilling. He picked out the names one by one, handing them to the under manager. Sitting beside him was the lodge secretary to see that there was no fiddle. The atmosphere was tinged with hope and a superstitious custom was to put the cat in a warm oven while the cavils were being drawn. The name would be read out – 'Ye bugger, there we go again, another bloody wet cavil'. If you got a good number we called it the 'piano flat' for you could make good money and buy something extra. Cavilling was general to hewers, to putters and to stonemen.

At first there were individual cavils but with the coming of machines and longwall working, teams of men were cavilled for the face on which they worked. Invariably, in a multi-seam pit the seams were not cavilled through: if you were in the Brockwell seam you were only cavilled in that seam. Changes in the working of the seams were discussed between the management and the lodge officials prior to the cavils being drawn when it was determined if it was necessary to transfer men from one seam to another. This was also done by cavilling. However, if the change had to

The men who were imprisoned during the 1926 strike

take place during the quarter one of the cavil rules was the last cavil came out: that is the places at the bottom of the list were the first to be changed regardless of where the men had been working. Drawing of the cavils was a very serious matter and the list was treated with respect: one copy was held by the management, one copy by the lodge and one copy was posted in the Institute – but you couldn't go to the club and see a copy.

Durham had a long tradition of trade union solidarity and by the 1890's it was a fully organised county. This was shown in the big strike of 1891 when the men were locked out for refusing to accept a 13% reduction in wages. The Durham men were also part of the Mineworkers Federation of Great Britain and took part in the first national miners' strike – the Minimum Wages Strike of 1912. Chopwell lodge was part of the bigger picture. In the event of trouble at the pit the lodge secretary would first see the official in charge. Failing satisfaction he would see the undermanager after which he would ask for a meeting with the management. At the regular meetings with the colliery manager the case would be outlined. If it was not settled then one of the full time officials of the union came down to meet the agent of the company. Generally, they would effect a settlement especially in Durham where there was a long record of negotiated settlement. Chopwell lodge, especially in later years, always tried to effect a settlement without calling in head office. The managers also preferred to have things settled at the pit because if a manager wanted to stretch something it was better that his betters didn't know.

In Northumberland and Durham there was a joint committee of the owners and the unions to deal with compensation cases which met in the Coal Trade Hall, the headquarters of the Coal Owners Association in Newcastle. The checkweighman at the colliery, a man of substance among the miners who had been elected by them, generally represented the injured man. You had your doctor's report and the coal owners had their doctor's report and they were always in dire contradiction to one another. It was farcical but it was much better than going to the County Court. The union would have a go at the committee with even the flimsiest cases but not the court because of the expense. There was never anyone satisfied. A fella who had suffered grievous injuries down the pit got little compensation. As soon as he was able to limp around they would say that he was fit for light work – but they had no obligation to provide such work. There were tragic cases throughout the village - there were dozens of fellas disabled. Sometimes they got a job at the screens, which was a blow to their pride and future hopes, but at least they retained their house.

Pit Work

The agent for the Consett Iron Company was Mr.Kirkup, who was known locally as 'the tsar'. There were three under-managers. Each had several overmen under his command who were responsible for a district within the pit. Below them in the chain of command were the deputies who were responsible for a flat or a number of working places. The deputies were promoted from the coalface and the overmen were promoted from the deputies – both jobs required responsible men who were able to control output in a particular part of the pit. The relationships between the management and the men below ground was usually very good. Pits couldn't work unless there was the proper sort of co-operation from all sides. The legal position of the men in charge always ensured that there was discipline within the pit which you didn't get in other industries. You didn't require the boss cracking whips. If there was continual antagonism there would be chaos.

In the old days the miners worked the bord and pillar system. Firstly, the main access road known as the mothergate was driven to open up the seam. A succession of roadways known as bords were driven into the face from the mothergate working with the grain of the coal. A pair of hewers worked at each bord or stall. Cross-cuts were driven - called walls - across the grain of the coal leaving pillars to support the roof. The plan of the workings was like a great checkerboard. When the boundary had been reached the men would work back splitting the pillars at regular intervals as they went. This was known as 'comin back brockins'.

In general, the longwall method of mining was practised at Chopwell in the twentieth century. By this system two roadways were driven, one called the tailgate the other the maingate, about one hundred yards apart. A dozen or so men worked as a team at the face which was a hundred yards long. At the beginning of the shift the conveyor belt would be quite close but after two shifts of coal getting the men would be working some six to eight feet away. A special team of conveyor shifters moved the Blackett conveyors forward during the maintenance shift ready for the hewers to start again the next day. The men used to rotate each shift and day by day move down the face so no one was having it canny.

There was no recognised training for miners except the hard school of experience. A boy starting in the pit knew in a shift or two that he was part of the machinery of the pit. He had a job to do and the others depended upon him. Lads progressed from driving to putting and then to hewing as the opportunity arose but this depended upon the pit. In some places progress was so quick that a lad could be putting by the age of sixteen or seventeen. But not at Chopwell the number of putting flats was limited due to the conveyor belts being used. The putter was dependent upon face vacancies to become a hewer and he moved forward on seniority or length of service at the pit. Chopwell was a place where there was little change in personnel – in fact the fellas who were here were here all their lives. This meant that the chances of getting on hewing were slight and you could be putting until you were in your thirties. While putting at the face a lad would get the odd chance to do a bit of filling and learn the hewer's job.

The hewers bought their own picks but at Chopwell the drills were provided. They formed conveyor sets which were groups of twelve marras working a particular face. The team was formed by mutual arrangement amongst the men. At one time the management would have liked to pick the teams to work the face for its lifetime. But we would have none of that in the Durham pits – the conveyor flats were cavilled quarterly in the same way as the single cavils. Some flats were easier and more productive than others, therefore it was only fair that they should have their cavils so that one set of men were not having it all good and another set all bad. The formation of the teams of marras was part and parcel of the cavilling system – it was a necessary preliminary before the cavils were drawn. The teams were paid by 'the weight of mineral gotten' as the Act says. The men were paid as a team and they would settle with the deputy the price of the job at the pit face. On payday the men took turns at paying out to their marras according to the number of shifts they had worked. The system was very democratic – everyone was an equal member of the team.

The deputy would go into the pit an hour before the men to inspect the flats to see if they were in a workable condition and he would come back to his kist in time for the men coming into the pit. The kist was the deputy's tool chest which also served as an office desk. The kist was designated in law as the meeting place where the men had to congregate underground before going to their work places. The deputy would give them instructions before they were allowed at the face. The hewer's first job was kerving or undercutting to enable a cleat of coal to fall down from the roof. This was

The winding engine at No. 3 Pit Chopwell at the time of its installation in 1910

done by hewing away with a pick at the base of the seam. In a naked light pit like Chopwell, where there was no fear of explosive gases, the next job was blasting. The men used to collect their explosives, which they bought themselves at the powder magazine on the surface, and take it in-bye. Black powder was used. It was made into squibs which were very sophisticated fireworks. The hewer drilled a hole and packed in the black powder. A pricker was inserted and then they stemmed the hole with clay. It was illegal to use anything else but there was never any clay available so we used clarts. They withdrew the pricker which left a hole through to the powder into which they inserted a squib. When they lit it, it shot into the hole and ignited the powder. There were any amount of accidents with that stuff: that's why you see so many men with blue patches on their faces.

It is impossible to imagine the working conditions in the pit unless you've been underground especially in the thin seams where a man could be hewing coal on his side in eighteen inches headroom. Bad air could be a problem but generally the ventilation was good at Chopwell. The men used to say that the pit hadn't sufficient water. If there had been a good deal more water falling down they would have done more about trying to get rid of it. But because it was just trickling it wasn't worth having better pumps.

The hewers shifted the coal onto the Blackett conveyors which fed into tubs in the mothergate or maingate. The drivers brought the tubs out from the mothergate into a landing using ponies. This was a siding with one side for full tubs and one side for empty tubs. From this landing a 35 horse power haulage engine with a main and tail rope ran the tubs in sets of fifteen or twenty according to the run of the ground to the main landings. There were a few self-acting inclines where the weight of the full tubs descending hauled the empties up. A larger haulage engine of 150 h.p. brought the tubs to the principal landing, the last one before the shaft which was a mile or so out-bye. The main haulage engine of 500 h.p. was situated near the shaft and hauled sets of sixty tubs. It served six districts at different levels by means of drifts from one seam down to the next.

At the shaft bottom the onsetter was responsible for accepting men into the mine or sending men to the surface in the main cages. He also took the empty tubs out of the cages. The men behind the shaft, the 'hangers on' as they were called, put the full tubs into the cages. At the surface the coal was fed into tipplers and graded into three sizes before going to the screens where the boys and men picked the stones off the belts. The boys started work at five o'clock in the morning or one o'clock in the afternoon and worked an eight hour shift. They were on piece work and paid by the box of stone. For five shifts they earned 9/6d. The main hazard was the coal dust which was terrible especially on the belts with small coals. Some of the older boys worked on loading timber into trucks to send in-by or on tipping stone out over the stoneheap.

At the pithead there was a large backup force of fitters, electricians, joiners, blacksmiths and saddlers to keep the colliery in operation. The joiners were responsible for repairing the trap doors underground, for repairing tubs, for making crackets and shoulder boards for the hewers. They were responsible for the shafts. Every six month, six foot was cut off the socket end of the wire rope and sent to the manufacturers who tested the strength of the rope, either passing or condemning it. At Chopwell, the cage ropes were changed every three and a half years. A lot of the haulage machinery was driven by electricity so the electricians were also important members of the team. There was a power station which fed 5,000 volts A.C. into the underground sub-station where it was transformed down to 650 volts for the pit machinery. The power station also supplied direct current for the house lighting and street lighting in Chopwell village and for the electric cars on the Whittonstall railway.

The Coke Ovens.

There were four sets of bee-hive coke ovens at Chopwell. The very tall building beside No.1 shaft was the hopper. Below that, on ground level, coal, particularly from the Five Quarter Seam which was good coking coal, was fed into a crusher and then transported by a conveyor up to the top of the hopper. There was a tunnel in from each bench of coke ovens for the coal car to get in, get filled up, come along the bank of coal ovens it was feeding and fill the empty oven. The coal car was an electric truck powered from an overhead line. It had two hoppers and was capable of filling an oven with one load. At the ovens, the leveller had to level the coal in the oven with a long rake so that it was tightly packed and it would all burn together. He then bricked up the front of the oven and lifted the dampers on each side. The heat from the ovens on each side which were burning would ignite the coal which burned for three days.

The drawer's job was a very hot and arduous one. It was always one of the lads' job to go and seek water for the cokemen. He used to collect their gallon cans, some had barley in the bottom and some cold tea leaves. You just kept filling the cans up – they drank a tremendous amount. To empty the coke oven the drawer first took one brick out and played a hose on the coke. It used a terrific amount of water. There was also a range of pipes on top of the ovens to quench the coke. The cokemen were on piece work and as soon as the coke was cool enough – although still as hot as hell – they would start bring it out onto the coke bench. To begin with they had short rakes but as the job got further in they had great big rakes hung on a pulley. At the end of the coke bench was a gulley which, because it was at a lower level, made loading easier. The fillers loaded the coke into trucks with great wide gripes which were like a garden fork but much bigger. The filler filled with his gripe until the trucks were loaded. The coke was shipped down the waggonway to Derwenthaugh and shipped for export. Some went to Consett Iron Works. When the new coke ovens were opened at Derwenthaugh in 1928 production at Chopwell was reduced until the ovens finally stopped work in 1941.

Conclusion

This account of Chopwell in the early to mid twentieth century is typical of village life throughout the northern coalfield. It is easy to romanticise life in the colliery villages especially after visiting the neat row of cottages preserved at Beamish Museum where the smell of bread cooking in front of a roaring open coal fire arouses memories of an idyllic past. There were however aspects of life in these communities, as in all communities, which were less appealing. William Patterson's account of the struggles to establish Primitive Methodism in the mining districts contains many examples of the work of devout and respectable members of society. However, his writings also contain many examples of the activities of the less attractive elements in society. When the evangelist William Clowes, for example, visited the Bishop Auckland area including 'notorious Cockfield', in 1820, he noted 'centres of gamblers were broken up; confirmed gamblers burnt their dice, cards and books of enchantment; drunkards, hopeless, incurable sots were freed from the tyranny of fiery appetite; pugilists, practised and professional, cock fighters of terrible experience, turned from their brutalities'. In the 1860's Ryhope Colliery 'had a bad reputation for drunkenness, gambling, fighting and dog racing'. After the visit of the preachers 'among the converts were the best public-house fiddler, the most popular bar-room singer, the leading boxer and drunkards and 'dog men' of every degree'. In 1867, at Ouston, 'many of the leading blackguards in the locality turned from their evil ways'. The church often received assistance from the mine owners for, as one owner commented, 'I will help you for your preachers have done so much good amongst our men that we have much less to subscribe for policemen and for trials of misconduct'. One Methodist minister at Ashington in 1936 harangued the gamblers declaring 'I loath the Greyhound Racing Track, with its hideous totalisator, its crowd of simple greedy fools who prey and are preyed upon by the Gambling Vampire'.

However, gambling, like alcohol, taken in moderation, was a pleasure which many working men enjoyed without destroying their lives and bringing misery to their families. The tanner accumulator placed with the (then illegal) bookmaker was the highlight of many a man's working day. In the larger mining communities the workingmen's clubs played an important part in the social life of the village although there was often a division between club and chapel. Ashington, in 1914, claimed to be the largest mining community in the world and had 15 churches – it also had 17 workingmen's clubs. There was also often a division between the supporters of the Colliery Institute and the club. The founders of the social clubs claimed to provide places for fellowship and good comradeship which facilitated social drinking and condemned drunkenness. They certainly contributed greatly to the social life of the villages through providing entertainment; their support of cricket and football teams; their sponsorship of flower, vegetable and leek shows; their organisation of day trips outside the area; and their provision of assistance in time of need. Many lives were enriched by membership of a workingman's club.

The mining communities were divided in another respect. There was a division between the management and the workers, between the gaffers and the men. Promotion from the ranks was not unusual but even after nationalisation there was a feeling that the worker had gone over to the other side. Also, although the vast majority of men in the villages worked at the pit, they did not all earn the same amount of money. There was a considerable difference between the income of a hewer working an easy cavil and the unskilled men labouring on the surface jobs. Some had to accept this inferior work after injury in the pit and the loss of status was keenly felt.

Like the civilian settlements around Roman forts and some of the region's medieval villages, several colliery villages have ceased to exist as communities following the closure of their colliery and they are now part of the archaeological heritage of Northumberland and Durham. Colliery villages such as Bigges Main and Netherton, North Seaton Colliery and Marsden have returned to grassland. Others have been subsumed by major developments such as the building of the new towns at Killingworth and Washington.

The scattered and diverse nature of Gosforth colliery housing is a reminder that the standard of housing for the miners varied greatly. The improvement in housing during the nineteenth century is graphically shown in Steve Martin's photograph of South Row Bedlington in 1968. Embedded in the late nineteenth century colliery row (which is now demolished) are the remains of a pit cottage built in 1839.

Chopwell was a very politicised mining community earning the title of 'Little Moscow' because of the enthusiasm for socialism in the community and especially because of the activities of miners' union leaders during the General Strike of 1926. However, in other respects the account of life in a colliery village in the early to mid twentieth century is typical of northern coalfield at large. The dominance of the pit in the daily life of the community, the physical nature of the work down the mine, the importance of the union, the difficulties facing women trying to manage the home, the separation of the roles of men and women in the community, the importance of the Methodist Church, Co-operative Store, the Club and the Miners Lodge in the social life of the community – all are shared in common with other mining villages. Despite all the hardships, at the heart of village life was the sense of family, comradeship and community and this is captured in the works of two northern pitmen. The writings of Sid Chaplin and the paintings of Norman Cornish express a great love of humanity: despite all the dehumanising influences of mining life, it is this humanity of the mining communities which is triumphant. Sid Chaplin's poem 'Hame', written in 1943, captures something of the miner's love for their community and especially the people within:

> Sight of the green smoke-flecked valley,
> With the mist tinged mountains beyond the moors.
> Sight of you, my own love,
> And the light in your eyes for me.

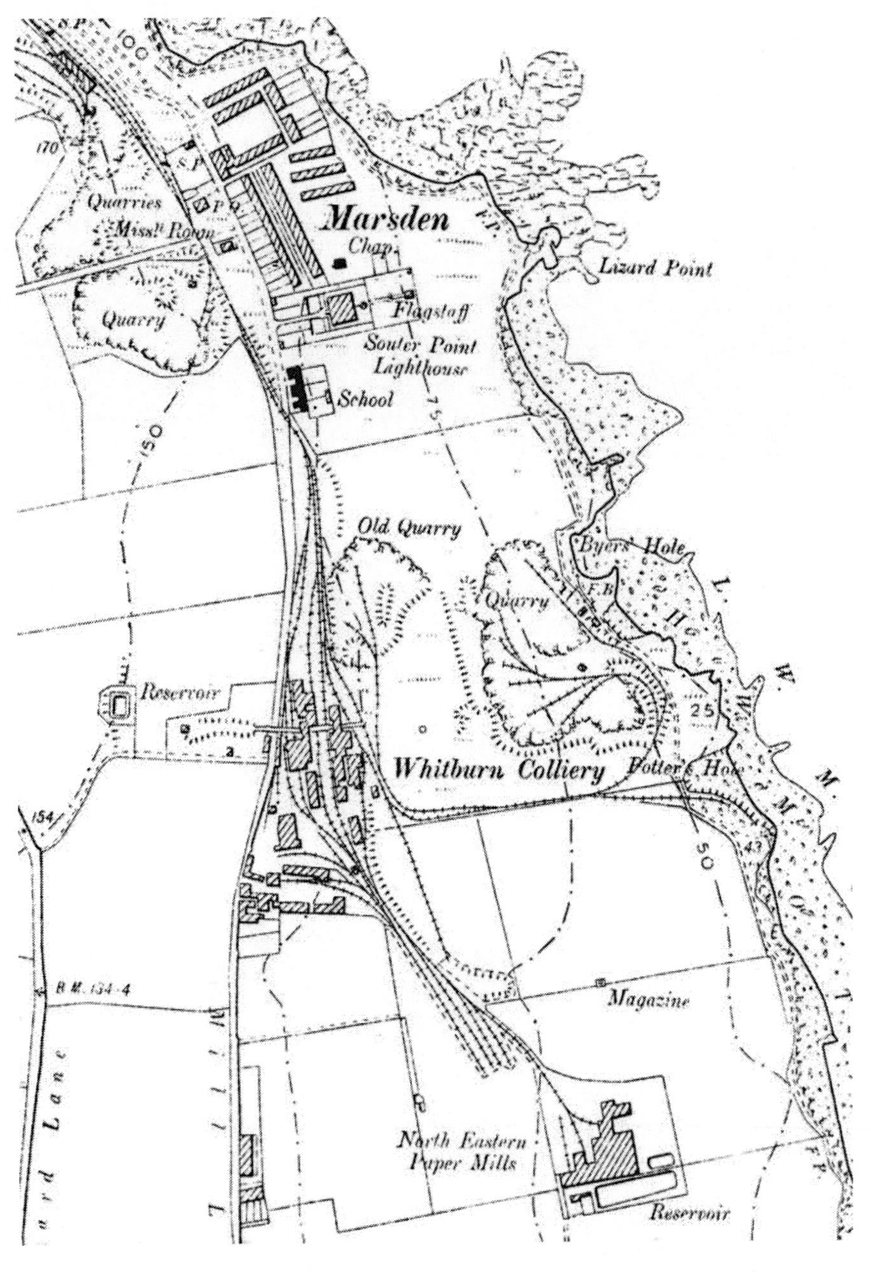

Marsden 1898

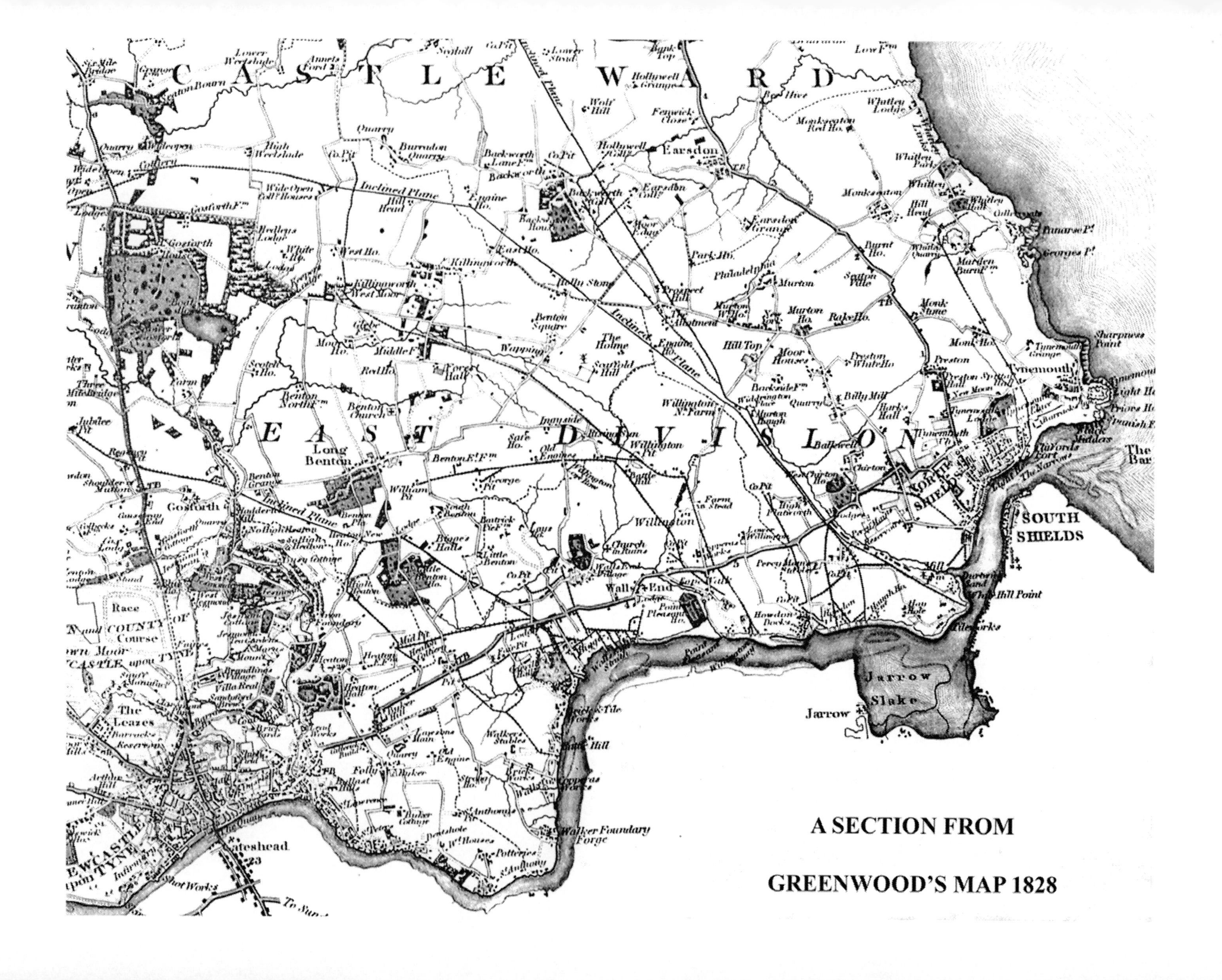

A SECTION FROM

GREENWOOD'S MAP 1828

Chapter Five – Glimpses of the Lost Railways of Newcastle

> *'Clap hands for daddy coming down the waggonway*
> *With a pocket full of pennies for Geordie everyday'.*

William Thomas, the colliery engineer for Denton Colliery, read a paper to the Literary and Philosophical Society of Newcastle on the 11th February 1800 in which he proposed building a cast-iron railway between Newcastle and Hexham which would carry not only coal and other freight but also people. This is the first recorded suggestion that passengers could travel by rail. On the September 27th 1825, this idea was put into practise when the Stockton and Darlington Railway was opened and the world's first public railway, built to the design of another Tyneside engineer George Stephenson, began operations. Within a decade railway lines were carrying people between Liverpool and Manchester and Birmingham and London. Also, the first cross-country railway linking Carlisle with Newcastle was in service. On 21st May 1839, the Newcastle and Carlisle Railway Company transferred its terminus from Redheugh in Gateshead to the Forth in Newcastle; and on 22nd June, the Newcastle and North Shields Railway Company opened its passenger service to Manors. These were the first public railways into the city.

However, for over two hundred years prior to these important events, waggonways had carried coal from the region's coal mines to staiths on the banks of the rivers Blyth, Tyne and Wear and these early railways are the focus of this chapter. Before the building of the Newcastle and North Shields Railway, the company had fought battles with the landowners including the Duke of Northumberland, who feared that the railway would divert traffic from the waggonways with the consequent loss of revenue to the landowners. William Tomlinson, the historian of the North Eastern Railway, noted that the line from North Shields crossed nine waggonways in the first 3.5 miles of the route. The North Shields line is now part of the Tyneside Metro and evidence of these early railways can be seen from the

Cartouche from Casson's Map of 1801

carriage windows. From Walkergate Station eastwards, the railway was built on a high embankment to enable the company to construct bridges over the waggonways which the railway was forced to cross. Although these early railways have been closed for many years, the openings in the railway embankment survive and serve as a reminder of the lost colliery waggonways.

In 1863, the local historian Richard Welford's wrote enthusiastically about Seghill, a mining community in South East Northumberland, commenting that 'wherever we look we see collieries in action; pairs of wheels revolving in opposite directions; titanic pumping beams majestically raising with their loads of water from the very bowels of the earth'. This description of the activity at the pit conveys the feelings of excitement, pride and awe which heavy industry invoked and could have applied to the coalfield in general when the waggonway, the subject of the popular children's rhyme, was everywhere to be seen. By the beginning of the twenty first century, the landscape had changed dramatically both at Seghill and within the coalfield at large. Considering the impact that over six hundred years of coal mining had upon the North East of England surprisingly little remains to be seen today outside the museums and the preserved railway lines. However, the rich collections of archive material relating to mining within the region enable the local historian of today to recreate a picture of this lost industry and its railways which were a vital part of the transport infrastructure of the coalfield.

The principal source of information for this chapter is the archives within library of the North of England Institute of Mining and Mechanical Engineers. The maps and working drawings of the colliery engineers provide an invaluable and often unique source of information about the Great Northern Coalfield. Much use has already been made of these maps in the previous chapters where plans of Heaton, Longbenton, Byker and Walker have been reproduced. In this section the archive is used to illustrate the landscape of the area now known as Newcastle during the period 1750 – 1850 with the particular purpose of discovering the routes of some of the lost railways of the region. At this time the city of Newcastle was still largely confined within the city walls and the area now comprising Newcastle was mainly farmland in which was scattered the country houses of the large landowners most of whom were involved in the coal trade.

There are several general maps of the coalfield which provide an overview roughly every decade from Gibson's map of 1788, to Casson's map of 1801, then Galloway's map of 1812, Greenwood's map of 1828, and finally William Bell's map of 1845. These maps are essential reference material and show the transitory nature of some of the early waggonways. They are referred to throughout the text and sections have been reproduced where appropriate. The early Ordnance Survey maps, dating from the mid nineteenth century, are invaluable for tracing old waggonways many of which were derelict when the first surveys were made. However, because a comprehensive collection of early Ordnance Survey maps of the North East is available within the local libraries and record offices, and on the internet, these maps are used only occasionally to illustrate this chapter, despite their value to the industrial archaeologist. Rather the space has been used to reproduce some of the more rare estate maps originating from the eighteenth and early nineteenth century. It is hoped that the inspiration of this small sample will lead others to use the resources of the Institute to research their locality and add to the history of the coalfield. Some of the other archive material has been used in an attempt to provide an outline history of mining activities within the area of modern Newcastle but much more detailed research like the study of Heaton in Chapter Two is needed before a comprehensive history can be written.

The special collections within the Institute, especially those of John Bell and John Watson, also provide insights into the social history of the coalfield. For example, a notice placed in a local paper by Elizabeth Stephenson, a miner's wife from Walker, provides an illuminating comment upon marital relations in 1811. It reads: 'my husband, having thought proper to advertise me as one whose Debts he will no longer be answerable for, I am under the necessity of stating to the Public that, owing to his repeated Debaucheries and otherwise perfidious Conduct, I have been compelled to leave his house'. Accidents on the waggonways also appear, often as coroners reports, such as the one at Walbottle in December 1844 when John Reid, the gardener of the viewer Mr. Oliver, 'was walking across an inclined railway leading from Duke Pit at Walbottle to Lemington when, being rather dull of hearing, some coal wagons that were passing knocked him down'; and on the Fawdon waggonway where John Charlton 'having got upon the wagons was incautiously standing up while they were running and passing under a bridge his head came in violent contact with the arch' with fatal consequences. There is even evidence of an early animal rights movement in the clamour caused in the local press by the rumour that redundant pit ponies had been burnt alive at Fawdon Colliery.

Heaton

A detailed study of the collieries in Heaton and their waggonways has been provided in Chapter Two. The first railway was the waggonway from Low Heaton through Walker to Wincomblee. This main way was also used by the branches from Heaton Banks Colliery until its closure in 1745. The Longbenton Colliery, which like Heaton belonged to the Grand Allies, joined the Heaton waggonway in Walker and the colliery used this route until its closure in 1766. The routes adopted for the later Heaton Main Colliery, initially via the Lawson's Main waggonway to St. Anthony's, and then linking up with the Kenton and Coxlodge waggonway to Wallsend, have already been discussed.

Walker

The early history of mining in Walker royalty is obscure but borings were being made in the early eighteenth century to assess the accessibility of the coal seams. It is likely that William Brown of Throckley, perhaps the most famous of the mid eighteenth century viewers, was in charge of the winning of Walker Colliery at the Fair Pit in about 1753. The West Engine Pit was sunk 100 fathoms to the High Main seam in 1766. This was closely followed by the Ann Pit and in 1770 by the East Engine Pit. By the late eighteenth century, Walker had become one of the most important collieries in the coalfield and was the site of several important technological developments. In 1758, two rotary mine ventilators were operated by converting the reciprocating motion of the pumping engine into rotary motion. In 1763, William Brown supplied four boilers to provide sufficient steam for the pumps and this was an early example of the use of multiple boilers. When Gabriel Jars visited the colliery in 1765 he observed that the miners worked only six to seven hours per shift and noted the uniqueness of the horse gin which was driven by eight horses and could wind a corf containing 6cwt of coal from a depth of 600 feet in 2 minutes. The gin was replaced in 1769 by a machine driven by both steam and horses and this innovation doubled the drawing capacity. This in turn was replaced by a water gin which used the water drawn from the mine by the pumps to power a double water wheel which drove the winding apparatus. A rotary winding engine was erected at the colliery in 1784 and in 1796 one of James Watt's new steam pumping engines was installed. By 1795, only the pillars were left in the High Main seam and John Barnes, who had succeeded William Brown as the viewer, introduced the practice of robbing the pillars. Walker was one of the first collieries to use cast iron to tub the shafts also in about 1795. In 1801, the Caroline Pit was sunk 963 feet to the Low Main seam but the coal was found to be unsatisfactory.

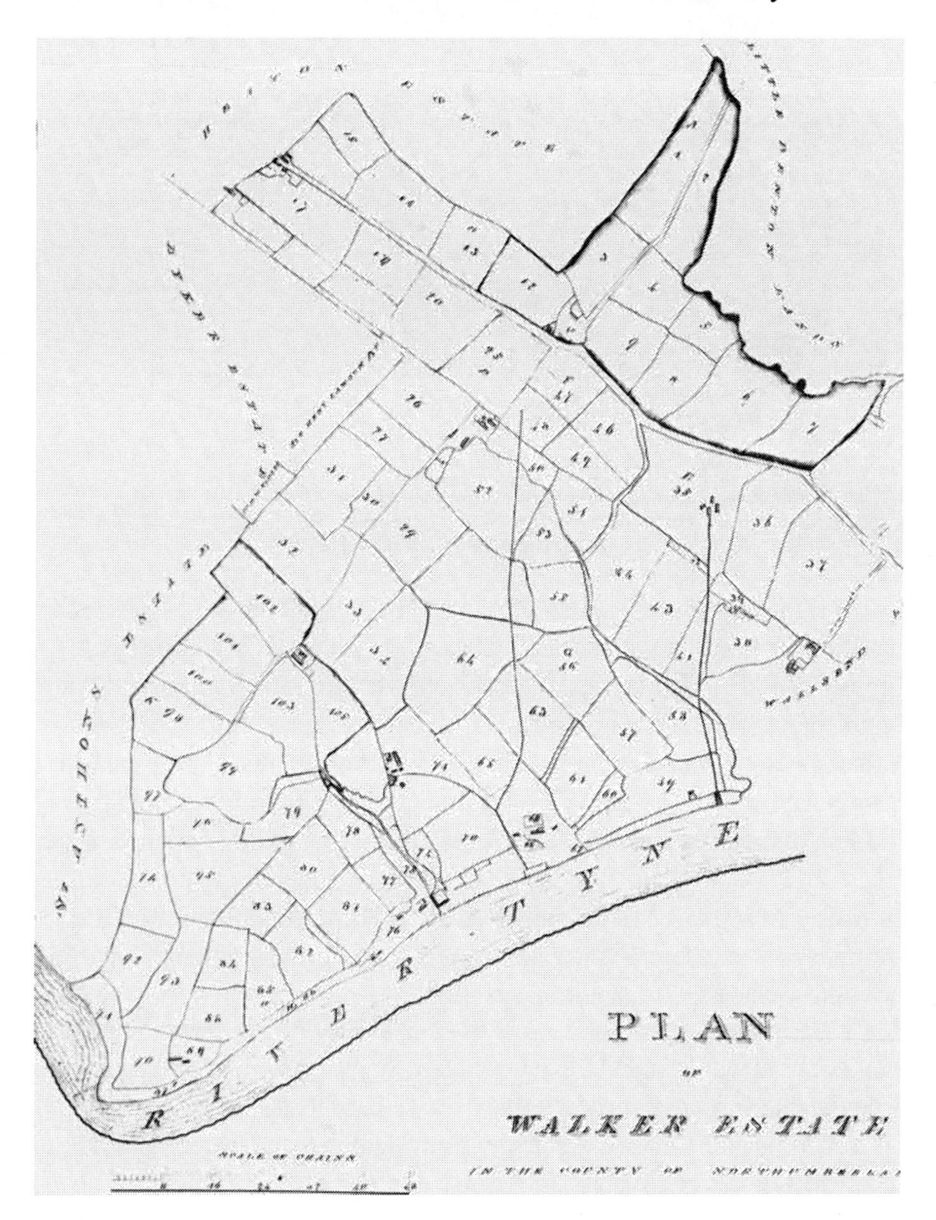

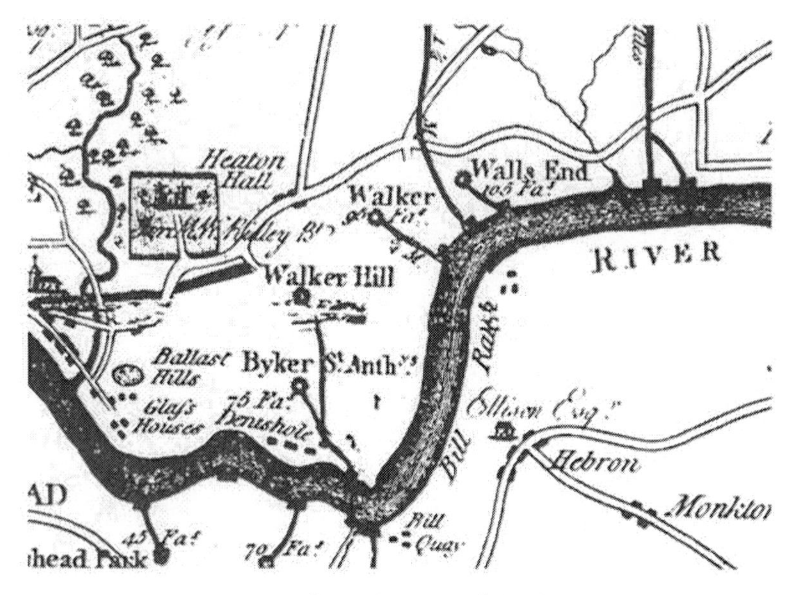

Gibson's Map of 1788

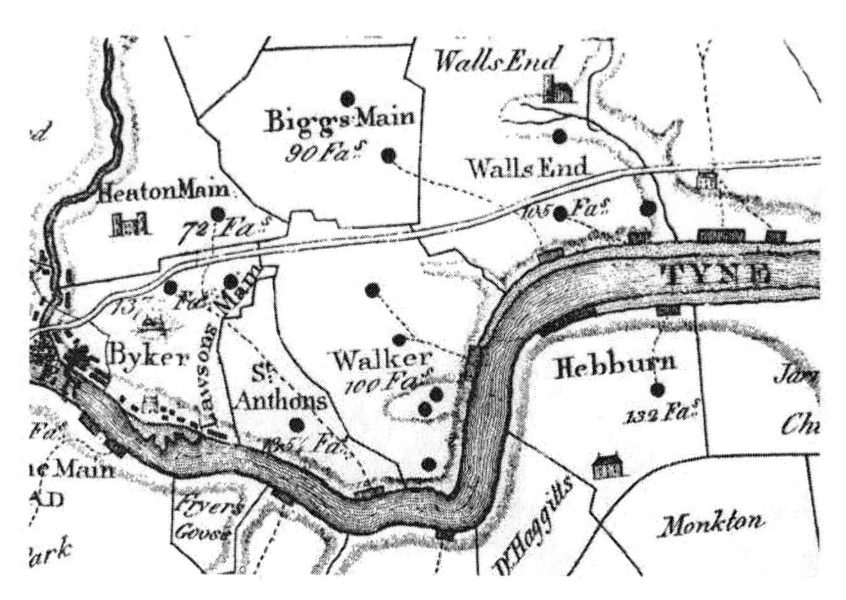

Casson's Map of 1801

By 1811, the High Main was exhausted and because of the difficulties with firedamp the mine was abandoned. There were several sales during the summer of 1811 offering eighty underground horses, one Boulton and Watt steam engine of twenty horse power and four coal keels 'the property of Walker Colliery' onto the market. The invention of the safety lamp enabled the mine to be re-opened in 1817 and it continued in production until the flooding of the Tyne Basin in 1857. The colliery was again re-opened in the 1860's and operated first under N.G.Lambert and then the Walker Coal Company. In 1914, the Beaumont, Bensham, Brockwell, Busty and Low Main seams were being worked and 1,303 men were employed. However, the colliery was finally abandoned in 1920.

Walker estate was bought by Newcastle Corporation in somewhat dubious circumstances in 1715 and it was used by Richard Ridley to thwart Cotesworth's plans for a waggonway from Heaton to the River Tyne. The matter was finally resolved by the High Court and a line was built to Wincomblee in the 1720s. The line of this waggonway from Heaton Banks Colliery, which was joined by the waggonway from Longbenton Colliery in the 1740's, is marked on Isaac Thompson's plan of Walker dated 1745 (see p 38). The Heaton waggonway, built circa 1725, and the branch from Longbenton, built circa 1745, follow an entirely different route to Wincomblee from the waggonway serving the Walker pits.

Heaton Banks Colliery closed in 1745 and Longbenton Colliery in 1766 which dates the plan of Walker (p105) to after 1766. The West Engine Pit sunk in 1762 is marked while the East Engine Pit sunk in 1770 is not marked. Thus, the plan was drawn between 1766 and 1770. Shields Road from Byker Hill to Wallsend High Street West and the road to Longbenton (now Benfield Road), are the only highways shown. To the south, the line of Hadrian's Wall formed the boundary between Walker and Byker royalties; the Wall can be traced in the straight line of hedgerows past the village of Old Walker, Stotts House Farm and on to Carville House in Wallsend. Walker Dene runs from Scrogg House eastwards past the West Engine Pit and the Ann Pit to the river. Further north two streams join to form another dene, Stott's Gill, which formed the boundary between Walker and Wallsend as it approached the river. There are two waggonways marked. The northerly one from the Fair Pit runs south-west across the dene to a staith. Later, the site was occupied by Walker Oil Mill and the Neptune shipyard. This line was built in 1753 for Walker Colliery and today it is remembered in the name Oil Mill Road. A second waggonway is shown running from an empty field to the north of Walker village, which was later to be the site of the Gosforth Pit, to staiths at Wincomblee, where it is joined by a branch from West Engine Pit. These staiths are downstream from the site of the earlier staiths built for Heaton Colliery.

The later history of the waggonways of Walker is complicated by changes as new pits were sunk and production was moved from one pit to another but much of this history can be followed on the early Ordnance Survey maps on which most of the waggonways are marked as earthworks. In 1770, the East Pit was sunk on the south side of Stott's Gill about 180 yards south west of where the waggonway from the Fair Pit crosses the burn. A branch line was constructed to the railway line from the Fair Pit and this waggonway linked the East Pit to the northern staith. This staith was closed by 1801 when Casson's map was published. There is no line from the East Pit marked on Greenwood's map. However, an alternative route for the East Pit running from the southern staith past the East Pit and on to connect with a line heading towards Wallsend is shown as abandoned on the first edition Ordnance Survey map. An advertisement dated September 1839 records the 'Railway leading from Walker Colliery East Pit Eastwards past Carville and Wallsend, to the Shipping Place adjoining Gosforth Colliery Spouts'. Whether this is the route marked as abandoned by the Ordnance Survey or another route which left no trace on the first edition is a matter of conjecture.

Curiously, the southern waggonway and staith are not marked on Gibson's plan of 1788 but they do re-appear on Casson's map of 1801 which shows the line serving the Delight Pit and the Gosforth Pit. The West Engine Pit, the Ann Pit and to the south the Jane Pit (sunk in 1790) are marked but without connections to the railway. Galloway's railway map of 1812 shows the line serving only the West Pit, the Ann Pit and the Jane Pit. A rich supply of brine from Walker Colliery (probably the Jane Pit) was the reason for John Losh, the cousin of the owner William Losh, establishing an alkali works in 1798 to produce caustic soda. The Jane Pit was also ideally situated to supply coal to the neighbouring iron works founded by William Losh, Thomas Wilson and Thomas Bell. Walker Iron Works was one of the early manufacturers of iron rails for the waggonways. It was later connected by rail to the Jane Pit.

Greenwood's map of 1828 shows major changes in the southern waggonway (p 102). The line runs from the staith to the Delight Pit, the Gosforth Pit and further north to the Henry Pit. A branch runs eastward from the Gosforth Pit, via the Fair Pit, to a second staith in Wallsend; and there is another branch from the Delight Pit which joins the first branch east of the Fair Pit. Most of this route can be traced on the first edition Ordnance Survey map by which time the railway was derelict. Then the only railways operational were the lines connecting the Jane Pit, Ann Pit and West Engine Pit to the river at Wincomblee which served Walker Colliery until it closure in 1920.

Field 27 on the plan of Walker is an area of great interest to the railway detective. The waggonway map of Heaton dated 1805 (see p 55) shows an 'old waggonway' running from Lawson's Main Colliery. It passes through the land marked field 27 on the plan of Walker estate dated 1766 – 70. Did the railway go straight on to Wallsend or did it turn south and join the Walker line heading for Wincomblee – that is the mystery? Fifty years later the Ordnance Survey map shows an 'old wagonway' running from the south east boundary of field 27 on the same alignment and heading eastwards.

Byker

Byker Colliery was one of the leading enterprises of the early eighteenth century and the visit of Sir John Clerk to see the new fire engines has been discussed in Chapter Two. The numerous pits in the area between Shields Road and the East Coast Main Line railway are shown on the map on page 9. Whether there was a waggonway for this colliery is not known. From the middle of the eighteenth century Richard Ridley's interest lay in Sir John Lawson's lands to the south of his own property on the escarpment leading down to the river at St. Peter's. This colliery is shown in the map opposite and the earlier Byker Colliery and Heaton Colliery are shown as drowned. There is evidence to suggest that there was a waggonway operating to St. Peter's staith from 1743 but was replaced by 1751. William Brown was active in building pumping engines at Byker and in 1769 there were six in situ. The engine at the Success Pit, the High Engines and the engines at Dent's Hole (not named but marked near the Chance Pit) are shown on the map. A Boulton and Watt engine was installed in 1778, once again placing Byker at the forefront of pumping technology which was indicative of the great difficulties which the colliery faced from water, being situated on the edge of the Tyne Basin.

The later eighteenth century Lawson's Main Colliery is not marked on the map but the land is shown as 'Part of Byker Grounds Unwrought'. The colliery was probably developed in the 1770's with initially a railway link eastwards through Walker shown as 'old Waggon Way' on the map of the Heaton railway dated 1805. The route was changed to run south to St. Anthony's Quay and this waggonway is shown on Gibson's map, Walker Hill being an alternative name for Lawson's Main. The line was shared with Heaton Colliery from 1792 which is shown on Casson's plan (p106). There were two pits – the Delight and the Recovery. The Delight Pit was sunk 72 fathoms to the High Main. Later the Low Main was reached at 131 fathoms but was not developed. Lawson's Main closed in 1811 following the flooding of the mine when Felling Colliery ceased pumping from the High Main seam. Several decades later there was a small landsale colliery named Lawson's Main which is marked on the first Ordnance Survey map on an entirely different site further west.

St. Anthony's Colliery was won at the Farewell Pit in 1769 where the High Main seam was 74.5 fathoms from the surface. A new machine for drawing coals invented by James Storey was tried in November 1786. Nearby, in 1787 the Nightingale Pit was sunk 123 fathoms to the Low Main. The colliery is shown with a waggonway link on Gibson's map but not on Casson's. This pit and the High or Restoration Pit were the main shafts of the colliery which was operated by George Johnson, John Johnson and William Rowe. George Johnson was prosecuted for trespassing below the river into the royalty of Felling but eventually agreement was reached and the map on page 9 shows St. Anthony's Colliery mining part of Felling royalty. Attempts were made to develop the Low Main in 1805 without success and the colliery was abandoned in 1815. It was offered for sale in December 1830.

The High Main seam at St. Lawrence's Colliery on Corporation lands in the west of Byker was worked in the eighteenth century but was drowned. The building of the Friar's Goose pumping engine encouraged the viewer John Watson and his partner Robert Todd to take the lease of St. Lawrence Colliery in 1831. The Low Main seam 5'10" high was found to be in excellent condition and on Wednesday 7th August 1833 'the neighbourhood of Newcastle was enlivened by the firing of guns, and other tokens of joy, at the loading of the first vessel from the low main seam at St. Lawrence Colliery, near Newcastle, called Picton Main'. The workings extended under the river and westwards beneath Sandgate and underground inclined planes were used to transport the coal in square tubs to the winding shaft. This was one of the first collieries to replace corves with tubs and to fit cages in the shaft. On the surface another inclined plane 400 yards long carried the tubs to the staith. Working conditions were difficult especially in the Bensham seam and there was the ever present threat of accidents. The wasteman, James Richardson, reported to the Commissioners in 1842 that there are 'places here as long as 200 yards

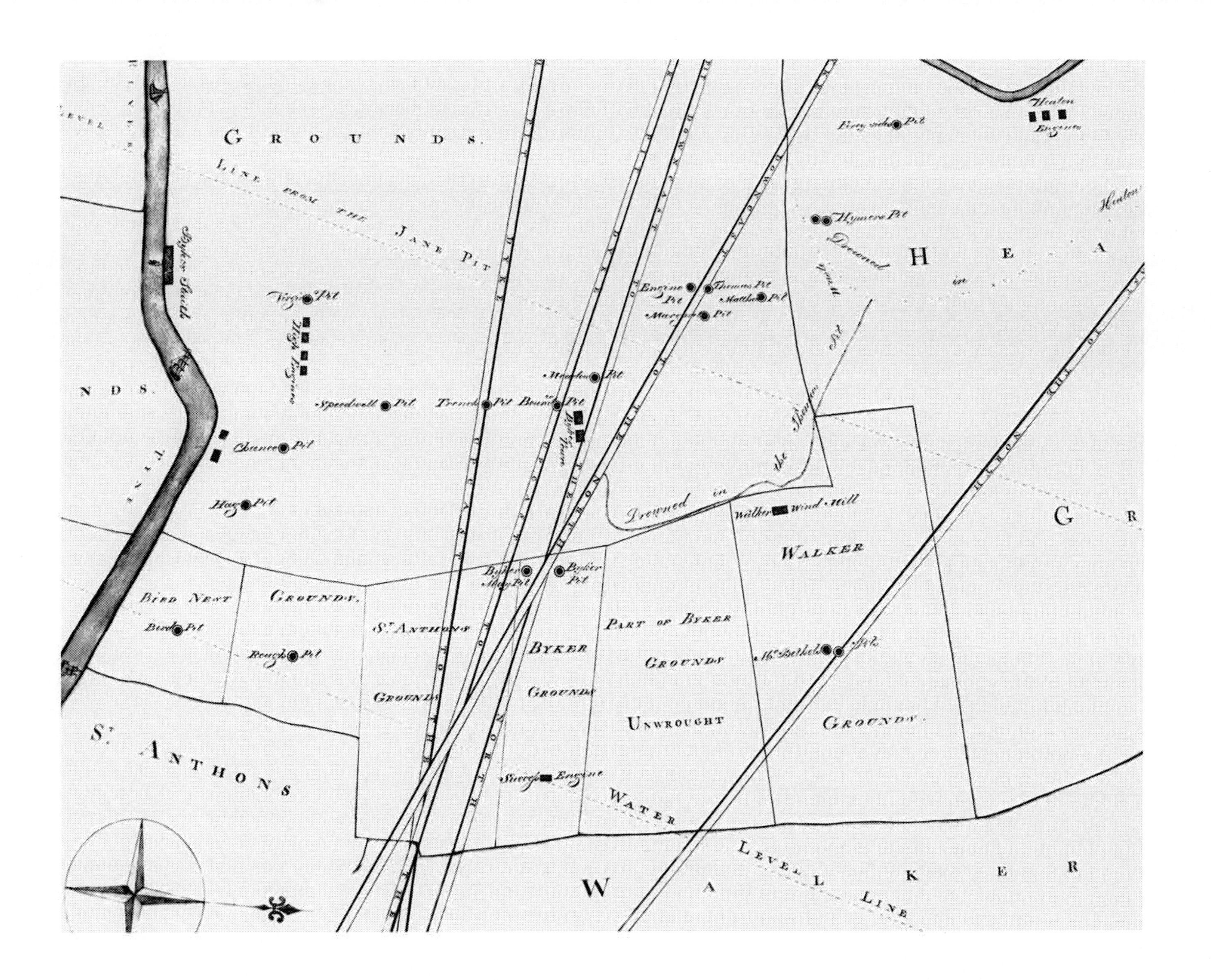
GROUNDS.
LINE FROM THE JANE PIT
Speedwell Pit
Chance Pit
Engine Pit
Thomas Pit
Drowned in the
Walker Wind Mill
WALKER
BIRD NEST GROUNDS
Bird Pit
Rough Pit
St. ANTHONS GROUNDS
Byker Pit
BYKER GROUNDS
PART OF BYKER GROUNDS UNWROUGHT
WALKER GROUNDS
St. ANTHONS
WATER LEVEL LINE
WALKER

where the height for the hewers is not more than 26 inches'. An explosion took place on 24th November 1834 killing John Gray, Thomas Hedley and his cousin Robert Watson which left three wives and sixteen children without support. The colliery was closed by the mid nineteenth century. The coals are sometimes referred to as Picton's Main on lading bills one of which provides this interesting engraving of the colliery (page28).

Shieldfield

How the landscape can change is dramatically shown in the map of Shieldfield Colliery which dates to about 1840. The estate to the east of central Newcastle had been the scene of mining since the Middle Ages. The High Main seam outcropped in Shieldfield and as late as 1806 an advert for the sale of the estate referred to the 'MINES, MINERALS and QUARRIES OF COAL within or under the said Shield Field'. The nineteenth century mine with its three pits is shown on the map. The

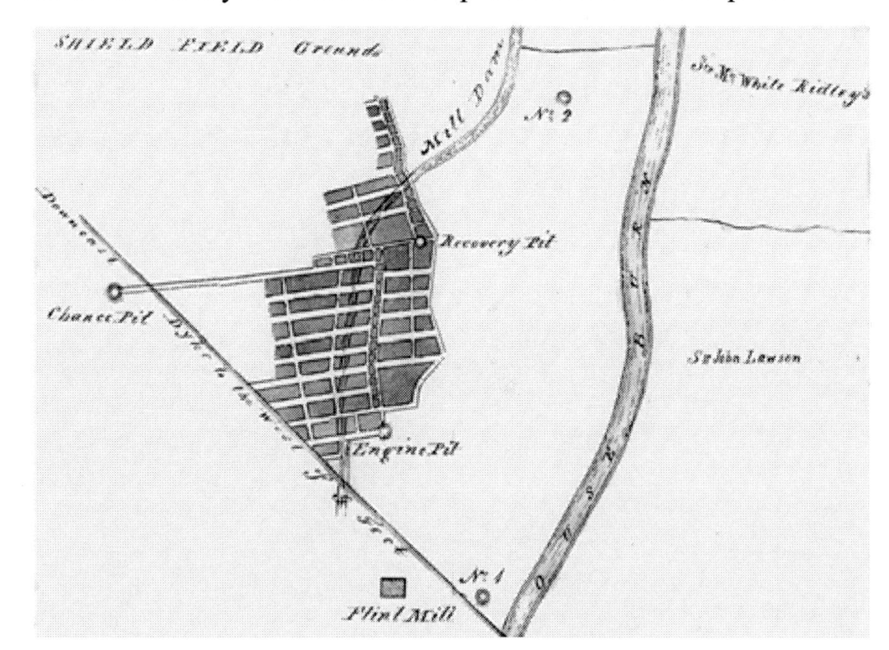

Shieldfield Colliery

advertisement also remarked that 'the intended Waggon-way from East Kenton to Coxlodge Collieries, to the River Tyne, will pass through' which was included as an incentive to prospective purchasers who would enjoy certain and tentale rents from the users of the waggonway. Unfortunately, Kenton and Coxlodge owners selected a different route taking their waggonway five miles upstream to Wallsend.

A mill stream from the Ouseburn runs above the mine to a flint mill which produced raw material for the pottery and glassmaking industries by grinding flint brought in as ballast by the colliers. The mouth of the Ouseburn was an important centre of both these industries and the site of large ballast hills. Other flint mills were powered by the burn upstream at Deep Dene House and Millfield House. There was also a steam driven flint mill on the opposite bank which worked until 1898. The mill shown on the map was situated between Byker Bridge and the railway viaduct and was part of Stepney pottery.

The Shieldfield Colliery was abandoned in the 1770s but was re-won by Matthias Dunn in February 1838. The local newspaper noted 'the workmen amounting to upwards of fifty were regaled with a handsome supper' by the owner Thomas James. The enterprise seems to have been short lived for on Tuesday the 24th May 1842 at eleven o'clock 'An Assortment of COLLIERY MATERIALS, comprising Engines, Boilers. A Weighing Machine, Tram Ways, Pumps, Wooden Work Shops, a Coal Staith, Timber of various Sorts, and other Colliery Materials' were to be sold by auction. Apart from the reference to 'tram ways' there is no indication that Shieldfield Colliery had a railway. However, the underground waggonway from Spital Tongues ran through Shieldfield to the River Tyne. The site of the colliery was later occupied by the Ouseburn Lead Works before becoming a corporation rubbish dump, the City Stadium and now an open recreational area. Even the Ouseburn disappeared from view at the beginning of the twentieth century when it was directed through a culvert and the escarpment filled to accommodate a new road from the growing suburb of Heaton to the city centre – the modern Warwick Street.

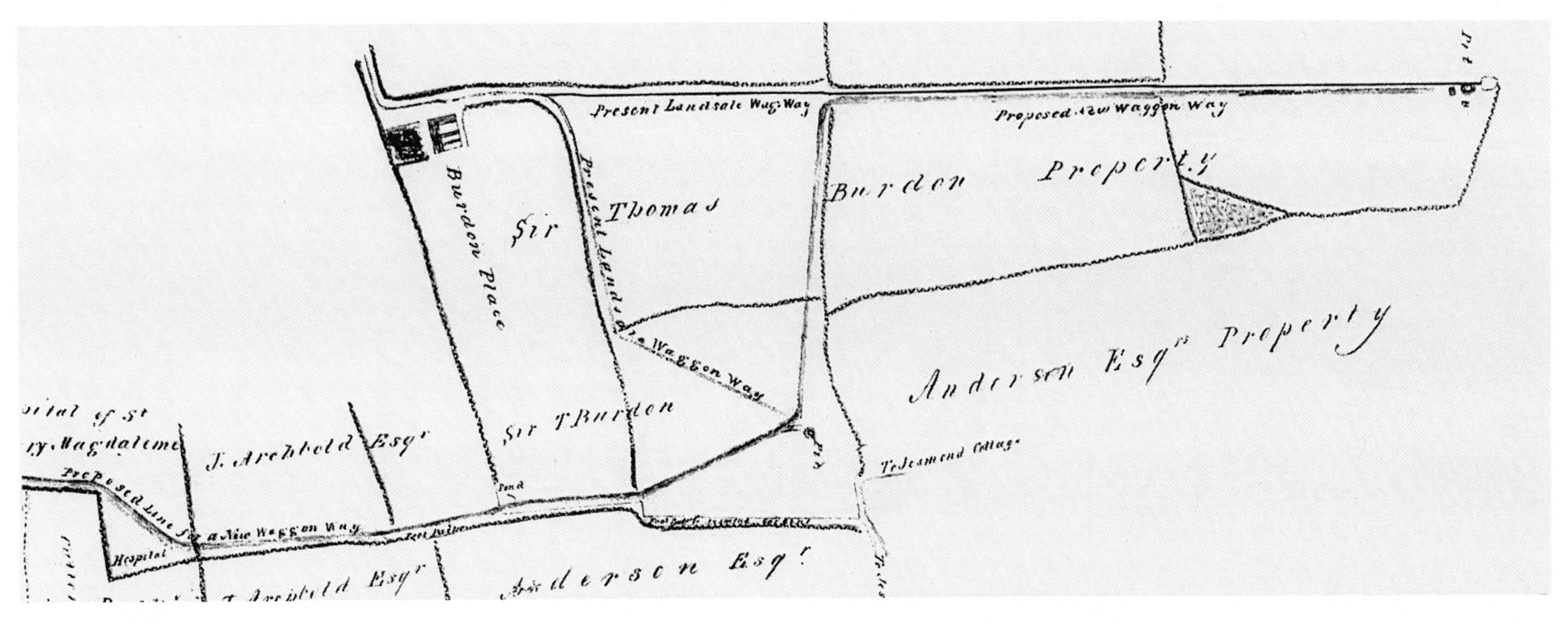

Jesmond

Adjoining Shieldfield to the north was Jesmond royalty. The outcrop of the High Main seam ran through the southern part of Jesmond estate and mining had taken place since at least the beginning of the seventeenth century. There was a large colliery in Jesmond during the eighteenth century employing steam engines for pumping and it was the water from the wastes of this colliery that flooded into Heaton Main Colliery in 1815 with catastrophic results. This colliery is illustrated on maps in Chapter Two and is likely to have had a waggonway. The map above dates from the early nineteenth century and shows Sir Thomas Burdon's mine in North Jesmond.The wagonway runs south following a course later to be adopted by Osborne Road and is joined by a branch line from the east before proceeding along the future Clayton Road to the staith on the Town Moor situated a short distance from Barras Bridge. It is interesting to find a waggonway for a landsale colliery. The map was drawn to show the line of a proposed new waggonway to the Ouseburn via Sandyford Bridge and Shieldfield to give access to the more valuable seasale trade. This railway does not appear to have been built and Jesmond remained a landsale colliery mining the High Main until it was sold in 1835. The lower seams were later mined from North Elswick Colliery. There had been other proposals for waggonways through Jesmond to the mouth of the Ouseburn. In 1720 Newcastle Corporation granted Matthew White wayleave for his pits in Jesmond, Gosforth and Coxlodge for a waggonway along the edge of the Town Moor; in 1763 there was another plan along the same route; and in both 1790 and 1800 there were schemes which included Kenton Colliery. None of these intended railways seem to have been built.

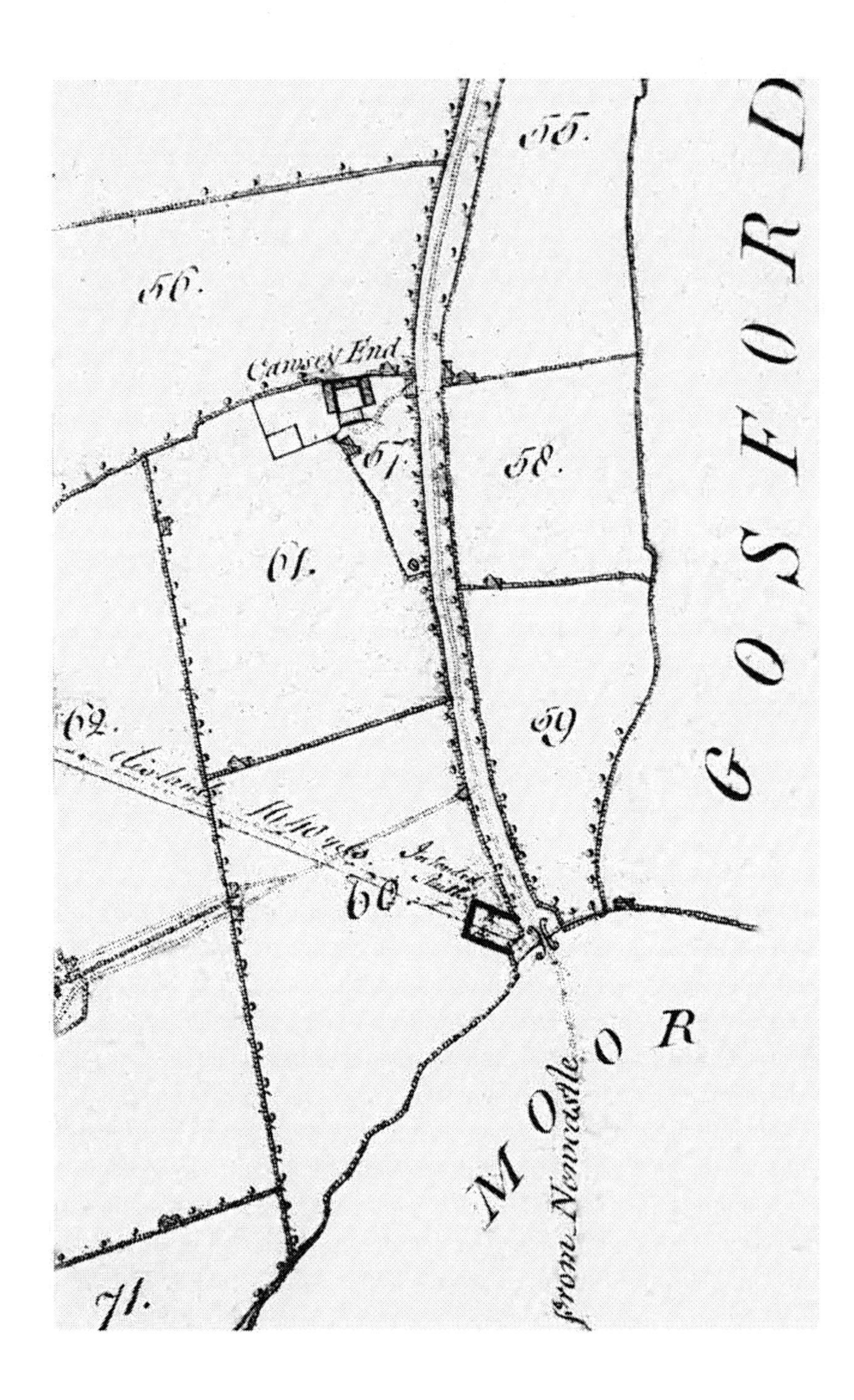

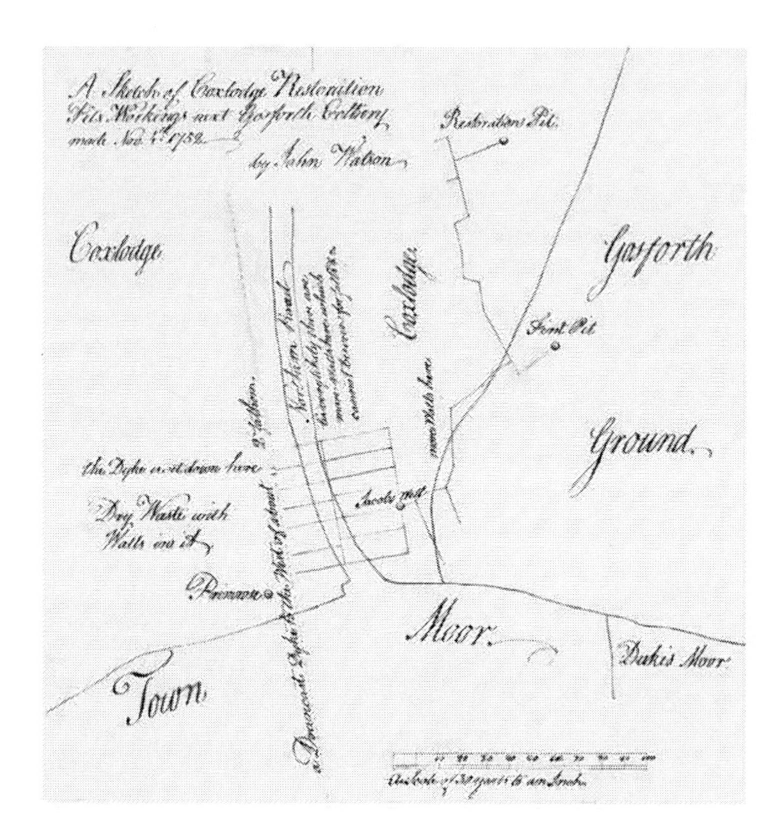

Gosforth

Evidence of another waggonway to a landsale staith survives in the form of an early nineteenth century map showing the proposed line of a waggonway 1,640 yards in length from Kenton Colliery to another staith on the main road north from Newcastle. The coal workings under this site (now the residence of the Bishop of Newcastle) are shown on a sketch by the viewer John Walton dated November 4th 1752 of Coxlodge Restoration Pit and Gosforth Colliery. There was another landsale colliery in Gosforth at Haddrick's Mill. The later seasale colliery was developed by the Brandlings between 1825 and 1829 when a drift was driven through the Ninety Fathom Dyke to the High Main seam on the northern side. It is shown on the Ordnance Survey plan and in the engraving from a lading bill

on page 86. After the death of the Rev. R.H. Brandling in 1853, the mine came into the possession of John Bowes. This colliery was served by the Kenton and Coxlodge waggonway which closed with the Gosforth Colliery in 1884. On the second edition of the Ordnance Survey map a short section of the Kenton and Coxlodge waggonway survives as a mineral line connecting the Jubilee and Regent Pits of Coxlodge Colliery with the Gosforth Colliery and the Blyth and Tyne Railway. All the pits are marked as disused. In 1901, part of the route was re-opened as a tramway and a service operated between Gosforth and Wallsend until 1930. Today, a large section is still in use as a footpath east of the Ouseburn.

The Hatton Gallery in the University of Newcastle houses an important collection of watercolours made by Thomas Hair in the 1830s which depict many of the important collieries of the Great Northern Coalfield. In an age before photography these illustrations are invaluable sources of information about the coalfield. The illustration above of Gosforth Colliery is drawn from Heaton and the artist is looking across the waters of the Ouseburn to the colliery buildings on the hillside opposite. A cart crosses the road bridge and behind a rake of chaldron wagons is being hauled up the incline across the imposing viaduct en route eastwards to the River Tyne.

Spital Tongues

Across the Town Moor was the Castle Leazes where the coal had been mined since medieval times. In 1835 Porter and Latimer took out a lease for 31years and developed Spital Tongues Colliery. The location of the colliery next to the barracks (next to the site of the B.B.C. Centre) is

shown on the map of the 1830's. By the time of the first Ordnance Survey map of 1861 an interesting industrial community had developed comprising the colliery and a rope works. The view of the colliery is taken from a lading bill. The waggonway opened in January 1842 was particularly interesting. It ran in a tunnel, named the Victoria Tunnel after the young queen, 2.5 miles to the staith on the River Tyne near the Glasshouse Bridge at the mouth of the Ouseburn. There was a total fall of 222 feet: the loaded wagons descending took the rope and at the pit a stationary engine of 40 h.p. was used to draw the empty wagons back. The engine was capable of loading twelve keels in an hour. Not all trips ran smoothly. In April 1843, a train of ten wagons was passing through the tunnel when the rope broke. Some of the wagons went into the river while the others landed on the deck of the vessel being loaded. Incredibly, only one man was slightly injured.

The tunnel was sold in 1859 and remained derelict until it was re-commissioned as an air-raid shelter during World War II. On occasions it is open to the public.

Elswick

Hadrian's Wall and the turnpike road to Carlisle, now known as the West Road, run along the top of an escarpment to the west of Newcastle; between Hadrian's Wall and the river several of the principal coal seams from the High Main to the Low Main outcrop. There is evidence to suggest that the Romans at Benwell fort made use of this asset. Certainly, during the Middle Ages the monks of Tynemouth who owned the manors of Elswick, Benwell and Denton were actively involved in the coal trade. Records of mining exist from the thirteenth century and coal was extracted from this area until the mid twentieth century: Benwell Colliery closed in 1934, Elswick Colliery in 1940 and the Montague Colliery in 1959.

Elswick was the scene of some of the earliest recorded mining accidents. The County History notes that 'Richard of Ryton dug for coal in the field of Elswick and the earth fell on him and crushed him' and Thomas Bridock and Nicholas Laker suffered a similar fate; while the parish records of St. Andrews record that on 'April 24th 1695 were buried James Archer and his son Stephen who in the moneth of May 1658 were drowned in a coal-pit in Galla Flat by the breaking in of water from an old waste'. In 1644, during the Civil War, the headquarters of the Scottish troops under General Leven was at Elswick and local pitmen were coerced into undermining Newcastle's town walls. The story of mining in Elswick is similar to that of Heaton with diggings first taking place at the outcrops and then pits being sunk to increasing depths as the technology of pumping improved. The colliery was active throughout the seventeenth century and in 1682 seven pits were at work. Tempest and Carr's pits near the river were served by a short waggonway in 1698. The purchase of a pumping engine in 1724 enabled Mr. Wortley and Partners to re-win the colliery. This colliery was drowned in 1740.

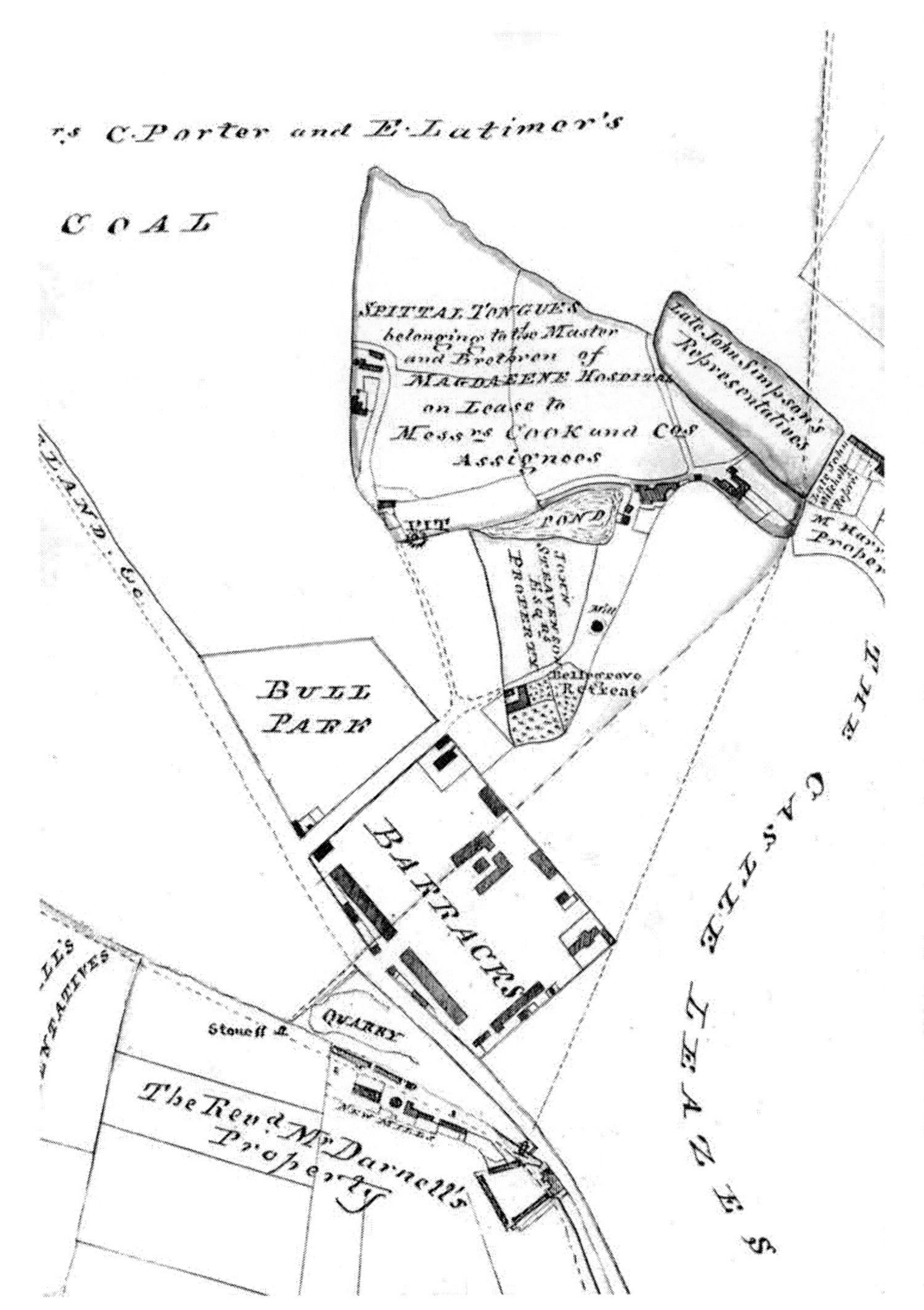

C.Porter and E.Latimer's
COAL
SPITTAL TONGUES
belonging to the Master
and Brethren of
MAGDALENE HOSPITAL
on Lease to
Messrs COOK and Cos
Assignees
Late John Simpson's
Representatives
PIT
POND
BULL
PARK
BARRACKS
QUARRY
THE CASTLE LEAZES
The Revd Mr Darnell's
Property

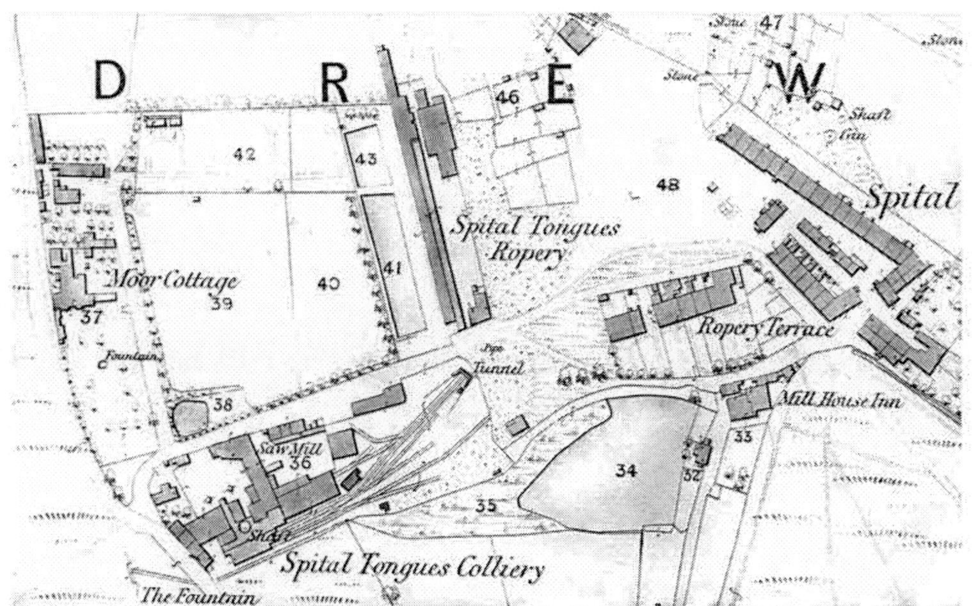

D
R
E
W
47
46
42
43
48
Spital
Spital Tongues
Ropery
Moor Cottage
37
39
40
41
Ropery Terrace
Fountain
Tunnel
Mill House Inn
38
Saw Mill
36
34
33
32
35
Spital Tongues Colliery
The Fountain

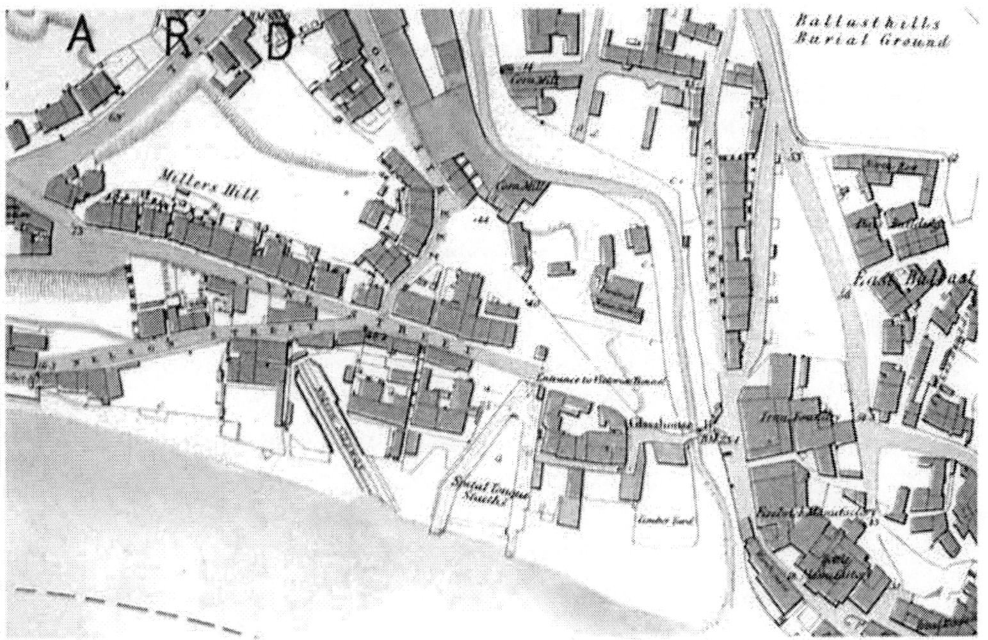

A
R
D
Ballasthills
Burial Ground
Millers Hill
Corn Mill
Entrance to Victoria Tunnel

A section of a plan of the estate dating to the late eighteenth century is reproduced opposite and it shows a series of pits in the west of the estate between Elswick Road and the River Tyne. Benwell Colliery is described as 'full of water – coal all wrought away' and the ominous comment is added 'dare not work near this waste'. There are bore holes to the Low main seam marked which was 62 fathoms deep at 'A' but only 25 fathoms in the south east corner of the estate (not shown) near the curiously named residence of 'Cats Arse'.

John Buddle had responsibility for the colliery between 1804 and 1843. Improved pumping engines enabled the Low Main seam to be won about 1805 at 219 feet from the Wortley Pit situated near the eastern boundary of the estate west of Elswick Lead Works. There was a short inclined plane from the pit to the staith. Further west was the Beaumont Pit with another short inclined plane to the staith. It was situated amid an interesting industrial complex comprising a glue factory, a copperas works, a bleach factory and another pit, the Billet Pit, also with a short waggonway to its coal staith. In 1828, the waggonway from the Beaumont Pit was extended to the Mill Pit which was near an old corn mill on the West Road, called Sinton's Mill, which is shown on the eighteenth century plan. Later a third pit, the Fenham Pit, was added. This was marked as the North Elswick Pit on the first Ordnance Survey outside the north west boundary of the Elswick estate in Fenham; and there are indications of a waggonway running south to the West Road. Presumably, it then turned east to link up with the line from the Mill Pit. A lading bill dated the 5th September 1846 recording a consignment of small coals from Elswick loaded on board the ship '*Magdalene*' has an interesting map for decoration (page118). It shows only a small section of waggonway from the Beaumont Pit, marked as Wortley Main. The whole colliery was sold by auction in October 1850. Amongst the sale were the malleable iron rails, stone blocks, incline rollers, incline wheels and chaldron wagons of the railway. In 1853, the colliery was bought by Alexander Brodie Cochran who founded the Ormesby ironworks in Middlesborough. An enterprising industrialist, Cochran was responsible in 1860 for the installation at the colliery of the first steam driven Guibal ventilating fan in the country.

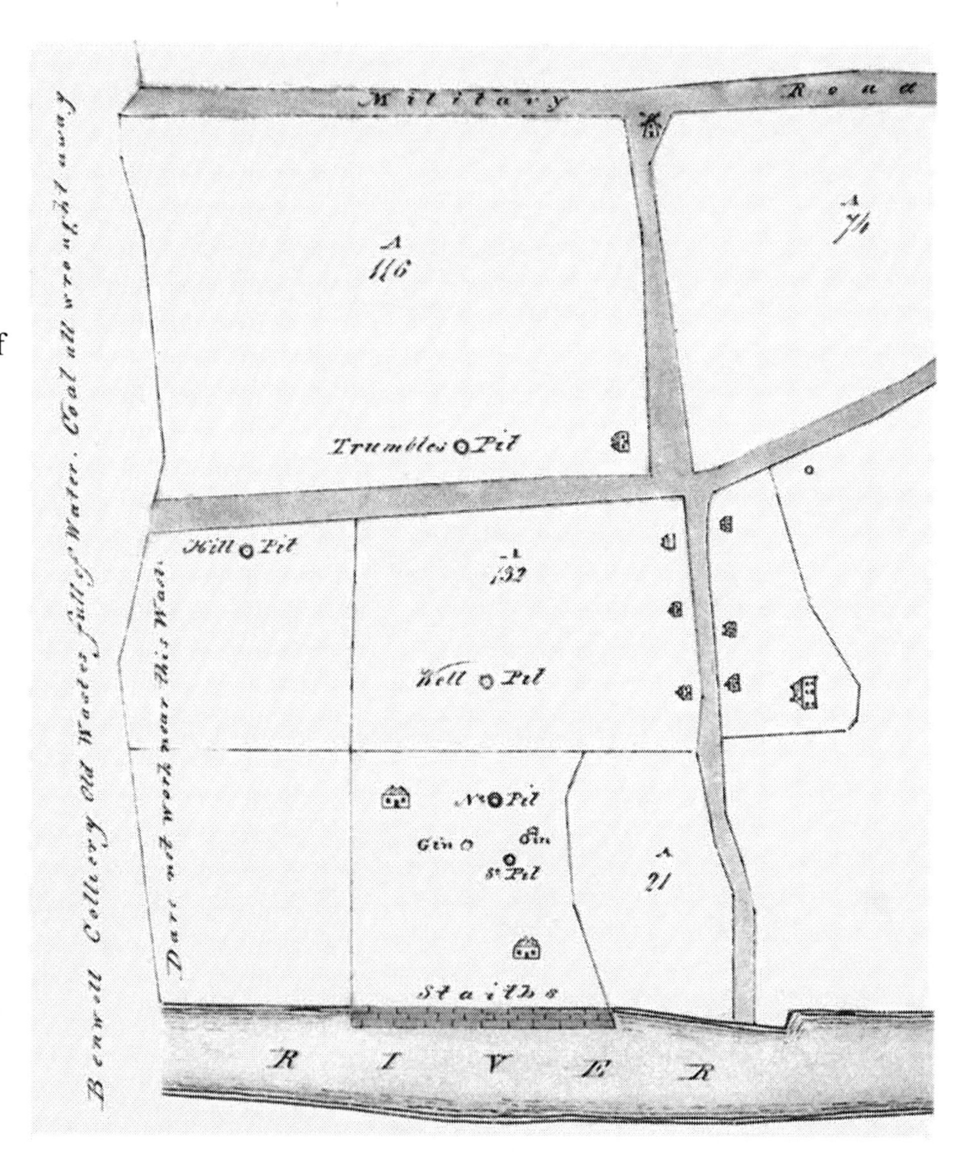

There was yet another colliery in Elswick known as North Elswick Colliery (situated a short distance north of Westgate Cemetery) which was sunk to the Low Main in the 1830's. Clay was also mined from the colliery and there was a brick works in the pit yard. It appears to have been a landsale pit supplying the brick works and the neighbouring town with fuel. The

THE Public are informed that they may be supplied with

COALS,

OF SUPERIOR QUALITY,

Worked from the BEAUMONT SEAM,

IN THE NEW PIT,

At Elswick Colliery,

NEAR SINTON's MILL,

Adjoining the CARLISLE ROAD, and a very short Distance from the Westgate, at the undermentioned Prices,

Best Round 6s. a Fother,
Small 2s. 6d. Do.

Elswick Colliery, 3d Jan. 1829.

Preston & Heaton, Printers, 98, Side, Newcastle.

colliery was offered for sale in February 1841 because of the bankruptcy of Robert Wilson, one of the partners. Later, in 1847, the engine house was destroyed by fire and the colliery was abandoned. It is shown as derelict on the first Ordnance Survey map. Another landsale colliery working the Metal seam at Todd's Nook, near the Leazes, advertised its coal as Adonis' Wallsend in September 1829.

The Elswick Coal Company was formed in 1881. It worked the lower seams from the Beaumont Pit and re-opened the North Elswick Colliery with three pits in 1883. The North Elswick Colliery also mined the lower seams beneath the Town Moor and Jesmond. The Beaumont Pit was linked to the engineering works of Lord Armstrong, one of the great Tyneside industrialists, who began his industrial empire by building hydraulic cranes in Elswick. The works were progressively enlarged as Armstrong's interests turned to the manufacture of guns, naval vessels and railway locomotives. A remnant of the enterprise still survives on Scotswood road producing tanks and armoured vehicles but the Elswick works have been redeveloped as a business park. The Elswick Coal Company operated the collieries until their closure in 1940 when 449 men were employed. Today, the collieries are remembered in the names of Beaumont Street and Pitt Street.

Benwell

The High Main seam outcropped to the south of Elswick Road and northwards from Benwell village along the eastern bank of the Denton Burn. The early mining was from this outcrop and the lower seams which broke onto the surface further down the escarpment. Mining records date from the middle of the sixteenth century and in the 1620's Benwell was one of the greatest collieries in the coalfield. However, by 1632 only one of the forty pits near the river was working and production moved further uphill. In the 1630's, between Hadrian's Wall and the West Road, there were 22 working pits and a waggonway was constructed to transport the coal to the river. It is shown on a map of 1637 reproduced in the Northumberland

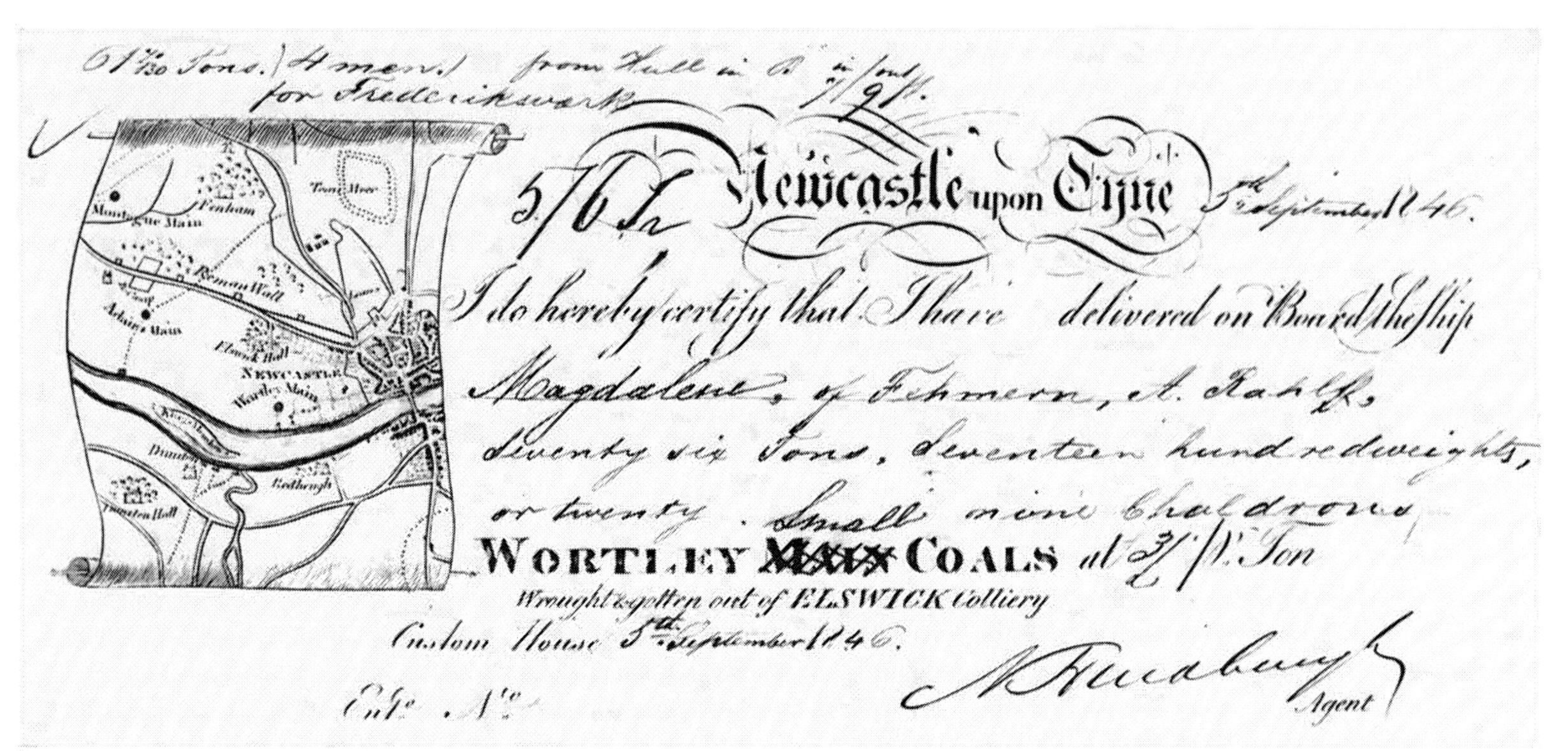

61 1/20 Tons.) 4 men.) from Hull in B. in port
for Frederikwark 7/9th.

576 La. Newcastle upon Tyne 5th September 1846.

I do hereby certify that I have delivered on Board the Ship

Magdalene, of Fehmern, A. Rahlf,

Seventy six Tons, seventeen hundredweights,

or twenty . Small nine Chaldrons,

WORTLEY ~~MAIN~~ COALS at 3/ pr Ton

Wrought & gotten out of ELSWICK Colliery

Custom House 5th September 1846.

Ent. No.

Agent

County History Volume XIII. The colliery appears to have been productive until about 1670 when the pumping technology of the time could not cope with the influx of water. Benwell acquired notoriety because of the fire at the colliery where a coal seam burnt from 1673 until 1702.

Charles Montague and George Baker took out a lease for 31 years in 1698. They re-opened the colliery and the earliest miner's bond to survive is an agreement dated 1703 between Charles Montague and the Benwell miners. The Montagues had a waggonway from 1708 but the venture appears to have been short lived and the colliery soon drowned. In 1762 the celebrated engineer William Brown of Throckley built a powerful pumping engine with three boilers for Benwell which enabled the colliery to be re-won. This is probably the 'Old Engine' marked on the map of Benwell royalty. The Beaumont Pit was opened in 1766 to work the Beaumont seam four hundred feet below. The eastern part of Benwell is marked as full of water on the plan of Elswick and no pit is marked on Gibson's map of 1788. However, according to Matthias Dunn a self acting inclined plane was constructed in 1797 to connect Benwell Colliery with the staith on the river a half mile away; and Benwell Colliery is shown as Adair's Main on Casson's map of 1801 and is served by a short waggonway. The Aubone Pit and Engine Pit are also marked but without connections to the railway line.

The map of the Benwell royalty dates from about 1826 when the colliery was leased to Aubone and William Surtees and operated under the direction of John Buddle until his death in 1843. The Beaumont Pit, situated in an area of Benwell known as Paradise. In 1809, the Charlotte Pit was won north of Benwell Lane and in the same year the Edward Pit was sunk to the north of Fox and Hounds Lane across the West Road. The waggonway for this later colliery is shown running from the Edward Pit,

through the Roman fort of Condercum, then down the escarpment by means of a self acting incline, to the staith, passing the Charlotte Pit and the Beaumont Pit. There was an underground railway linking the Edward Pit to the Fenham royalty which was mined from Benwell Colliery. The engraving from a bill of lading above is probably the Charlotte Pit.

The Elswick lading bill reproduced on page 118 shows alterations to the railway by 1846. It then ran from the staiths to the Charlotte Pit, marked Adair's Main, from which it headed in a north easterly direction through Fenham towards the Town Moor. The Benwell Colliery worked until 1848 when the Beaumont seam became exhausted. The Beaumont Pit was sunk to the Brockwell seam in 1821 but attempts to develop this seam proved fruitless because the coal was unacceptable to the house coal trade. The colliery was re-opened in 1851 by William Cochran Carr for fireclay and was worked from the Paradise Pit and Charlotte Pit and from a drift near Elswick Station adjoining the firebrick works. It continued in operation mining both coal and fireclay until 1934 when it was closed making 478 men redundant. Delaval Colliery operated as a separate enterprise under John Scott, mining both coal and fireclay from the 1850's until its closure in 1901. It was a much smaller concern: in 1896 it employed only 43 men – 34 below ground. Another landsale colliery, known as Adair's Main, operated on the site of the Edward Pit in the 1860's.

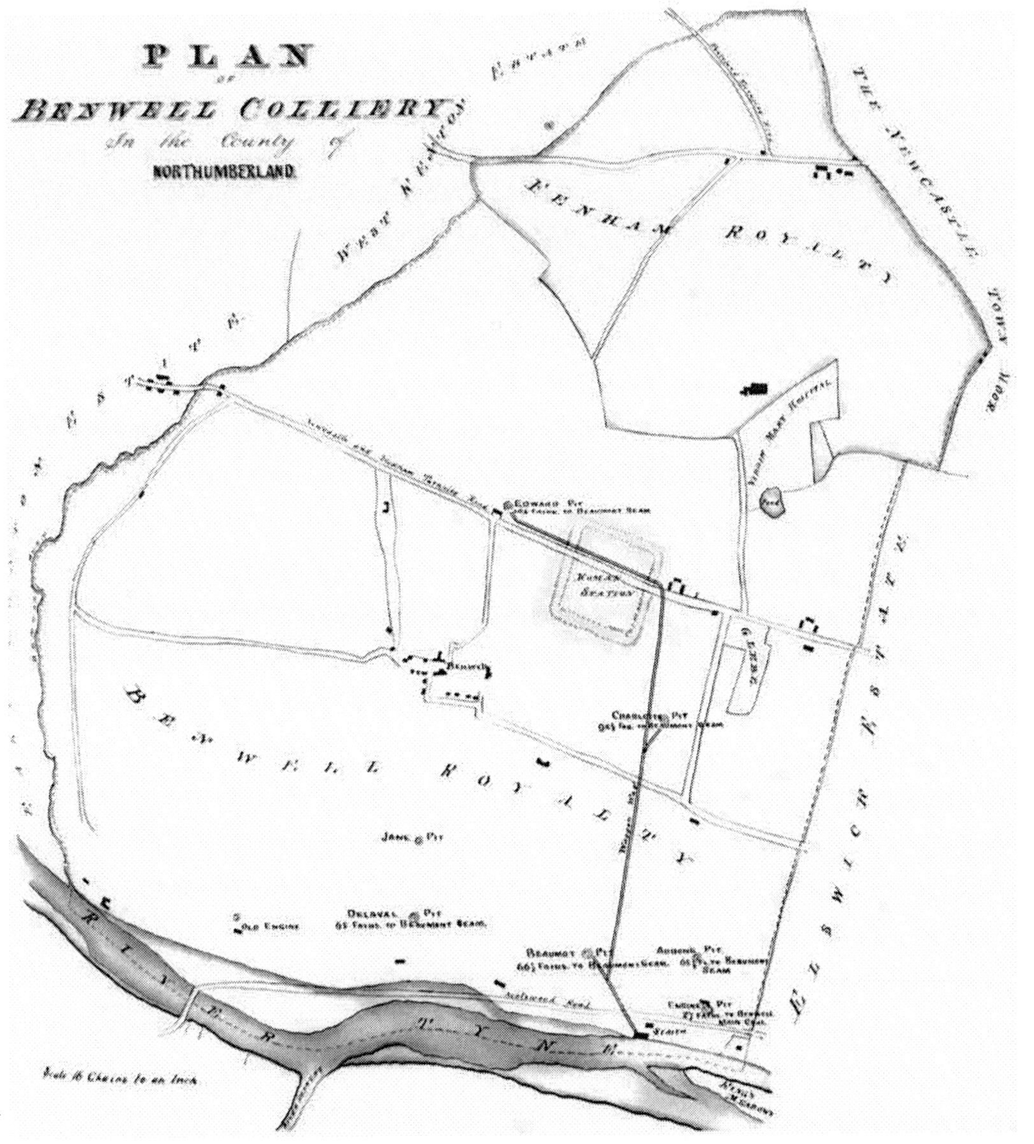

Denton

Like Elswick and Benwell, Denton had belonged to the Priors of Tynemouth until the dissolution of the priory in 1539 after which the Errington family acted as bailiffs for the Crown in the three estates. Records survive of Anthony Errington's lease of a coal mine for 21 years from 1585 at £10 p.a. The will of Roger Errington dated November 1616 records his wish that 'outt of his colery … his debtes should be first paid'. John Rogers succeeded to the Errington's estate in Denton and was party to the restrictions which the hostmen placed upon the trade in 1665 when he 'agreed not to work his collieries from May 1st to September 29th large quantities of coal being accumulated at the pits and staiths'. Another disruption to trade occurred in the form of the weather. The River Tyne was frozen over in the winter of 1739 – 40 and two hundred pitmen from the area were employed to cut a channel through the ice from Lemington to the bridge at Newcastle to enable the trade to proceed.

A plan dated circa 1758 shows the Denton estate divided into three: East Denton and Lemington belonging to Edward Montague and West Denton belonging to his relative John Baker. The Ninety Fathom Fault bisects the estate. The 'Winning Engine' is shown near the River Tyne in the south east corner of West Denton and on Isaac Thompson plan of 1754 (below) a fire engine and coal staith are marked at the same position. This was the beginning of Baker's Main Colliery marked on both Gibson's map and Casson's map with a short waggonway to the staith.

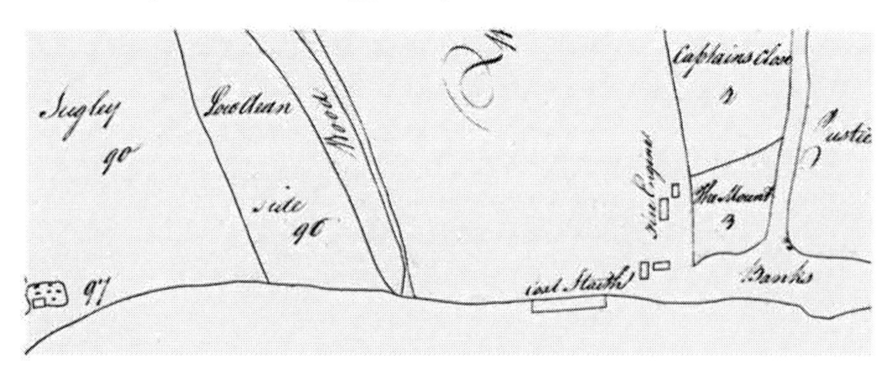

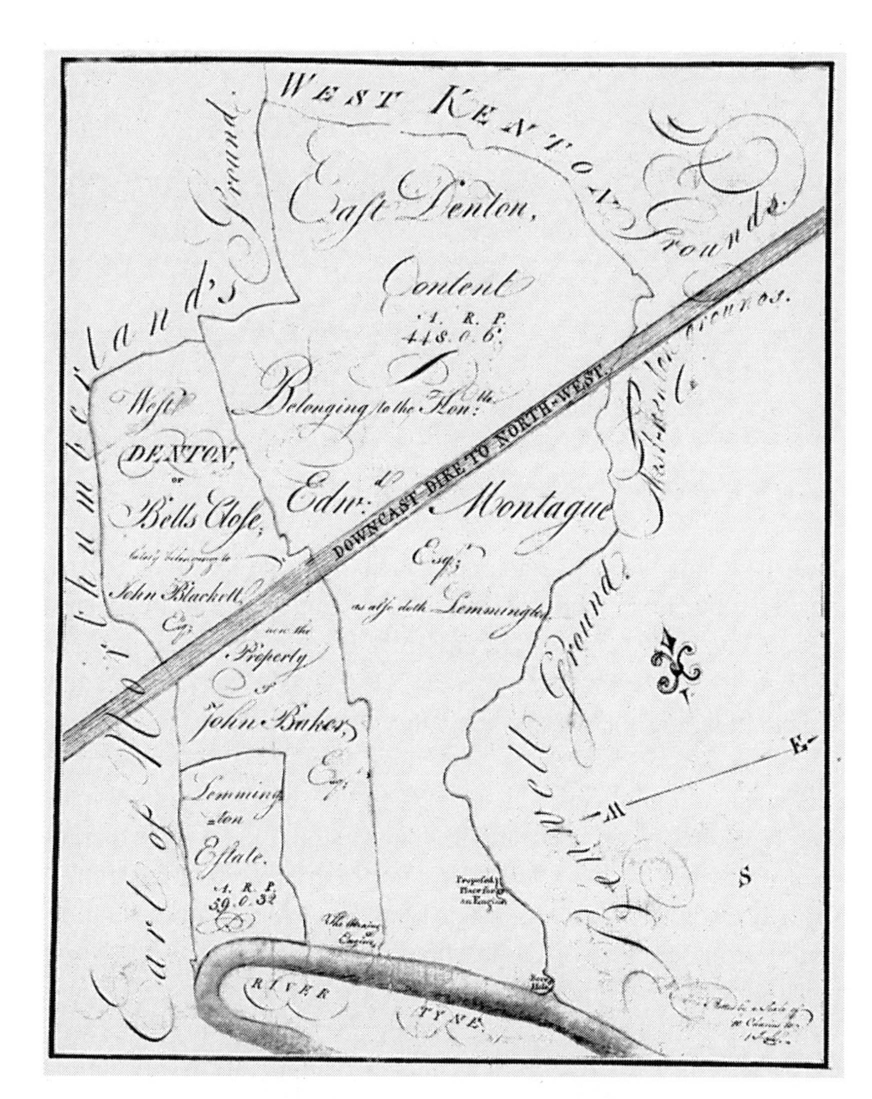

Also on the map of Denton estate, in the south east corner of East Denton, the site of the 'Proposed Place for an Engine' is marked which was the beginning of Edward Montague's East Denton Colliery . In 1758, Edward Montague inherited East Denton and Lemington. Edward had been a frequent visitor to the north in order to manage the coal mines of his father Charles Montague, a leading member of the coal trade. East Denton Colliery developed into a major enterprise in the later eighteenth century under the enthusiastic leadership of Mrs. Elizabeth Montague, his young wife. Several detailed plans of the colliery survive in the Institute showing twenty nine pits in operation working the Beaumont seam to the south of the great dyke and some of the upper seams to the north. The proposed engine was built and the winning was made at the Montague Pit and the View Pit near the river in 1765. A second engine was installed further north at a depth of sixty four fathoms to drain the coal beneath the great dyke. A waggonway from the Caroline Pit to Scotswood is marked on the maps of Gibson and Casson. The leases expired in May 1799 and in November 1796 Mrs Montague's shares were advertised for sale.

The correspondence of Mrs Montague provides some interesting details of the mining community. 'As for Denton, it has mightily the air of an ant-hill; a vast many black animals for ever busy. Near fourscore families are employ'd on my concern here. Boys work in the colliery from seven years of age. I used to give my colliery people a feast when I came hither, but as the good souls (men and women) are very apt to get drunk.... I dare not trust their discretion to behave with proper gravity, so I content myself with killing a fat beast once a week, and sending to each family, once, a piece of meat. It will take time to get round all my black friends'. In 1767, Mrs Montague founded a school for the children of the pitmen at Denton and hoped to establish a spinning, knitting and sewing school for the girls. Mrs Montague commented that the colliers 'speak a dialect that is dreadful to the auditor's nerves' and that she could not reconcile herself 'to seeing my fellow-creatures descend into the dark regions of the earth; tho', to my great comfort, I hear them singing in the pits'. Mrs Montague last visited Denton in 1789 and died in August 1800 at her house in Portman Square, London, aged eighty years.

In 1796 an accident occurred in which six lives were lost when the Denton miners broke into the flooded workings of an old mine at Slatyford. The viewer, William Thomas, one of the first members of the Literary and Philosophical Society in Newcastle, read a paper to the society on the need to lodge the plans of abandoned workings with the clerk of the peace. 'When a colliery gives up working any particular seam, there should be a public record of the exact limits of the waste at the moment the works cease; as on this depends in a great measure, the security' of the mine. Unfortunately, his advice did not get the support of the coalowners. After the inundation at Heaton in 1815, William Chapman revived the proposal – again to no avail. The South Shields Committee, formed after the explosion at St.Hilda's Colliery in 1839, which claimed 59 lives, published a report recommending the compulsory registration of plans and the formation of a mines inspectorate. Although the principle of government inspection was recognised in the Mines Act of 1842, the registration of plans did not take place until the next century. The Montague Colliery suffered another tragedy as a consequence: in March 1925 the miners at the View Pit broke into the abandoned workings of the Paradise Pit of Benwell Colliery flooding their workplace and killing thirty eight men.

In the nineteenth century, East Denton Colliery appears to have been operated intermittently by first Cookson Cuthberts and Company and then by Carr and Ridley. An advert for the sale of 'about ten tons of metal railway plates and a quantity of metal chairs' from Slatyford Colliery appeared in the local press on 31st October 1833 suggesting the abandonment of the colliery and its railway. In 1857, it was bought by Benson and Hawthorn and the Bensons remained in the possession of the colliery until nationalisation. Benson deepened the Caroline Pit to the Brockwell seam and began mining the coal north of the Ninety Fathom Fault in Denton and the neighbouring royalties. Fireclay was also an important product of the colliery. In the 1920's the colliery employed over one thousand men and it closed in 1959 with a loss of 850 jobs.

There were other smaller enterprises within the royalty. Carr's Drift in Denton Dene mined iron stone and coal in 1816. It is shown on the first Ordnance Survey map as mining clay and coal in 1864 and was connected by a waggonway to the brick and tile works in Bell's Close. West Denton Colliery, south west of Dumpling Hall, operated between 1914 and 1924.

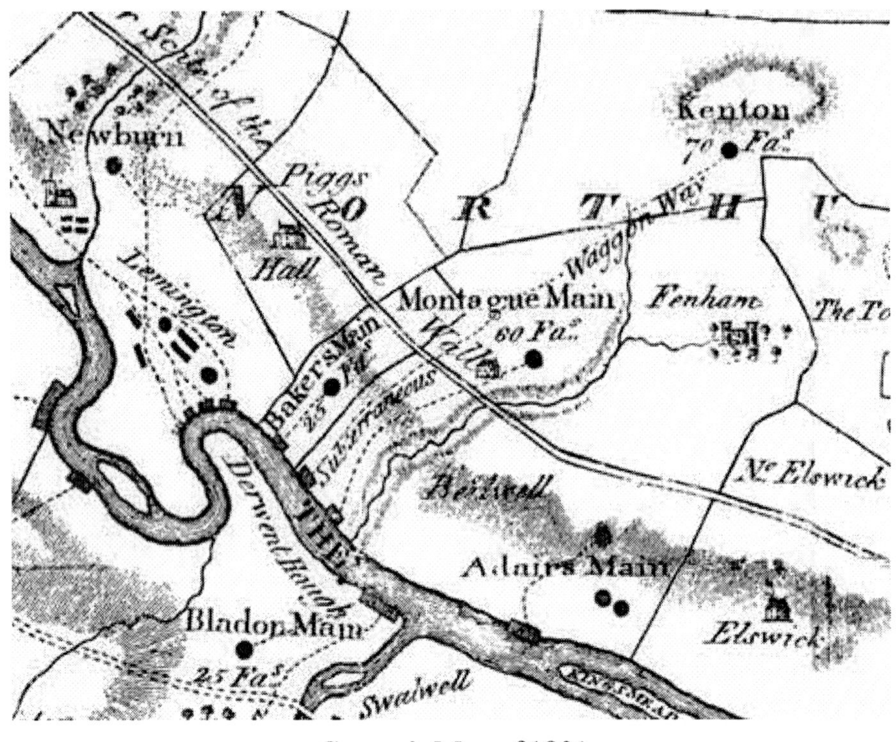

Casson's Map of 1801

It was a small landsale colliery employing about 30 men. Scotswood Colliery, situated immediately west of the Montague Pit, was a drift mine established in the 1860's which mined coal and fireclay. In 1950, it was bought by Adamsez Ltd, a major producer of sanitary ware, and continued in operation with about ten employees until 1975.

The Denton estate provided an important corridor along the west bank of the Denton Burn for coal traffic from the north to the river at Scotswood. There was a wain road from Newbiggin Hall where the High Main seam outcropped. Marked as the coal road on Isaac Thompson's 1754 plan of Denton, it survives today as Newbiggin Lane, Beaumont Terrace, Thornley Road and Copperas Lane. Between 1818 and 1826 the Fawdon waggonway used an incline from Hotchpudding to the river and in 1837 a waggonway ran from Callerton, south through Denton, to Scotswood. A line from Kenton to the Tyne via Copperas Lane existed from the late seventeenth century and this waggonway may have had a branch to Fenham Colliery. In the mid eighteenth century it was joined by a branch from West Brunton and there was also a branch to Montague Main. This is shown on Gibson's map (see page 10) and Casson's map above. The railway followed the contour above the Denton Burn on the line of the present Slatyford Lane and Broadwood Road to join the Kenton way at Dentonwood House. The last part of the route was lost in the construction of the western by-pass. There was even an underground waggonway from Kenton to Scotswood known as Kitty's Drift which is discussed on page 132.

Newburn

The coal seams outcropped on the Duke of Northumberland's estate at Newburn and mining had been carried out there from medieval times. A survey of 1613 recorded that the 'old pitts are worne out of use' and that 'there are no woods … of any value nowe left within the manor for that they have been greatly wasted … for making of Steythes and timbering of cole pitts'. Like elsewhere the story is one of pits being drowned and re-opened as pumping technology improved.

Isaac Thompson's map of 1754 shows a colliery with four pits and a fire engine near the river at Lemington. There is a wain road, probably from Newbiggin via Hill Head Road and Union Hall Road, leading to Mr Humble's staith. Gibson's map of 1787 shows four staiths at Lemington serving two important waggonways - the Wylam line running five miles to the west with its branch from Heddon , and the Callerton line from the north with its branches from Greenwich Moor and Walbottle Moor. By the late eighteenth century Lemington was already an important industrial community with several large iron works and glassworks near the staiths. The eighteenth century brick kiln of one of the glassworks is preserved as a monument to the glass industry which was an offspring of the coal trade. This was the area where George Stephenson spent his youth and the

Isaac Thompson's Map of 1764

Wylam waggonway was the location for Ralph Hedley's experiments with the steam engines 'Puffing Billy' and 'Wylam Dilley'.

By the time of Casson's map of 1801, the Duke Pit had been established in Walbottle and it was served by the waggonway from Callerton. Robert

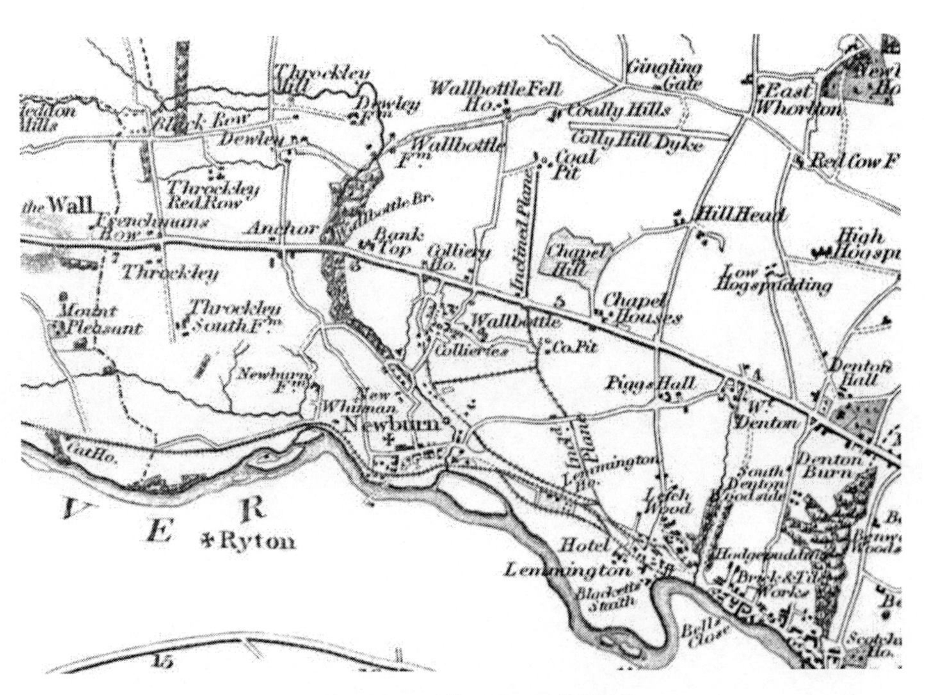

Greenwood's Map of 1828

Hawthorn, another distinguished Tyneside engineer, worked at Walbottle Colliery and in 1839 he was presented with a silver snuff box in recognition of 'his faithful services as their Engineer for upward of fity years'.

Greenwood's map of 1828 shows the rump of the Callerton line running from the Duke Pit of Walbottle Colliery to the staiths and a new line to the east linking the Coronation Pit and the Blucher Pit with Lemington. There was also a line connecting the Duke Pit to the new waggonway but this link had been abandoned by the time of the first Ordnance Survey in 1859 (see page 124). Walbottle Colliery was burdened with heavy feeders of water and in 1846 pumping was concentrated in one shaft near the river. The depression in the coal trade and the expensive battle against water caused the owners Lamb and Partners to surrender the lease in 1867. However, it was later re-opened by the Throckley Coal Company. The 1858 Ordnance Survey map (p. 124 above left) shows intense industrial activity in the valley of the New Burn. The waggonway from the Duke Pit passes

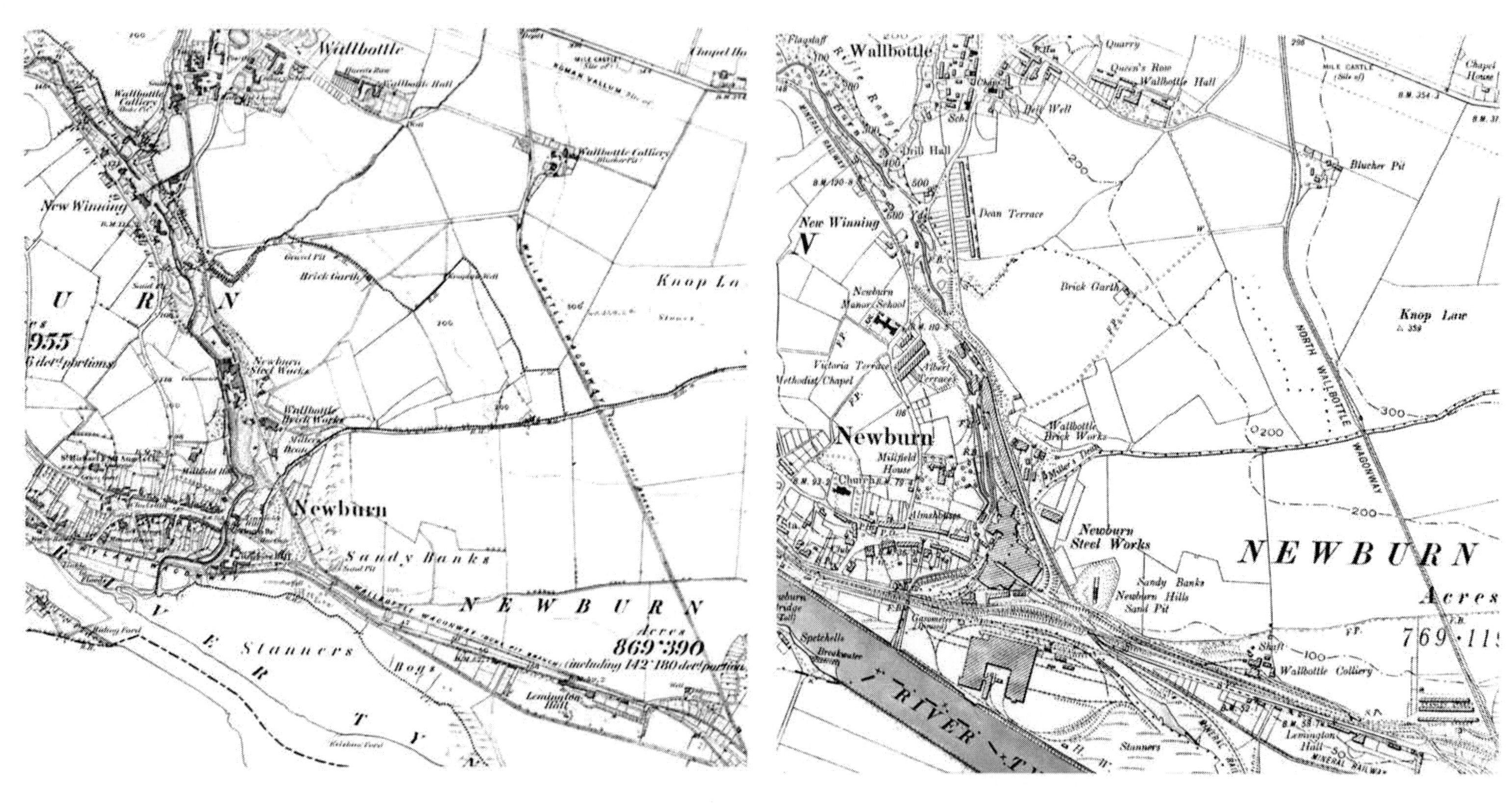

the steel works, the brick works and sand pits en route to Lemington. By the time of the 1899 edition (above right) the Duke Pit had been closed but the waggonway was used by the Throckley Coal Company which had re-opened Walbottle Colliery. The steel works had experienced a massive expansion and the Wylam waggonway had developed into the Scotswood, Newburn and Wylam branch of the North Eastern Railway.

Throckley

The map of Throckley Fell to the west was drawn in 1774. The lands had once belonged to the Radcliffe family but were sequestrated, because of the leading part played by the Earl of Derwentwater in the Jacobite rebellion of 1715, and given to Greenwich Hospital for Seamen. The plan shows the four seams outcropping – the Splint , the Main, the Three

Quarter and the Engine or Beaumont seam – north of the Newcastle to Carlisle turnpike road, the present B6528 Hexham Road. There are numerous pits clustered around the outcrops (marked "out bursts" on the map) which are the early mining ventures. The colliery was developed in 1765 by William Brown, the local engineer, and Matthew Bell, an important coalowner. A channel is marked carrying the water from Brown's pumping engine to Walbottle Dene. This later colliery is represented by the Pink, Success, Rye, Wardle, New Engine, Queen and Rose pits served by branches to the main waggonway. This is a typical arrangement of an eighteenth century colliery waggonway. Later, as ventilation technology improved, fewer shafts were needed and the coal was transported for long distances on underground waggonways which led to a single winding shaft. The line of the waggonway through Throckley and down the west side of Walbottle Dene to Newburn closed in 1780 but the route was used intermittently by other owners until the late twentieth century. By the time of Gibson's map, mining on Greenwich Moor had moved further north near to the road from Stamfordam and that colliery was connected to a waggonway down the east side of Walbottle Dene (see page 14).

Throckley appear to have lain dormant until the middle of the nineteenth century when the Throckley Coal Company re-opened the Meadow, Rye and Wardle pits and established a tile and brick works nearby. They adopted the same route for the northern part of the waggonway until the junction with the line from the Queen Pit after which the line continued downhill between Hallow Hill and Rye Hill, past Newburn Grange to join the Wylam waggonway. This route is shown on the First Edition Ordnance Survey map; but by the publication of the Second Edition the railway had returned to the route down Walbottle Dene. In 1867, the company sank the Isabella Pit in the south east corner of the estate near the site of the old East Engine Pit. The Second Edition Ordnance Survey map shows the colliery, the coke ovens and the mineral railway. Threatened with flooding from the abandoned pits of the neighbouring Walbottle royalty, the company leased part of that royalty in 1877 and established a colliery near

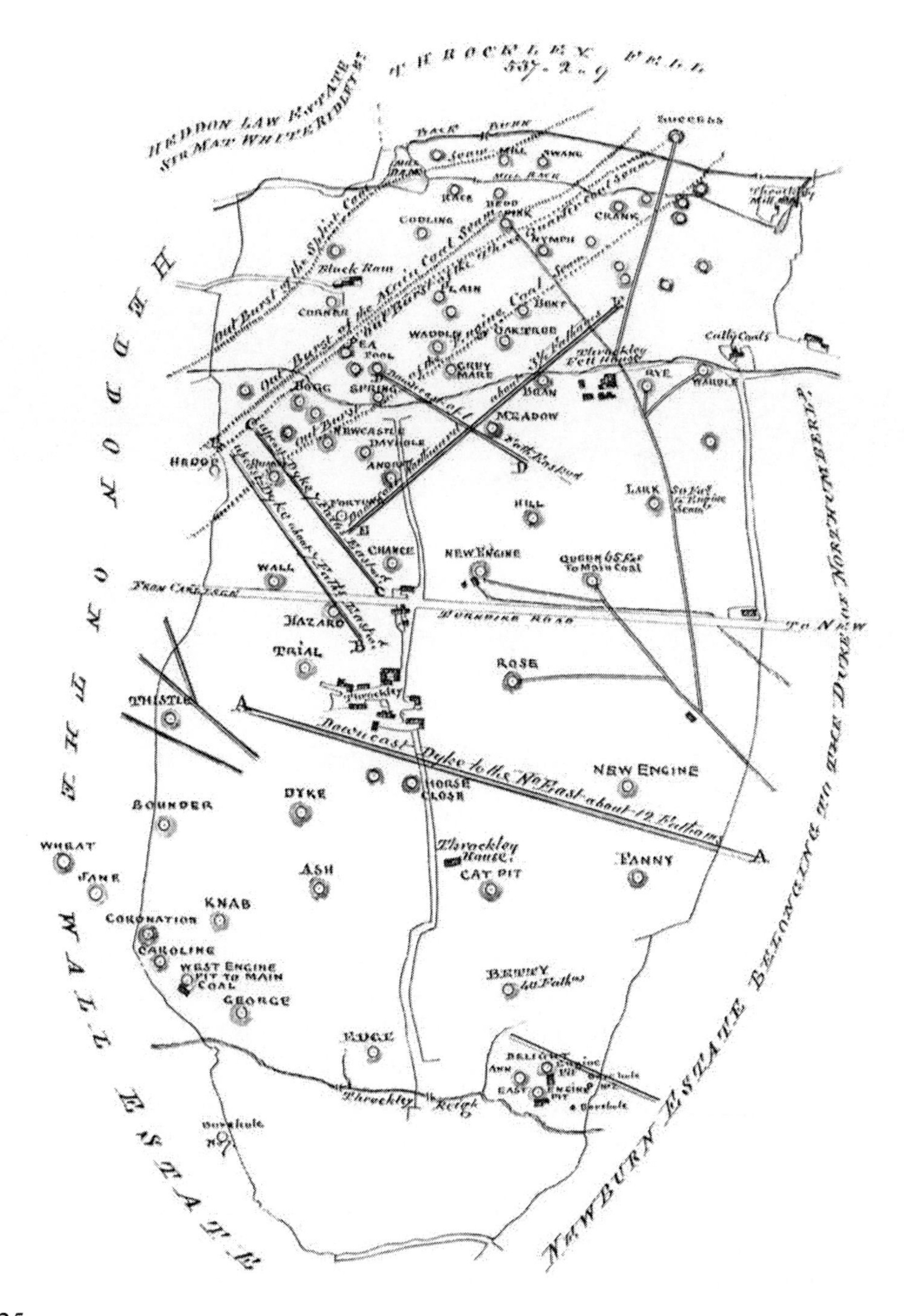

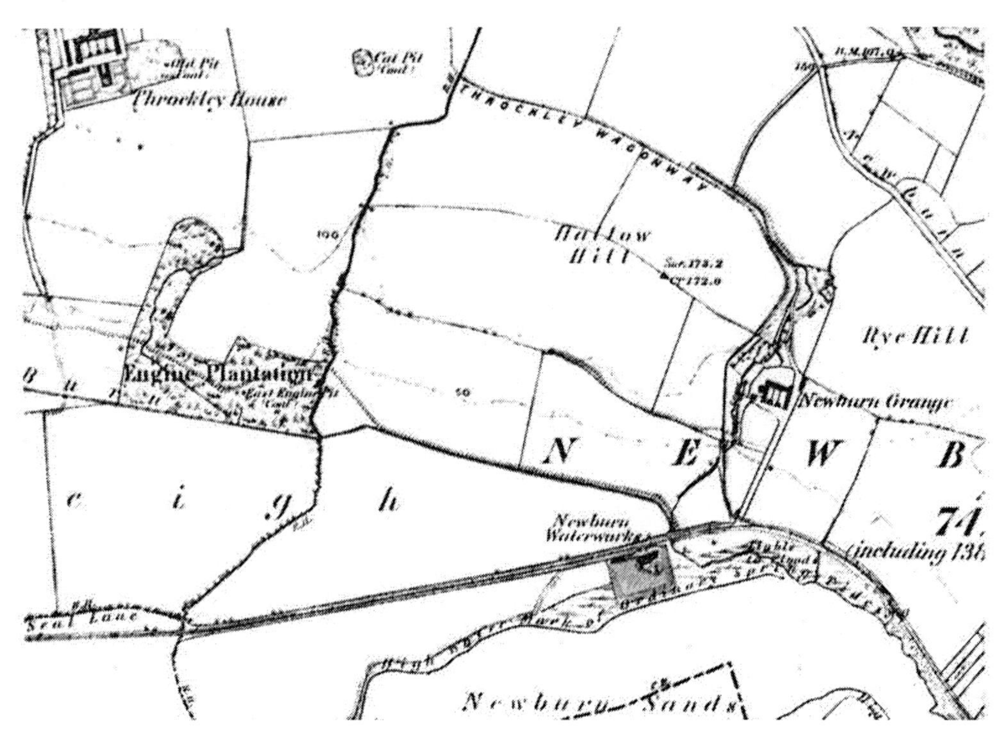

The Throckley Waggonway 1858

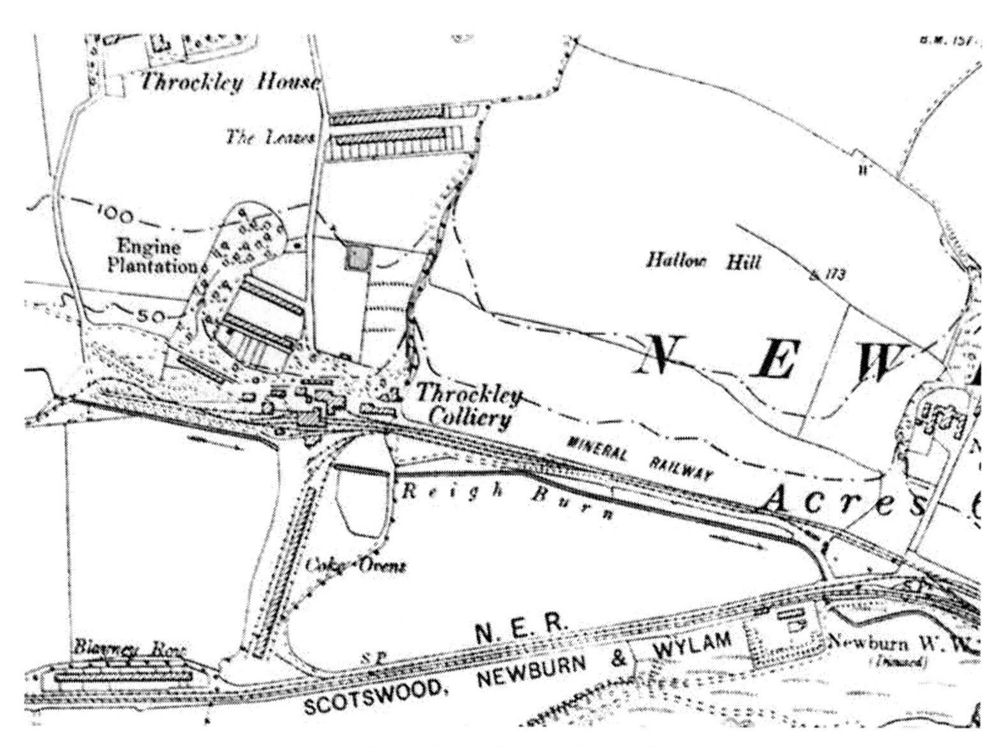

Throckley Isabella Colliery 1899

Lemington Hall. The Blucher Pit was re-opened in 1901. The Heddon Colliery to the west was added to the enterprise in 1902 and finally, the Coronation Pit was re-opened in 1925.

In about 1892, the North Walbottle Coal Company sunk the Betty Pit, near Westerhope, north of the Whin Dyke to the Beaumont or Engine seam here at a depth of 545 feet. The other seams worked in Walbottle and the neighbouring royalties were the Hutton (1'8"), Tilley (2'10"), Three Quarter

(2'6"), Low Main (3'1") and the Brockwell (4'2"). North Walbottle was a large colliery employing over a thousand men for much of the twentieth century. The coal was transported on an extension of the Coronation Pit waggonway to Lemington. Before it closed in 1968, North Walbottle had the distinction of being the last working colliery in Newcastle.

Callerton

The coal seams outcropped to the north in Callerton and Newbiggin estates and there were numerous pits working principally the High Main and Beaumont seams from the eighteenth century. One waggonway from Callerton linked Holywell Main Colliery with the staiths at Lemington and this is shown on Gibson's map. The colliery, 36 fathoms deep, was located at the west end of Callerton estate near Broom Hall. Traces of this waggonway and its branches are shown as abandoned on the first edition of the Ordnance Survey. Several pits are named. In 1827, at the east end of the estate, Callerton Colliery was opened: it was situated 'about 500 yards West of the Ponteland Turnpike Road, the Woolsington Bridge being South East of it'. The colliery was owned by Mr. Elsdon and operated for

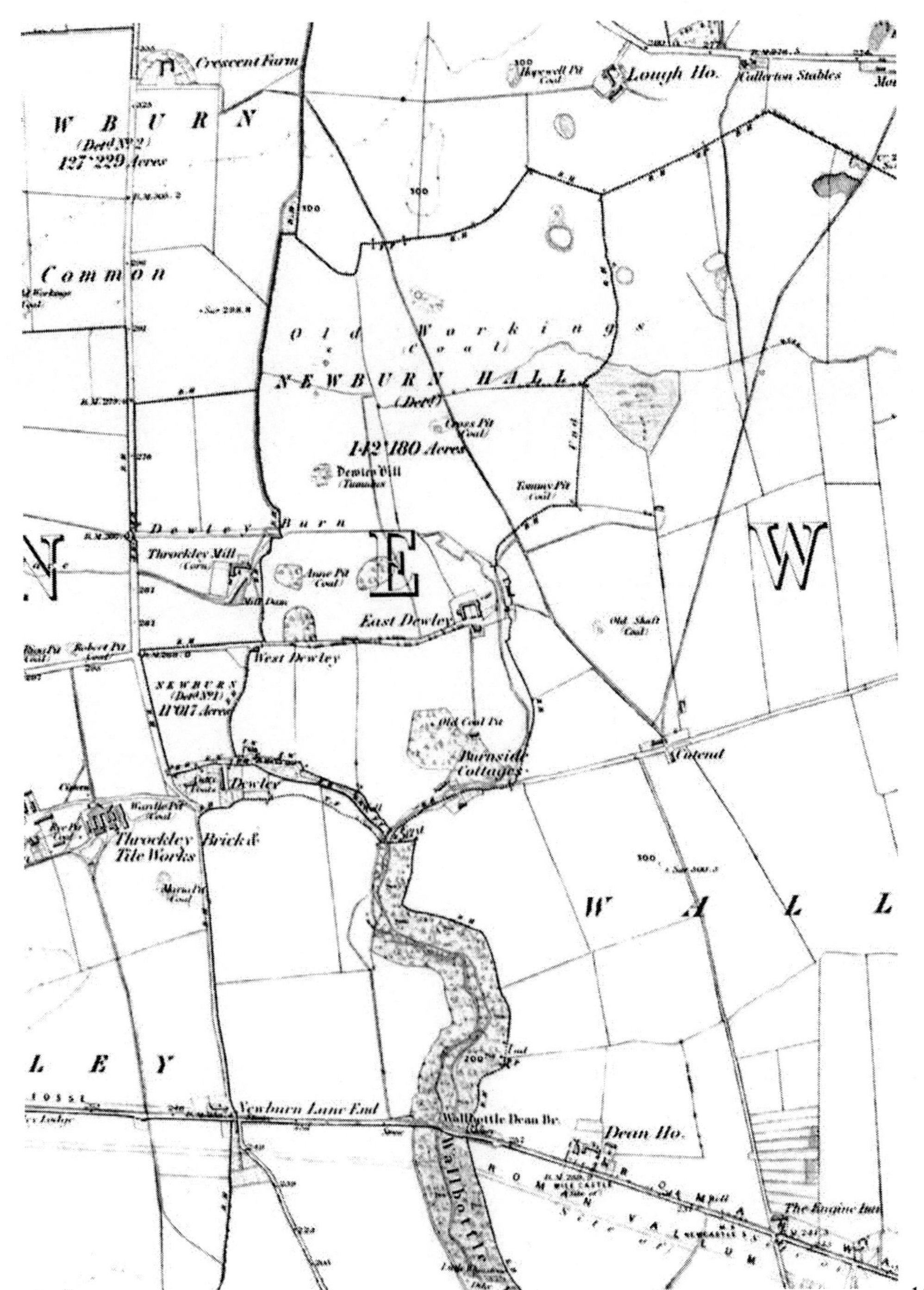

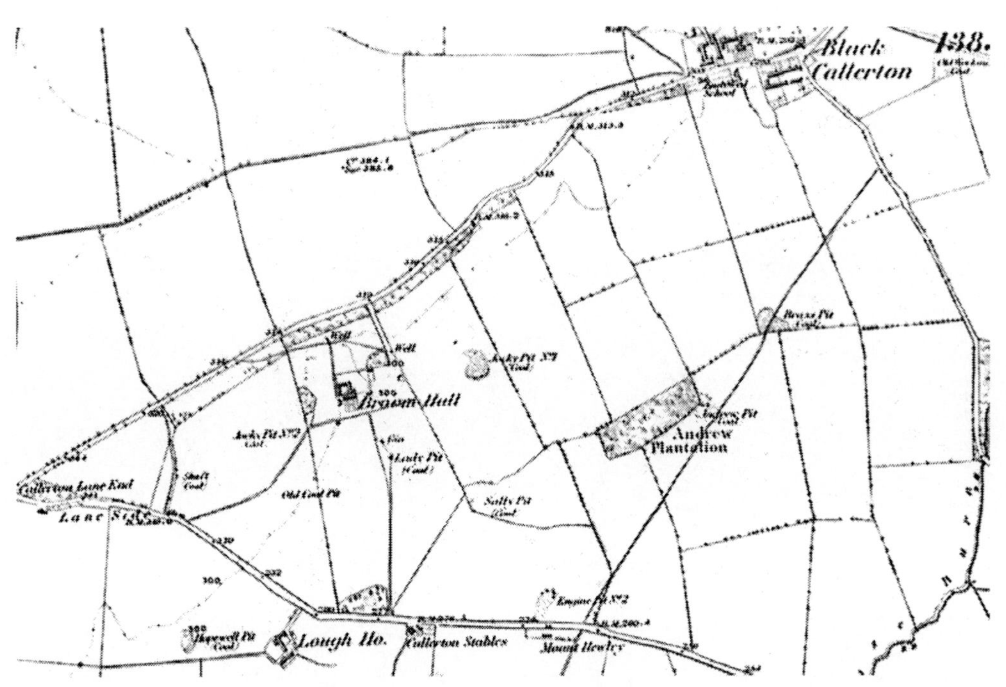

a decade. The contents of the colliery were offered for sale in April 1837 and these included a pumping engine of 50 horse power, a winding engine of 30 horse power and a railway engine of 24 horse power 'with rope drum etc.etc. Tram Plates; Malleable and Cast-Iron Rails; the Railway from the Colliery to the Staith on the River Tyne at Scotwood'. This was a different route from the one shown on Gibson's plan and it ran south to Scotswood avoiding Newburn. There were also 52 coal wagons in the sale and 'material of 44 workmen's cottages' – seemingly the closure involved the demolition of the mining village which is illustrated on the lading bill. In the 1860's, S. Forster opened another Callerton Colliery near Lough House. This was a small landsale colliery employing 64 men when it was abandoned in 1948. The N.C.B. attempt to redevelop the colliery on the other side of the road in the 1950's was short lived. Two sections from the 1858 Ordnance Survey Map are reproduced above. They show the remains of the Callerton way running from the Engine Inn at Walbottle north to Catend, Crescent farm, Broom Hall and Black Callerton.

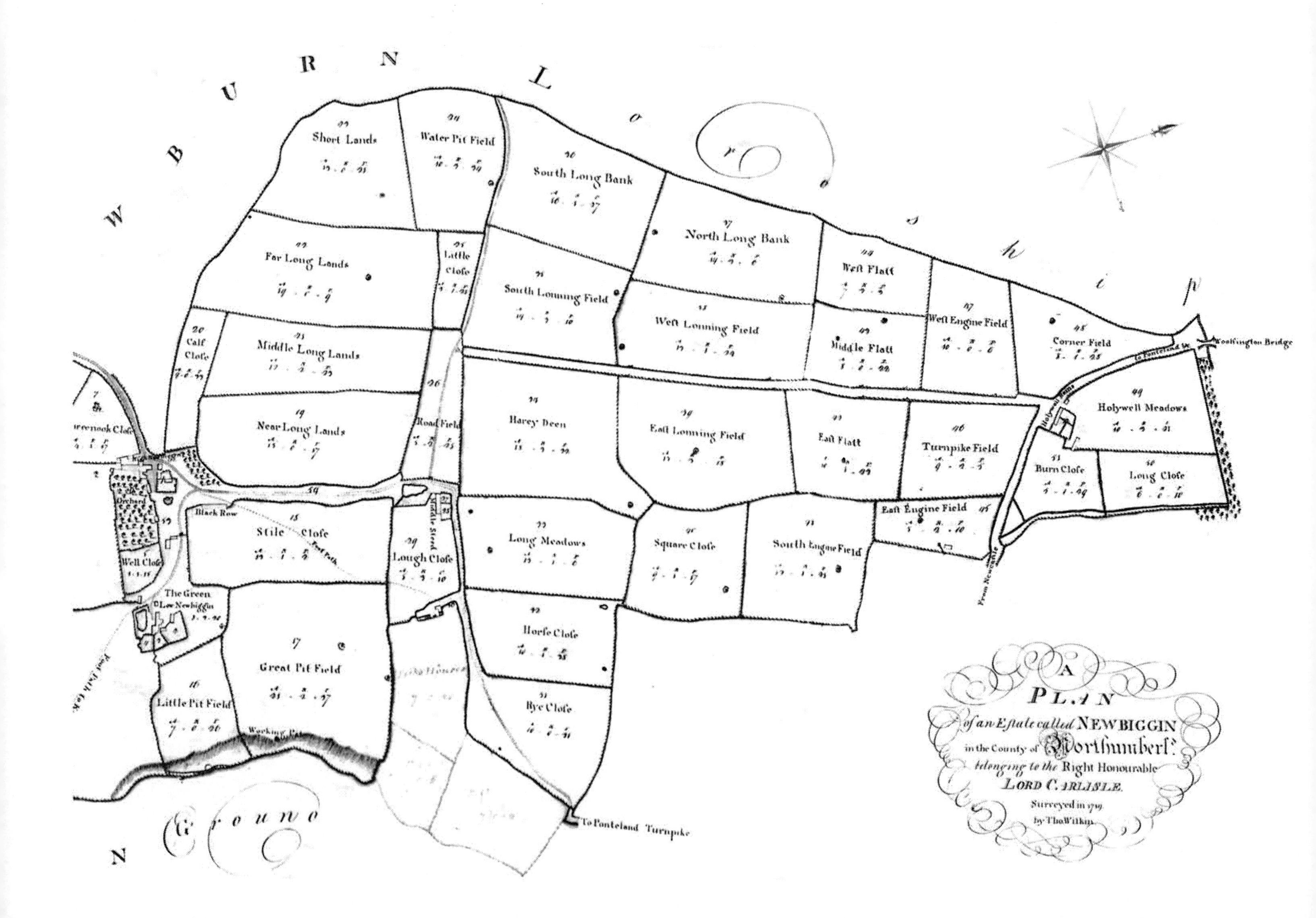

A PLAN of an Estate called NEWBIGGIN in the County of Northumberl.d belonging to the Right Honourable LORD CARLISLE.
Surveyed in 1719 by Tho Wilkin
Short Lands
Water Pit Field
South Long Bank
North Long Bank
Far Long Lands
Little Close
South Lonning Field
West Lonning Field
West Flatt
Middle Flatt
West Engine Field
Corner Field
Calf Close
Middle Long Lands
Near Long Lands
Road Field
Harey Deen
East Lonning Field
East Flatt
Turnpike Field
Holywell Meadows
Burn Close
Long Close
East Engine Field
Orchard
Black Row
Stile Close
Foot Path
Lough Close
Middle Steed
Long Meadows
Square Close
South Engine Field
Well Close
The Green
Low Newbiggin
Great Pit Field
Horse Close
Little Pit Field
Bye Close
Working Pit
To Ponteland Turnpike
From Newcastle
To Ponteland &c.
Woolsington Bridge
WBURN LORDSHIP
GROUND

Newbiggin

The northern part of the Earl of Carlisle's estate at Newbiggin shown in the section of Thomas Wilkin's map of 1789 (left) reveals a landscape of abandoned mining operations. There is a working pit on the edge of Newbiggin Dene in Great Pit Field, and by implication, the other 21 shafts scattered throughout the remaining fields are not in use.

A section of an earlier plan of Holywell Reins Colliery dated circa 1770 shows the pillar and stall workings in the area west of Ponteland Road as it passes from Bullock Steads to Woolsington. There are four pumping engines marked: the West Engine, the Old West Engine, the Little Engine and the Great Engine. Two waggonways converge on the Duke of Northumberland's Newburn estate: the southern one serving the John Pit, Unity Pit and Liberty Pit; the northern one running to the Anne Pit with branches to the Brunton Pit and the Old West Engine Pit. The route of the main line to the River Tyne is not known. On 7th September 1780 an advert appeared in the local press advertising the sale of 'Holywellreens Colliery, Several Gins, Waggon HORSES and underground GALLOWAYS all in good Condition. Also a Number of Waggons, nineteen Bolls each, two Coal Gins and several other Colliery Materials. Also about four Miles of old Waggon Way to be sold as it lies'. There were also two fire engines for sale. All enquires were to be made to Christopher Bedlington at Walbottle.

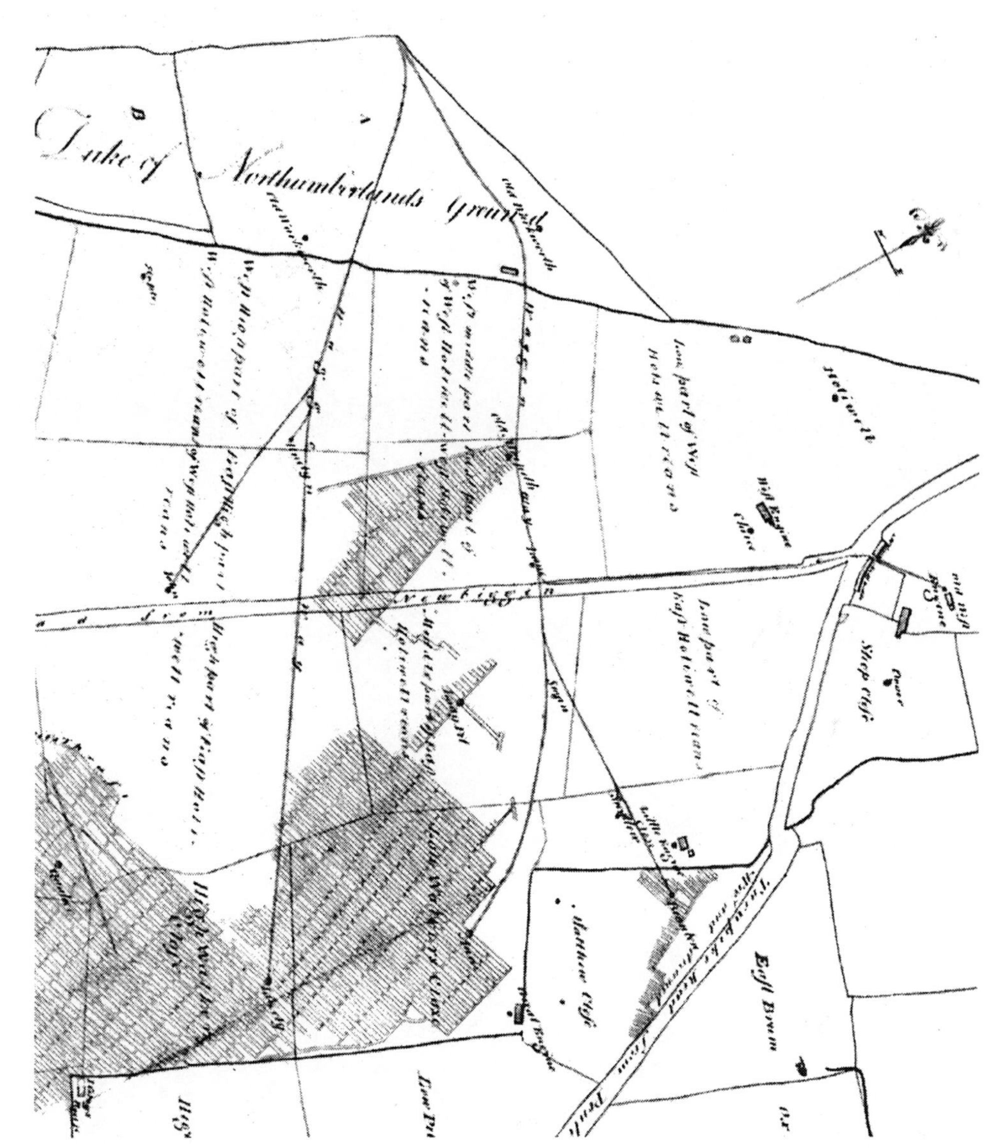

This area in the west from Newcastle airport to Callerton, Walbottle and Throckley was mined until after World War II first by private companies like the Throckley Coal Company, the Callerton Coal Company and the Lemington Coal Company before being taken over by the National Coal Board in 1947. Beside coal, fireclay was also mined as an important part of the work of many of these pits and Throckley Brick Works is still in existence. In 1951, there was a colliery at Prestwick, served by the Ponteland branch railway; at Walbottle served by a waggonway connecting the North Walbottle, Coronation and Blucher pits; and at Throckley where the Maria Colliery in the north and the Isabella Colliery further south connected with the Newcastle to Carlisle railway. These were amongst the last collieries to close in Newcastle – the Throckley Maria Colliery closed in 1953, the Throckley Isabella Colliery in 1954, the Coronation Pit in 1954, the Blucher in 1956, Callerton Drift in 1960, East Walbottle (Dinnington) in 1966 and finally North Walbottle Colliery in 1968.

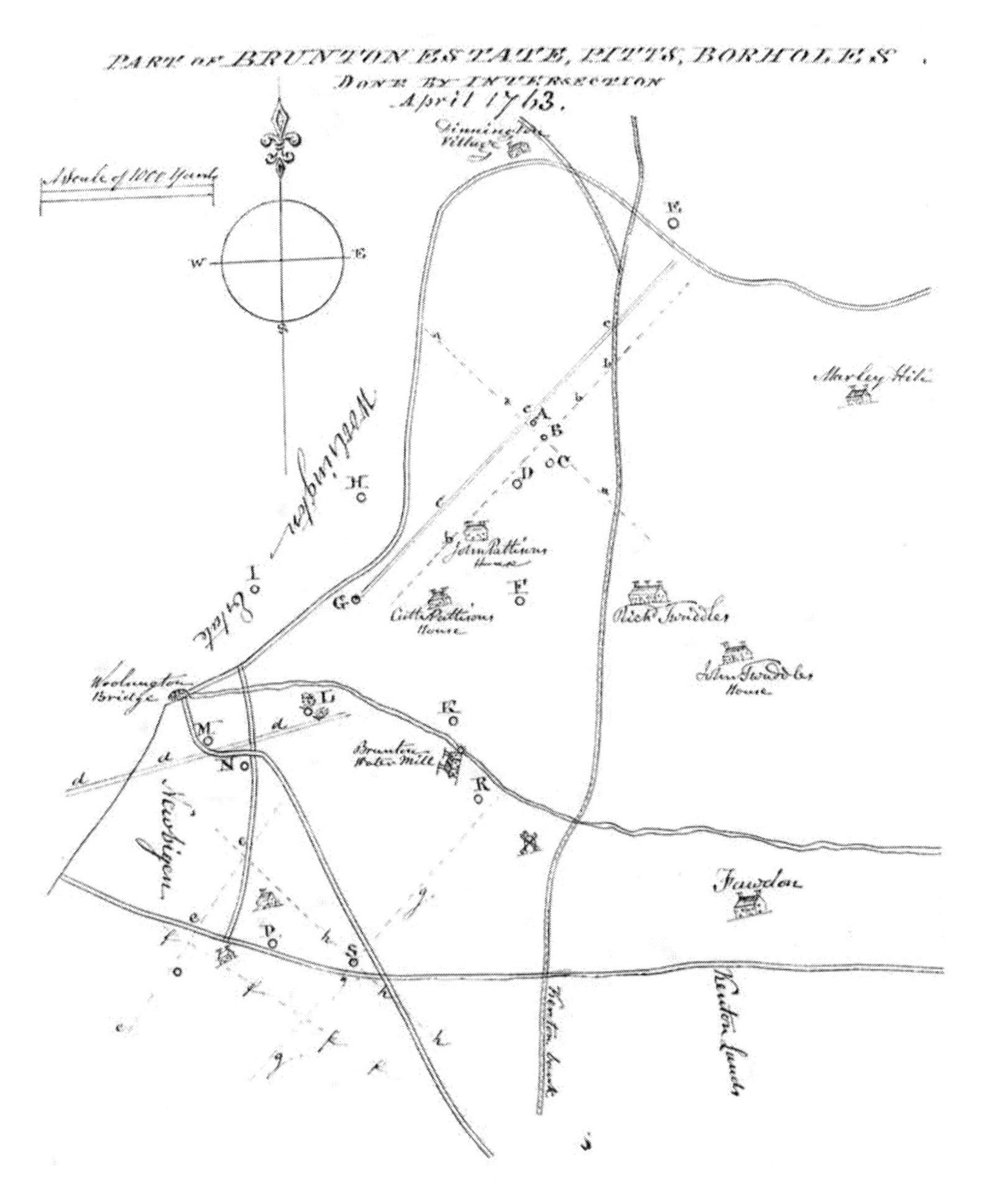

Brunton

In the eighteenth century, the land to the east comprising Dinnington, Brunton, Wideopen, Weetslade and Fawdon were the estates of Sir Arthur Hazelrigg. A report by William Brown dated 1752 observed that although coal was being worked near Bullock Steads and Woolsington 'all of these collieries are very disagreeably situated there being no level to get to drain them unless brought at great expense from the River Tyne or the water drawn by fire engines; and this last method has the experience of being very expensive'. In the eighteenth century, collieries were areas of known deposits of coal not necessarily mines in the modern sense. He concluded that it was 'not expected that they will be attempted to be wrought for a century or two to come'.

However, the tradition of experts being mistaken is a long one. A plan of Brunton estate dated 1763 shows a number of pits and boreholes. 'A' is the Whiney Pit sunk 18 fathoms to a coal seam six feet thick; 'B' is 22 fathoms deep to coal six feet thick; 'C' is the Water Gin Pit 26 fathoms deep to coal six feet thick which burns well; 'D' is the Threepool Pit 21 fathoms deep and 'E' is 'Mr Pecks fire Coal Pitt (in Mason Ground) 8 fathoms deep and Coal near 6 feet thick' which was in Dinnington.

The Ouseburn is shown running from Woolsington bridge westwards to Brunton Water Mill and Fawdon beyond. A windmill is marked near the Dinnington road at the foot of Kenton Bank.

The other map of West Brunton royalty dates to the early nineteenth century. An 'old Waggon Way' is marked running south from the three coal pits near the boundary with Dinnington through land now occupied by Newcastle airport. The railway crosses the Ouseburn and the Ponteland Road and leaves Brunton near the site of the modern Kenton Bank Metro Station. The line continued southwards through West Kenton to join the Kenton waggonway to Scotswood just north of the Carlisle road. It is marked on the map of Kenton on page 133.

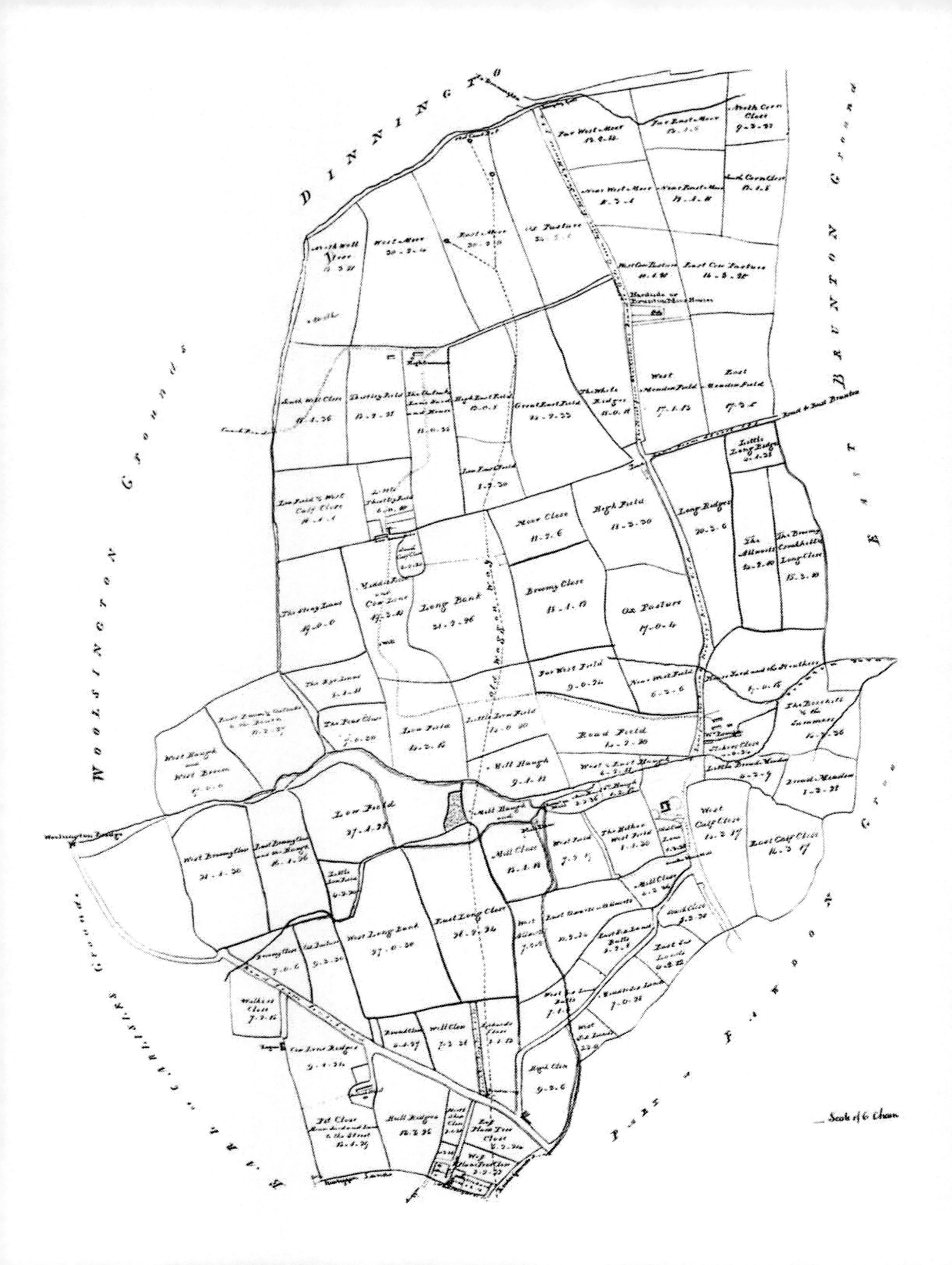

Far West Moor
Far East Moor
North Corn Close
West Moor
East Moor
Ox Pasture
West Cow Pasture
East Cow Pasture
South West Close
High East Field
Great East Field
The White Ridges
West Meadow Field
East Meadow Field
Little Long Ridges
Low East Field
Low Field & West Calf Close
Moor Close
High Field
Long Ridges
The Allwells
Broomy Close
Ox Pasture
The Stony Lonns
Long Bank
Far West Field
Road Field
The Pear Close
Low Field
West Haugh and West Broom
Mill Haugh
Broad Meadow
West Calf Close
East Calf Close
Low Field
West Broomy Close
Mill Close
West Field
East Long Close
West Long Bank
Walkers Close
Cow Lonn Ridges
Mill Ridges
High Close
Pit Close
WOOLSINGTON Grounds
EAST BRUNTON Ground
Scale of 6 Chain

Kenton

Kenton royalty has a complicated railway history. Mining to the south of the great fault dates to at least 1577, when Cuthbert Mitford, the mayor of Newcastle, bequeathed to his son Henry 'my hole lease in the cole myndes or pittes in Kenton which I took from Robert Fenwicke'. Later, Sir William Blackett obtained permission in about 1688 for a waggonway along the north western edge of the Town Moor. The Montagues had interests in the estate during the eighteenth century and were progressive owners despite Mrs Montague's view that the pitmen were 'little better than savages'. A line ran from West Kenton to Montague Main and on to Scotswood in 1707 but fell into disuse when the pit was drowned in 1715. There were several schemes for a waggonway from East Kenton to the mouth of the Ouseburn but none seem to have come to fruition.

The bulk of the royalty lay north of the Ninety Fathom Fault and in the 1770's work began on a three mile drift driven from Bell's Close to East Kenton to access the main coal in the northern part of the estate. The drift, opened in 1796, was designed as an underground waggonway by Christopher Bedlington: it was known as Kitty's Drift and was a tourist attraction in its day since it enabled visitors to experience a coal mine without the trauma of descending the shaft in a wicker basket. As a bonus, the drift was intended to drain both Kenton and Montague collieries. Unfortunately, the great fault threw the coal seams down about 500 feet at this point and the drift ran above the coal. Two shafts were sunk on the north side of the fault and the coal was raised to the level of Kitty's Drift. Also, a large pumping engine was erected to raise the water to the level of the drift. Although the drift ceased to be a waggonway in about 1808, it continued to serve as a drainage level. Kitty's Drift has attracted much attention but it was a minor venture compared with the much more extensive levels, like the Nentforce Level, being driven in the lead mines of the northern Pennines. The drift does not appear to have been able to handle the traffic from the colliery and a line above ground from East Kenton to join the old route to Scotswood from West Kenton was opened in the early nineteenth century. The Kenton waggonway is shown on a plan made about 1810 to consider various proposals for a railway from the new colliery at Fawdon. This has been superimposed upon an early nineteenth century map of Kenton estate to assist understanding. The insets shows the principal shafts of East Kenton Colliery.

The railway to East Kenton Colliery is shown following the line of the present Slatyford Lane from the 'turnpike to Carlisle', across Stamfordam Road and Ponteland Road to Kenton Pit. The waggonway continues eastwards to join the Coxlodge line opened in 1808. A short distance from the Carlisle road a branch heads north following the western boundary of Kenton royalty which is the waggonway to West Brunton. Two proposals are drawn for the Fawdon railway. One route runs south from Fawdon Pit via the Kenton waggonway and the other runs west to link up with the Brunton line. Neither of these proposals were adopted. A third options appears to have been added. This was to extend the inclined plane on Kenton bank to Bell's House at the bottom of the hill enabling the waggonway to follow a level route from Fawdon Colliery. This is considered later.

An evaluation of the estates of Grey Hazelrigg in 1809 noted that Kenton and Coxlodge, worked by Knowsley, Chapman and Co., should be joined with Fawdon into a single colliery since 'the whole coal is nearly exhausted or wrought out of Kenton Estate'. The amalgamation of the collieries did not happen but they did share a waggonway. In 1808, a new waggonway was built from East Kenton, through Coxlodge, Gosforth and Longbenton to Bigges Main and on to the staiths at Wallsend. This was known as the Kenton and Coxlodge waggonway and it had a long and distinguished history being involved in the early development of the steam locomotive. The line was used by Fawdon Colliery between 1810 and 1818 and Gosforth Colliery between 1829 and 1884. It was also used by Heaton Colliery from 1821 to 1852.

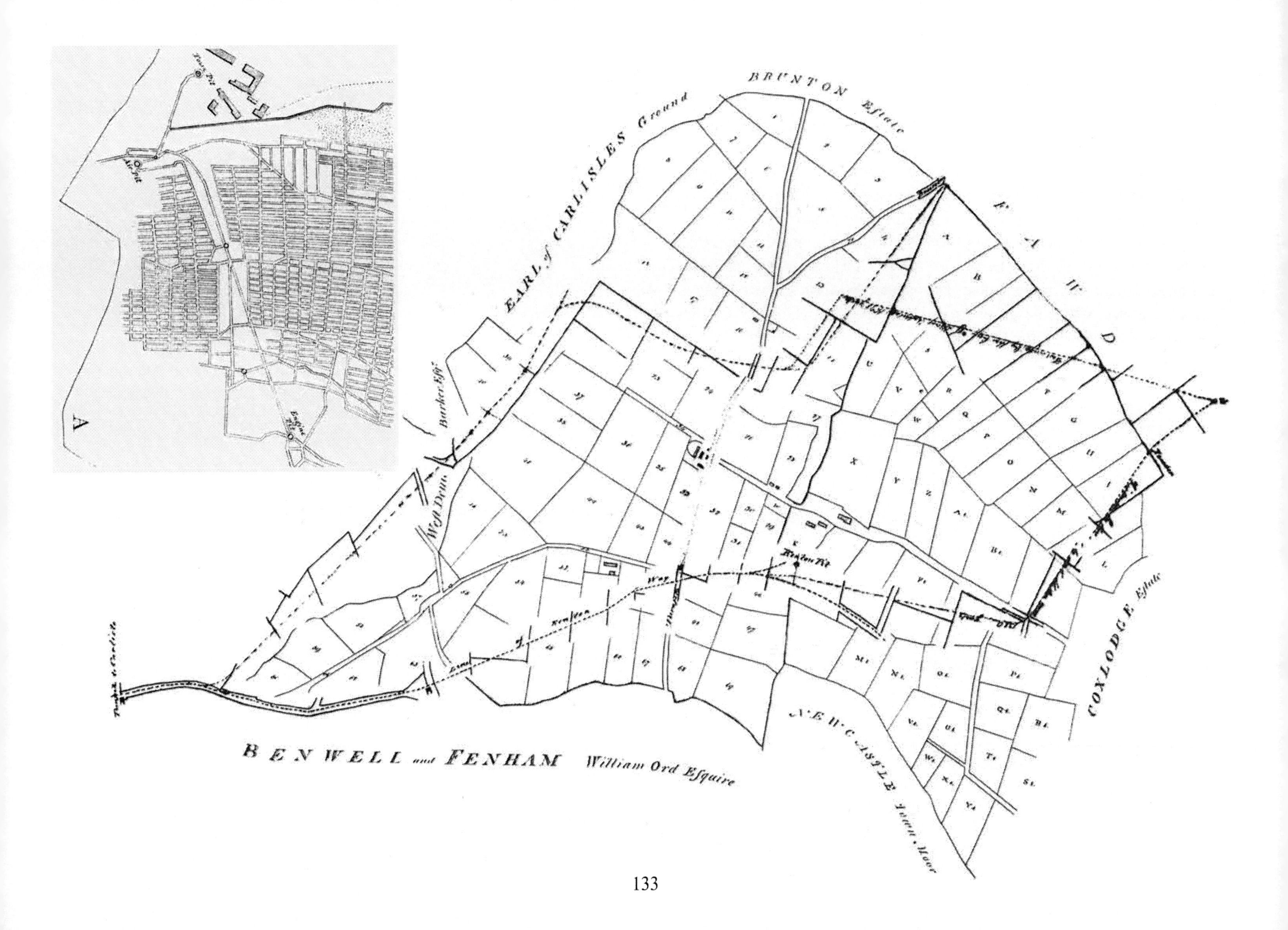
BRUNTON Estate
EARL of CARLISLES Ground
Barker Esqr.
West Denn
BENWELL and FENHAM William Ord Esquire
NEWCASTLE Town Moor
COXLODGE Estate
Kenton Pit
Newton
Way

Coxlodge

In 1809, the Hazelrigg royalty, which comprised 4,570 acres, was leased to John de Ponthieu and partners. William Rowe of St. Peters and John Watson were in the partnership. John Watson was also viewer of Kenton Colliery and there was a scheme for a waggonway to link Dinnington, East Brunton, West Brunton and Fawdon with the Kenton and Coxlodge waggonway which had opened in 1808. Unfortunately, only the maps for Coxlodge and Gosforth estates survive and it is not known whether the grander scheme was implemented. The plan for Gosforth shows the line from Benton crossing the Ouseburn and passing south of Gosforth Church to the Newcastle to Morpeth turnpike road – now Gosforth High Street. The plan of Coxlodge estate shows the waggonway running west in the direction of East Kenton Colliery. A branch runs north west to the Jubilee Pit of Coxlodge Colliery (below) and is continued in pencil to Fawdon Colliery indicating the proposed line. The colliery village of Fawdon Square (in reality a triangle) is added in pencil. The Regency Pit (opposite), marked in pencil on the plan, is not included in the original scheme although by 1812 it had its own branch. This dates the map to 1810/11. Two other lines to the north of Coxlodge estate are marked in pencil but there is no evidence to confirm that they were ever built. A water works is marked on the plan which was on the site of a former landsale colliery in Fountain

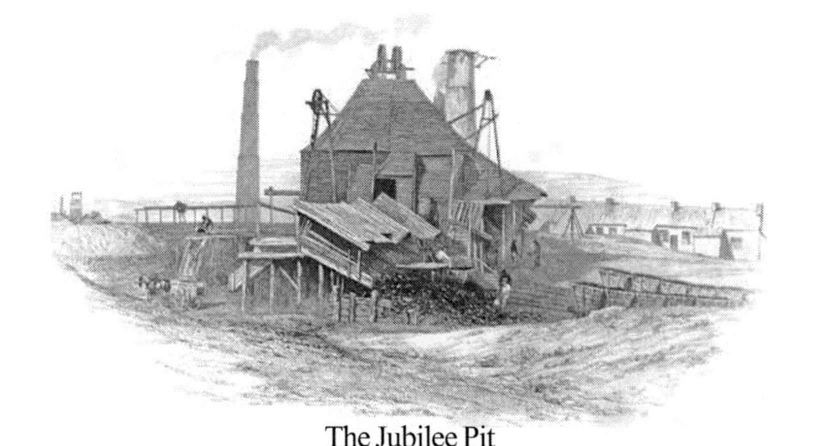

The Jubilee Pit

The Regency Pit

Close a short distance west of the Three Mile Bridge. This works supplied most of the water for Newcastle at the beginning of the nineteenth century.

The viewer, John Watson, was keenly interested in the development of the locomotive and corresponded with John Blenkinsopp, the agent for the Brandlings' colliery at Middleton near Leeds, and Matthew Murray, part owner of the engineering works which built 'travelling engines' to Blenkinsopp's design. The distinctive feature of this design was the rack placed along one side of the track which engaged with a cog on the engine. On 2nd September 1813 one of Blenkinsopp's engines later named 'Willington' had a trial run on the Kenton and Coxlodge line. Since a celebration dinner was held afterwards in the grandstand of Newcastle Race Course, then on the Town Moor on the site now occupied by Moor Court flats, it is likely that the trial took place on the section of line between Kenton and the Great North Road. The success of the trial led to an order for two locomotives which were delivered in 1814. These were used on the western section of the line between East Kenton Colliery, Coxlodge Colliery and the Ouseburn. To the east of the Ouseburn viaduct the gradient was 1:24 and 1:48 for 950 yards which was too much for the locomotives. A stationary engine was in use by 1817 on the incline and horses were employed for the stretch to the river via Bigges Main.

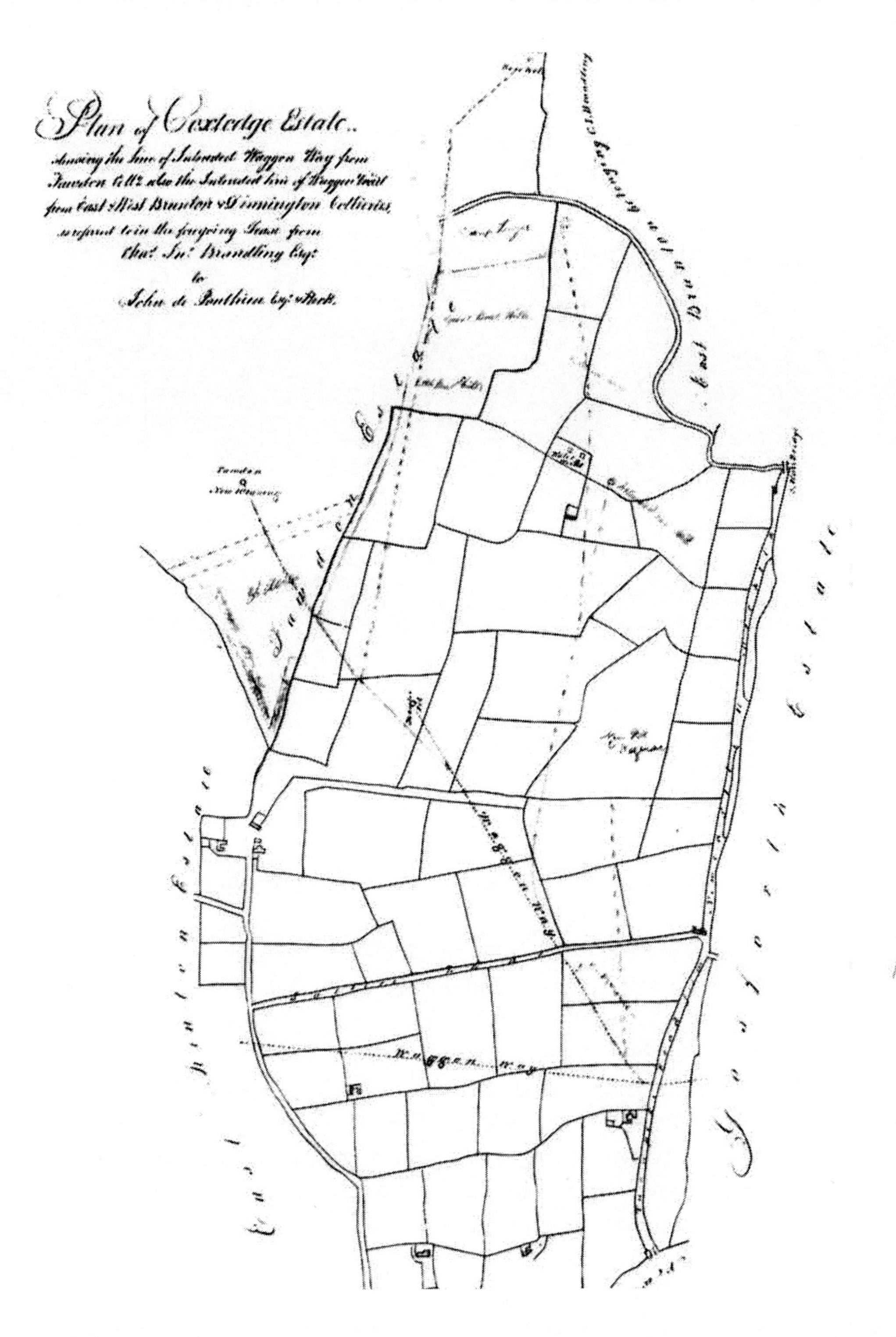

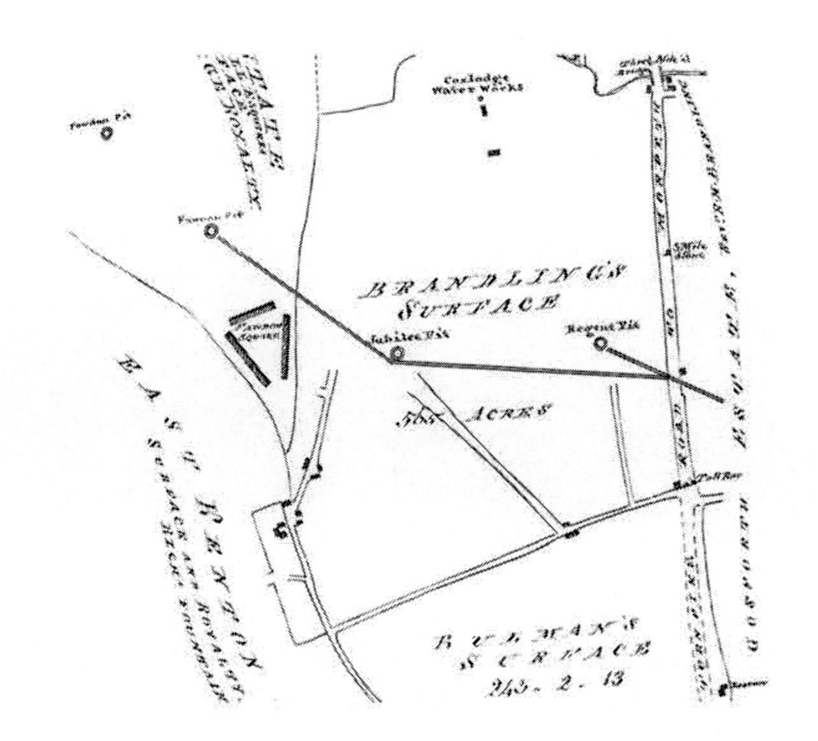

Plan of Line of Waggon Way
from Fawdon Coll.y & also from East & West Brunton and Dinnington Coll.s
over Gosforth and Long Benton Grounds,
from
Chas. John Brandling Esq.r
to
John de Ponthieu Esq.r & Park,
as referred to in the foregoing Lease.

Fawdon

Although Fawdon Colliery was won in 1810, the partnership collapsed and John de Ponthieu 'owing to the mismanagement of his colliery and the misconduct of his wife … fell by his own hand at his house in Portland Place the 26th April 1813'. The royalty came into the possession of John Newmarsh, his four sons and Benjamin Thompson who acted as manager of Fawdon. Thompson was an opponent of the travelling engine favouring instead fixed engines. The coals from Fawdon, which were transported along the Kenton and Coxlodge line, continued to be drawn by horses after the introduction of locomotives. This caused operational difficulties which were made worse by the allegation that the Fawdon horses were poorly fed and worked slowly. Complaints were made to the viewer, Samuel Williams, with the additional charge that, on the instruction of Thompson, he had ordered the removal of the locomotives to the Kenton section of the line to avoid interference with the traffic from Fawdon. The dispute led to the locomotives being withdrawn from service between May 1815 and March 1817. East Kenton Colliery had been acquired by the Brandlings in 1817 and was afterwards worked from Coxlodge Colliery. This was probably the reason for altering the line of the waggonway to exclude Kenton : it now ran from the Ouseburn Bridge, north of Gosforth Church to

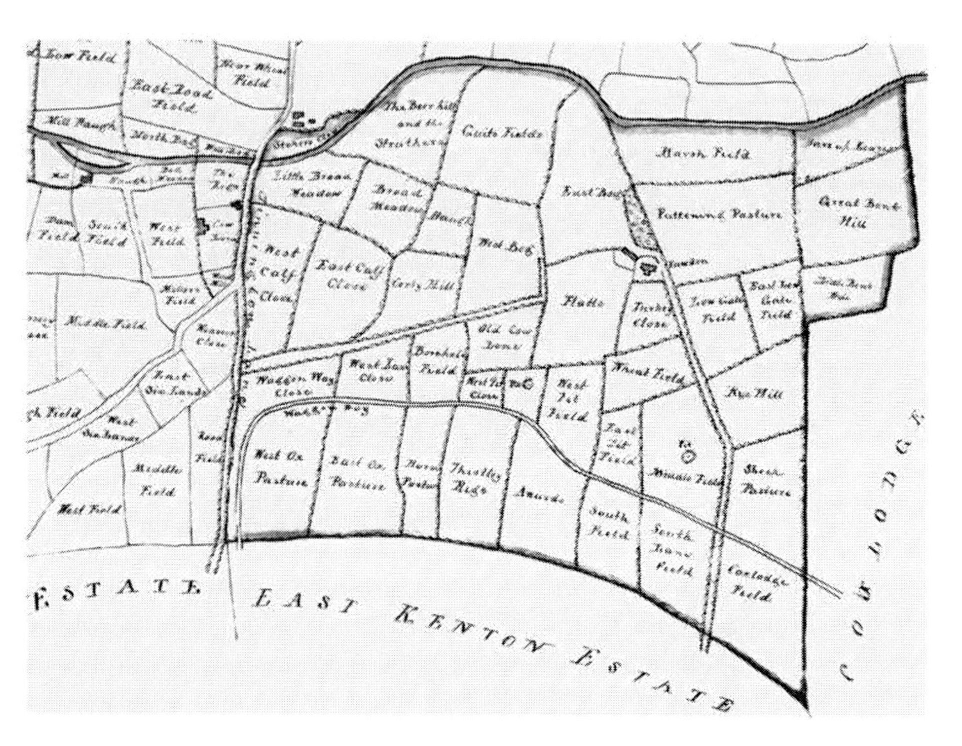

the Regent Pit, Jubilee Pit and Fawdon Engine Pit. Meanwhile, Thompson had designed a new route for the Fawdon traffic and did not renew the lease of the Kenton and Coxlodge waggonway when it expired in November 1818 - much to the annoyance of the Brandlings.

The map of the manor of Fawdon shows the route of the original waggonway running from Coxlodge to the Engine Pit, which was sunk 48 fathoms to the High Main seam in 1810. It followed the line of the present Jubilee Road. The new route ran westwards to the West Pit (opened in 1814), which is the line of the present Fawdon Park Road, to Bell's House at the foot of the incline to Bank Top. The Fawdon waggonway turned west at Bank Top (near the present hotel) and ran to the head of Newbiggin Dene before resuming its southerly course probably at first on the line of the old Brunton waggonway. However, it adopted a more

Wideopen Colliery

westerly line from the neighbourhood of Black Swine House to the head of the Hotchpudding incline. The line demonstrated Thompson's enthusiasm for stationary engines: besides the two inclines, one at Kenton and the other at Hotchpudding, fixed engines were later used to work the Bank Top to Hotchpudding section. In 1824, the Burn Pit was opened and it was connected to the waggonway at Bell's House.

In 1826, this system was replaced by the more ambitious Brunton and Shields Railroad which had five incline planes along its eight and a half mile length to Whitehall Point. The line ran from the Burn Pit (also known as Brunton Colliery since it became the only Fawdon pit to draw coals) north to Brunton Farm and then north east to Hazlerigg; it continued in an easterly direction across the main north road to Wideopen Colliery and on to Burradon; it then ran north of Killingworth before heading in a south easterly direction to the River Tyne. Wideopen Colliery was won in 1827 and used the line. Later traffic from Hazelrigg Colliery (1892 – 1964), Dinnington Colliery (1867 – 1960), Seaton Burn Colliery (1844 – 1963) and Weetslade (1903 – 1966) also used the railway which became known as the Seaton Burn waggonway. In 1892, a branch was built to the Jubilee Pit on the Coxlodge waggonway and was used until the 1960's to convey miners from Gosforth to Hazelrigg. Finally, a branch to the Havannah Drift (1950 - 1976) was added.

In autumn 1840, the 4,570 acres of the Hazlerigg coal mines 'together with a long established and current going colliery called Fawdon Colliery' where a new winning had been completed in 1837 were placed on the market. The sale seems to have been precipitated by the financial difficulties of the Newmarsh family who blamed the Scotswood Waggonway and the Brunton and Shields Railroad as the source of all their misfortunes. Thomas Newmarsh in a vitriolic letter to Benjamin Thompson claimed that 'you, as manager of Fawdon Colliery, dishonestly left the Coxlodge Railway for your individual advantage' and argued that 'Fawdon Colliery has had its profits diminished £212,959 by leaving the Coxlodge road'. Ultimately, Fawdon royalties, like those of Kenton, became part of Coxlodge Colliery. The pits were deserted at the time of the first Ordnance Survey but the old Engine Pit at Fawdon acted as a furnace shaft for Coxlodge. After the estates of the Rev.R.H. Brandling were sold in 1852, Coxlodge was briefly owned by Joshua Bower of Leeds before being bought by Lambert and Co. who established a large brickworks at the Jubilee Pit. Coal ceased being mined in 1894 but the bricks works continued until the 1940's.

Longbenton

The eighteenth century waggonway from the Grand Allies colliery in Longbenton to the staiths at Walker has been discussed in Chapter Two (p 38-9). On the map opposite, dated 1836, the Willington waggonway is shown running through the lands of Bewick and Craster from the William Pit to the George Pit, Christopher Pit and Bewick Pit and on to the River Tyne at Willington Quay (see Greenwood's map p 102). Later there was a link from the William Pit to the Bigges Main 'C' Pit which today survives as a footpath dividing Newcastle United's football academy.

The final map shows the area north east of Newcastle in 1836 when the Heaton waggonway was being lifted from the Middle Pit to the Far Pit. Three of the four waggonways which were instrumental in the development of the steam locomotive are shown: the Heaton waggonway, where William Chapman experimented with the chain locomotive; the Coxlodge line, where John Blenkinsopp tried the rack and cog system; and the Killingworth railway for which George Stephenson built several locomotives. Killingworth consequently became a place of pilgrimage for many of the early pioneers of the modern public railway. The Brunton and Shields Railroad where Benjamin Thompson, the opponent of the travelling engine, built stationery engines is marked skirting the northern boundary of Killingworth royalty.

In 1847, the main line north from Newcastle was to bisect the Willington waggonway as it headed through the royalties of Heaton, Bigges Main, Longbenton, Killingworth and Weetslade en route for Edinburgh. This necessitated the building of two bridges over the main line. Today only the west abutment of the southern bridge survives. It is fitting that one of premier lines of Britain's modern railway system should be surrounded by the archaeology of the old waggonways which pioneered the iron way and the travelling engine – a reminder that of Tyneside's many outstanding engineering achievements, perhaps the railway and the steam locomotive are the most important in terms of world history.

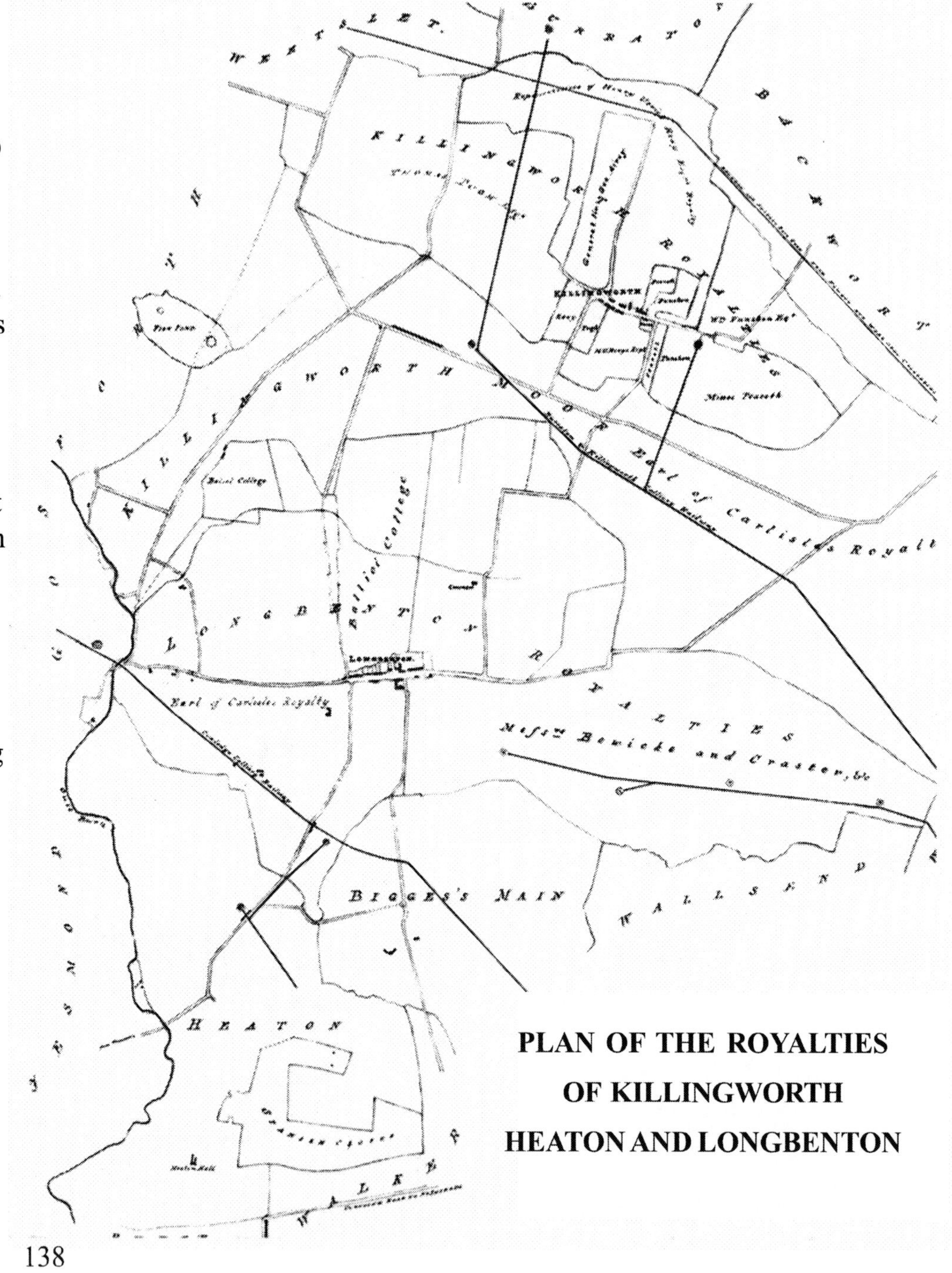

PLAN OF THE ROYALTIES OF KILLINGWORTH HEATON AND LONGBENTON

DIRECTORY OF THE PRINCIPAL COLLIERY OWNERS IN 1921

Reid's 'Handy Colliery Guide' for 1921 lists over 400 collieries in Northumberland and Durham. Many of these were small concerns such as that of R.J. Bewicke and Brothers who operated Mickley Bank and Mickley Grange collieries. Only the major companies are included in this abridged list and even within this group there was a great range in the size of the businesses. James Joicey's empire, which ultimately included the Lambton and Hetton Collieries, was probably the largest coal mining enterprise in the world. Administered from Cathedral Buildings in Dean Street, Newcastle, it was on a different scale to the Burradon and Coxlodge Coal Company next door in Milburn House.

NORTHUMBERLAND

Owners	Collieries
Ashington Coal Co. Ltd.	**Ashington Bothal, Carl, Duke, Linton, Woodhorn, Ellington**
Backworth Collieries Ltd.	**Church, Maude, Eccles, Algeron, Properous**
Bebside Coal Co. Ltd.	**Bebside, Choppington A and B**
Bedlington Coal Co. Ltd.	**Bedlington, Doctor, Barrington, Bomarsund, West Sleekburn**
Burradon & Coxlodge Co.Ltd	**Burradon, Hazelrigg**
Cowpen Coal Co. Ltd.	**Cambois, North Seaton, Cowpen Isabella, Straker, Mill**
Cramlington Coal Co. Ltd.	**Ann, Lamb, Amelia, Dudley, Scott, Daisy, Wrightson**
North Walbottle Coal Co.	**North Walbottle**
Seaton Burn Coal Co. Ltd.	**Dinnington, Seaton Burn,**
Seaton Delaval Coal Co. Ltd.	**Seaton Delaval C, D, E & F, Forsters, Hastings, Relief**
Throckley Coal Co. Ltd.	**Throckley, Blucher, Maria, Heddon**
Wallsend & Hebburn Co. Ltd.	**Wallsend G, Rising Sun, Edward, Hebburn (Durham)**

Hartley Staith

DURHAM

Bell Bros. Ltd.	**Browney, South Brancepeth, Tursdale, Heigh Hall, Bowburn**
Bolckow, Vaughan & Co. Ltd.	**Auckland Park North, A.P. South, Black Boy, Westerton, Westerton North, Leasingthorne, Shildon Lodge, Dean and Chapter No.1, No.2, No.3, Byers Green, B.G. Busty, B.G. Drift, Newfield and Hunwick**
Bowes, John & Partners Ltd.	**Andrew's House, Marley Hill, Burnopfield, Byer Moor, Dipton, Pontop, Kibblesworth, Springwell, Follonsby, Felling**
Consett Iron Co. Ltd.	**Eden, Medomsley, Derwent, Westwood, Langley Park, Busty, Hutton, Chopwell No.1, No. 2, No. 3, Garesfield Bute, Garesfield Ruler,Garesfield Towneley, Blackhill, Castle Drift, Delves, Whittonstall (Northumberland).**
Dunston Garesfield Collieries Ltd	**Dunston, Norwood, Swalwell, Garesfield**

Easington Coal Co. Ltd.	**Easington**
Harton Coal Co. Ltd.	**Boldon No. 1, No. 2, No. 3. Harton, Saint Hilda, Westoe, Whitburn No. 1, No 2.**
Horden Collieries Ltd.	**Horden, Shotton, Blackhall, Castle Eden**
Joicey, James & Co. Ltd.	**Tanfield Lea, Tanfield Moor, Beamish James & Mary, Beamish Second, East Stanley, Twizell, West Pelton, Handon Hold.**
Lambton & Hetton Collieries Ltd.	**Bournmoor D, Herrington, Houghton, Lumley Third, Lumley Sixth, Newbottle Dorothea, Newbottle Margaret, Harraton, North Biddick, Silksworth, Elemore, Hetton, Eppleton, Hazard**
Londonderry Collieries Ltd.	**Seaham, Dawdon**
Pease & Partners Ltd.	**Bowden, Close, Wooley, Roddymoor, Waterhouses, Esh, Ushaw Moor, Saint Helens, Eldon Harry, Eldon Harvey, Eldon John Henry, Windlestone, Witton Hall Drift**
Pelaw Main Collieries Co.	**Bewick Main, Ouston E, Riding Drift, Urpeth C, Ouston A, Winning, Blackhouse, Ravensworth**
Pelton Colliery Ltd.	**Newfield, Pelton, Tribley**
Priestman Collieries Ltd.	**Chester So.Moor, Waldridge, Shield, Row Drift, Victoria Garesfield, Garesfield Lilley, Blaydon Burn Bessie, B.B. Mary, Blaydon Main, Axwell**
Samuelson Sir B. & Co.	**Hedley Hope, Hedley East (Tow Law) Lady Durham, Sherburn House, Sherburn Hill**
Scott Walter Ltd.	**East Hetton, Trimdon Grange, Trimdon**
South Derwent Coal Co.	**South Derwent, Cresswell, Willie, West Shield Row, West Stanley**
South Garesfield Colliery Co.	**Lintz, Anna, South Garesfield**
South Hetton Coal Co. Ltd.	**Murton East, West, Middle, South Hetton**
South Medomsley Colliery Ltd.	**South Medomsley, Annie and Drift**
South Moor Colliery Co	**Charley & Hedley, Louisa Old, Louisa New, Morrison North & South, William**
Stella Coal Co. Ltd.	**Addison, Stargate, Towneley Emma, Greenside, Clara Vale**
Stobart, Henry & Co.	**Etherley, Jame, Railey Fell, West Tees**
Strakers & Love	**Brancepeth A, B, C, Drift Brandon A, B, C, Willington**
Washington Coal Co. Ltd.	**Washington F, Washington Glebe**
Weardale Steel, Coal & Coke	**Black Prince Five, Black Prince Main, West Thornley, Hedley Hill, Salter's Gate, Tudhoe, Croxdale, Thornley No.1, Thornley No.2, Middridge, Ludworth, Wheatley Hill No.1, No.2**
Wearmouth Coal Co. Ltd.	**Wearmouth A, Wearmouth B, Hylton**

Wear Bridge

Glossary

After damp	a mixture of carbon dioxide, carbon monoxide and nitrogen formed by the ignition of methane or fire damp. Also known as choke damp.
Bank	the top of the shaft hence banksman – the person responsible for controlling the ascent and descent of men and materials.
Board	a passageway. Narrow boards, about two yards wide, were usually the first part excavated to provide ventilation and access. Normally boards were four or five yards wide.
Boll	measure equal to 9,676.8 cubic inches: 22.5 bolls equalled a chaldron.
Bond	contract of employment between coal owners and workmen.
Brakeman	generally the engineman who attended the winding engine.
Chaldron	a measurement of coal by volume. The Newcastle chaldron became standardised at 53 cwt. and the London chaldron at 28 cwt. After the Coal Mines Act of 1872, cold was sold by weight only.
Corf	a basket made of hazel with a capacity of 10 to 30 pecks to carry coal which was supplied and maintained by a contractor known as a corver. Corves were gradually replaced by tubs from the 1830's.
Fire damp	methane gas.
Fitter	agent responsible for the selling of the coal who usually owned the keelboats.
Galloway	small, stocky pony used both above and below ground.
In bye	away from the shaft – into the workings.
Keel	oval shaped vessel about 40 feet by 15.5 capable of carrying eight Newcastle chaldrons.
Keelman	men who operated the keels and ferried coal down the river.
Onsetter	man who loader the corves at the shaft bottom.
Marras	workmates
Mothergate	main access route into the mine.
Pillar	a square or oblong formed by boards and walls left to support the roof.
Putter	usually a youth aged 14-20 years who moved the corves to the shaft.
Ramble	the thin stratum of shale found immediately above the coal seam.
Rolly	a carriage normally used to carry two corves underground.
Score	a number of corves varying from 20 on the Tyne to 21 on the Wear
Skreener	a man who separated the stones from the coal.
Steel mill	a machine used to provide light in gaseous pits.
Stenting	an opening between a pair of boards through which air circulated.
Ten	a measure of coal upon which the lessor's rent was based.
Trapper	a young boy employed to open and shut a door to assisted ventilation.
Tubbing	casing put into a shaft to keep water back.
Viewer	colliery engineer and manager.
Wailers	boys employed to pick out stones or pyrites which had escaped the attention of the screeners.
Wall	communication at the end of a pillar between two boards.
Wasteman	person responsible for checking the worked out part of the pit especially for accumulations of gas.

Wallsend Staith

FURTHER STUDY

The History of the British Coal Industry by the Clarendon Press, Oxford, is the standard work of reference. There are five volumes:

Volume 1 Before 1700 Towards the Age of Coal by John Hatcher;
Volume 2 1700 – 1830 The Industrial Revolution by Michael Flinn;
Volume 3 1830 – 1913 Victorian Pre-eminence by Roy Church;
Volume 4 1913 – 1946 The Political Economy of Decline by Barry Supple;
and Volume 5 1946 – 1982 The Nationalised Industry by William Ashworth.

Within these five volumes are numerous reference to individual collieries in the North East and extensive bibliographies of manuscript and printed material.

The North of England Institute of Mining and Mechanical Engineers has a useful websit (http://www.mininginstitute.org.uk) which contains an index to the library and special collections of archive material. The library is open to members of the public.

Durham County Mining Museum has a useful website (http://www.dmm.org.uk) which contains an extensive bibliography, details of individual mines, maps and numerous articles. It is a good starting point but needs to be used with caution.

Durham County Council's Geographical Information Service is available through the council's website (http://www.durham.gov.uk). This provides a comprehensive mapping service for the whole coalfield – including Northumberland – from the First Edition Ordnance Survey maps to present day maps and aerial photographs.

If this book encourages others to research the rich history of the Great Northern Coalfield then it will have served its purpose. The librarian of the North of England Institute of Mining and Mechanical Engineers, Jennifer Kelly, would welcome such studies to add to the collections.

Earsdon Staiths

Les Turnbull is a member of the North of England Institute of Mining and Mechanical Engineeers and he has written several books on the history of mining in the North East. 'Coals from Newcastle' is an introduction to the history and industrial archaeology of the Great Northern Coalfield and is illustrated with some of the rare maps and engravings from the archives of the Mining Institute. The book, written for the general public, is essential reading for all who are interested in the region. Lost colliery villages, coal mines and railways are re-discovered in the pages of this book.

CHAPMAN RESEARCH PUBLISHING
OXFORD

£10.95

ISBN 978-0-9561248-0-7